ABORTION

Questions & Answers

Love
   Them
      Both

by
JOHN C. WILLKE, MD
BARBARA H. WILLKE, RN

Abortion Questions & Answers

Why Not Love Them Both

ISBN — 910728-23-2
©January 2003

Hayes Publishing Company, Inc.
6304 Hamilton Avenue • Cincinnati, Ohio 45224
Phone (513) 681-7559
Phone/Fax (513) 681-9298
e-mail: hayespub@aol.com
web: hayespub.tripod.com

This book is the third in a series, each about the same subject, each quite different as it responds to the needs of our changing times.

The first American edition of *Handbook on Abortion* was published 1971, revised 1975 and 1979, with 21st printing March 1983.

Other language editions included Latin American (Hiltz & Hayes, 1974); French (France Empire, Paris, 1974); Malayan (India, 1974); Continental Spanish (EUNSA, Pamplona, 1975); Italian (Milano, 1978); Chinese (Hong Kong, 1978); Portuguese (San Paulo, 1980); Swedish (Jarfalla, 1980); German (Vorarlberg, 1982).

Abortion: Questions & Answers was published in 1985 and revised in 1988 and 1991. Its other language editions were Japanese (Tokyo, 1991); Italian (CEC Edizimi Internazionali, 1995); Spanish (Editorial Bonum, Argentina, 1992, and Hayes, Cincinnati, 1993); Russian (Moscow, 1992); Czech (Cor Jesu, Cesky Tesin, 1993); Slovak (Cor Jesu, Cesky Tesin, 1993); Lithuanian (Caritas, 1996); and Polish (Wydanie Uzupelnione, Gdansk, 1990); Korean Edition, 1997 Korea, Entervarcity Press, Seoul; Hungarian Edition, Abortuse, 1999, Pro Life Alapitrany, Budapest.

Love Them Both, Russian Edition, 2001, Moscow. Orthodox Church.

PREFACE

This is the third book in a series over 25 years. In 1971, at the insistence of many people, particularly our college daughters, we wrote *Handbook On Abortion*. In question and answer format, it attempted to present all of the arguments for abortion and to answer them in a rational, medical, and scientific way. The first edition, in June 1971, numbered 141 pages and contained 42 scientific references arranged for the reader's convenience immediately following the answer to a question.

Its 1975 revision increased its size to 208 pages with 180 references, and the 1979 revision totalled 210 pages with 210 newer references. In 24 printings, *Handbook On Abortion* sold well over one million copies and was translated into ten languages. Internationally, it became known as the "bible of the movement."

But time moved on. A flood of new scientific information, particularly the explosion of detailed information about the other patient (the tiny one) through recent technology and modern research, reshaped our answers. Historical, legislative, and legal developments had to be incorporated into our thinking. A few earlier "facts" had been disproved, but many new facts have been confirmed by scientific studies.

In 1985, we saw the need for a totally new book, and so we started with blank paper and wrote afresh. *Abortion: Questions & Answers* brought new areas, new questions and answers, new developments.

Except for a few classic papers, we used new and updated scientific articles to support our answers. It ended up larger, far richer and more useful.

It did fill the shoes of *Handbook*. With revisions and updates, it even inherited its "bible" status and added ten more languages.

It is now 26 years since we entered this struggle. We view this field of battle with mixed emotions — dismay that the slaughter continues, elation at the great progress the pro-life movement has made . . . and a quiet optimism that our children will see the day when this demon is slain.

Why Can't We Love Them Both proclaims the new theme that our research has shown is the way to turn the tide as we move into the 21st century.

Broad areas in society, major church bodies and political parties have joined the pro-life side, but,in opposition, we have not yet seen the full fury of the pro-abortion ideologies and of the pro-abortion industry.

Accordingly, we offer this new educational tool, hoping it too will fill the need its two predecessors did.

The issue today is still intensely personal, while being totally global. We echo Mother Teresa's words at the 1994 National Prayer Breakfast:

"The greatest destroyer of peace today is abortion, because it is a war against the child . . . and if we accept that a mother can kill even her own child, how can we tell other people not to kill one another?"

And we offer this book.

Dr. & Mrs. (John & Barbara) Willke
Anno Domini 1997

For help above the call of duty, our thanks to:

Bob Regner
Northern Printing
11383 Landan Lane
Cincinnati, OH 45245
(513) 772-0020

FORWARD – 2ND EDITION

We are in a new century. There are good signs. There is a decrease in total abortions. There are fewer abortionists and those still operating are aging. In spite of eight years of a vigorously pro-abortion administration in Washington, and a no longer even thinly veiled pro-abortion push by most of the national media, we have seen public opinion clearly becoming less supportive of surgical abortion.

Concurrent with this is the rise of chemical abortion. RU 486 is here. Emergency "contraception," more accurately termed "emergency" abortion, has raised its head. There is increasing awareness of the abortifacient action of other so-called contraceptives.

The relationship of abortion to later breast cancer can no longer be denied. The increasing aging of and the soon to be dying of Western nations has finally drawn international attention. AIDS spreads inexorably, as do a number of other incurable sexually transmitted diseases. And, of all things, chastity and the intact family are coming back in style.

The most dramatic and potentially far reaching developments are microscopic. What began with invitro fertilization has spread into genetic manipulation, stem cell research and cloning.

Finally, citizens of individual nations cannot rest content by coping with these developments in their own countries. This is increasingly becoming an interdependent one world. This has drawn sharp attention to the activities of the United Nations.

And so, it is time for a new edition, keeping the old that is proven and relevant and detailing much that is new. Accordingly, we bring you a revised edition of *Love Them Both*, building on its predecessors.

Anno Domini 2002

CONTENTS

PART I
INTRODUCTION

Chapter

CHAPTER 1

THE SITUATION

The situation in the United States, almost three decades after abortion became legal throughout the nation, seems to be at an impasse. Canada, presented with abortion (now on demand) throughout that nation four years earlier, is not that much different. One thing that is completely obvious is that the issue will not go away.

The other obvious fact is that the two sides remain completely polarized. There seems to be no middle ground, no chance for compromise. When one strips the issue to its bare bones, the reason for the lack of middle ground is only too obvious. This either is or is not a living human from conception. This living human either continues to live or is killed. It is obvious that this being can't be just a little human, or perhaps not human, at one point and then human at another. He or she either is or is not. Just as simply, there is either life or death. There is no middle ground.

Compromise?
Pro-abortion advocates, who call themselves prochoice, are unwilling to concede any ground at all. Would they allow passage of laws in either nation forbidding abortion in the third trimester for sex selection, to pick an extreme position or would they stop killing

babies during delivery (partial-birth abortion)? No! They have fought any such attempt.

Would true-blue pro-lifers, if they had their choice, allow abortion for pregnancies resultant from assault rape and incest, or for pregnancies when the developing baby is severely handicapped? No, they might be forced into this as a political compromise, and as a temporary measure. But, ethically speaking, no real pro-lifer would consent to this. It would seem, then, that the chance for compromise simply does not exist. On the other hand, it is obvious that people of goodwill must continue to try for a solution.

Ultimate Pro-Abortion Goals:

Many of the ultimate goals of those who favor abortion already exist. Abortion is legal in both of our nations until birth for social and economic reasons. Many areas use tax money to pay for elective abortions. What pro-abortion forces have not achieved has been to mainstream this procedure into the day-to-day practice of medicine. They also have not achieved a status of respectability, as the word "abortionist" still is one of low esteem, or even condemnation. Also, abortion is still strongly condemned by substantial segments of the cultures of both the U.S. and Canada.

The Ultimate Pro-Life Goals:

The ultimate pro-life goal is quite direct and very simple. Pro-lifers want an amendment to the U.S. Constitution, to the Canadian Charter of Rights that will give equal protection under the law, to all living humans from the time their biologic life begins at fertilization until natural death.

Understanding that such a goal remains yet in the future, pro-life people have an intermediate goal. It is a Constitutional Amendment returning the right to make decisions about abortion to each individual state in the U.S., and the equivalent in Canada, to each individual province. This would take federal judges out of the mix completely and make legislating on abortion a state's issue. States and provinces could then allow abortion, forbid it, or anything in between.

Since the above intermediate goals also remain yet unattainable, pro-life forces today are seeking more immediate goals, particularly so in the United States. These include parental notification and consent for abortion for minor daughters; specific public health regulations of free-standing abortion facilities; women's right to know, or informed consent laws; forbidding certain types of abortions (such as partial-birth abortion); forbidding of abortions for certain reasons, such as sex selection and after a certain age of fetal development.

Certain allied issues can also be legislated, such as forbidding destructive live fetal experimentation and forbidding human embryonic stem cell research and cloning. Freedom of conscience can be guaranteed, both for individuals and for institutions. Laws to ban the use of tax monies for elective abortions have been the first line of attack for pro-lifers, but much yet can still be done. There are many avenues where federal monies have been given to pro-abortion organizations. A major example is family planning, which includes abortion as a method of family planning, and routinely uses abortifacients. Government support for institutions that have encouraged and referred for abortions could be terminated and such monies redirected to those that support women before, during and after birth.

Adoption:

There are certain constructive areas that can be encouraged that should be non-controversial. An obvious one is adoption. Certainly, the pro-life side has been warmly supportive of this. Tragically, the pro-abortion side, while giving lip service to adoption, nevertheless has, in practice, strongly discouraged adoption to the point of not so subtly condemning it. The typical

Planned Parenthood type of advice to an unmarried teenager contemplating adoption is to hold it up as a fate worst than death for her unfortunate child. Sadly, adoption should be, but has not been, common ground.

Contraception:

A major thrust of pro-abortion rhetoric has been the assumption that if only young people were given adequate education in how to use contraceptives, and then adequate access to them, the problem would be solved.

A portion of the pro-life side has serious moral reservations about contraception per se. Many other pro-lifers do not share this. Almost universally, however, pro-lifers oppose contraceptives for premarital sex, for adultery, and for homosexual liaisons. They oppose so-called contraceptives that cause abortions in the first week of life. They also oppose our federal government exporting huge amounts of contraceptives for "population control."

Title X, the U.S. federal family planning program which has expended billions of dollars giving contraceptives to teenagers over the last three decades, has proven to be a colossal failure. Wherever its clinics have been established, an intense campaign has been launched to teach contraceptive use to unmarried teens. The result? The pregnancy rate has gone up. Sexually transmitted disease has gone up. The abortion rate has gone up. The age of first sexual encounter is younger. Planned Parenthood has reported that 60% of women getting abortions had used contraceptives the month they became pregnant. This evidence, along with other studies, has convinced many that the siren song of "give them contraceptives and the problem will be solved" is not part of the solution, but rather part of the problem.

But legalizing abortion was sold to us as a cure for many of our social ills.

Let's look at the record.

Social Concern	1970	1990
Illegitimate Births	10.7%	26.2%
Children with Single Mothers	11%	22%
Children on Welfare	8.5%	11.9%
Violent Crime Rate (per 100,000)	36.4	73.2

From the Index of Leading Cultural Indicators,
William J. Bennett.

Love Them Both:

Your authors have been teaching, writing, and lecturing in the field of human sexuality for forty-five years and have been in the thick of the struggle over abortion for thirty years. Is there any common ground? We certainly can take sides, and many do with great passion and dedication. We, however, see one glimmer of light that hopefully would appeal to both sides, and certainly would to those in the middle. It is the recent emphasis on the simple question, "Why can't we love them both?"

Why can't we all stand with the pregnant woman? Why can't we tell her that we share the agony of her decision? That we really know of no "convenience" abortions? Why can't we tell her that we stand with her, not against her? Why can't we begin to discuss constructive alternatives to abortion, adoption being an alternative par excellence?

Why can't we cooperate in giving her all the information there is to be given from both sides of this controversial issue? Why not fully informed consent? Give her all the reasons for abortion? The law allows, even requires this. But also give her all the reasons for waiting and, most emphatically, offer to her all of the constructive alternatives that now exist. If our laws continue to dictate that she be given that choice of life or death for her unborn, at the very least that choice should be a fully informed one. It should not just be informed in terms of technical information. No, it should also be a choice that is made in view of the fact that there is a warm and loving alternative to the technical quick-fix of abortion.

In the coming years, the hallmark of the pro-life movement, at least, should not be just to save the baby, but to love them both.

CHAPTER 2

THE THREE QUESTIONS

FIRST, SOME DEFINITIONS.

Define "Alive"

Alive means that this being is growing, developing, maturing, and replacing its own dying cells. It means not being dead.

Define "Human"

Human means one of the biological beings who belongs to the species Homo Sapiens. Such beings are unique from all other beings in that they have 46 human chromosomes in every cell. Such beings do not belong to the rabbit family, the carrot family, etc.

Define "Person"

Person is defined in at least a dozen different ways, according to the field or discipline in which you define it. In theology, it usually means when the soul is created. In law (in the U.S.), personhood begins at birth. Other countries have ruled that it begins at different ages. In medicine and natural science, person usually means when the being is alive and complete. In philosophy, it has multiple meanings and shades of meanings. We

8

strongly suggest that no one use this term without first defining precisely what you mean by it, for, unless you do, any discussion of personhood is foolish.

Define human life

This is the question that must first be considered, pondered, discussed and, finally, answered. It cannot be brushed aside or ignored. It must be faced and met honestly. Upon its answer hinges the entire abortion question, as all other considerations pale to insignificance when compared with it. In a sense, nothing else really matters. If what is growing within the mother is not human life, if it is just a piece of tissue — a glob of protoplasm — then it deserves little respect or consideration, and the primary concern should be the mother's physical and mental health, her social well-being, and, at times, even her convenience.

NOW THE THREE QUESTIONS

There are three questions that are basic to the entire abortion controversy:

The first is: "Is this human life?" As we will see, the answer clearly is Yes. That answer is a medical and scientific one, for we cannot impose a religious or philosophic belief in our nations through force of law.

The second question is: "Should we grant equal protection by law to all living humans in our nation?" or, "Should we allow discrimination against entire classes of living humans?"

The third question is about Choice and Women's Rights, as discussed in Chapter 27.

COMMENT

For two millennia in our Western culture, written into our constitutions, specifically protected by our laws, and deeply imprinted into the hearts of all men and women, there has existed the absolute value of honoring and protecting the right of each human to live. This has been an unalienable and unequivocal right. The only exception has been that of balancing a life for a life in certain situations or by due process of law.

- Never, in modern times — except by a small group of physicians in Hitler's Germany and by Stalin in Russia — has a price tag of economic or social usefulness been placed on an individual human life as the price of its continued existence.
- Never, in modern times — except by physicians in Hitler's Germany — has a certain physical perfection been required as a condition necessary for the continuation of that life.
- Never — since the law of paterfamilias in ancient Rome — has a major nation granted to a father or mother total dominion over the life or death of their child.
- Never, in modern times, has the state granted to one citizen the absolute legal right to have another killed in order to solve their own personal, social or economic problem.

And yet, if this is human life, the U.S. Supreme Court Decision in America and permissive abortion laws in other nations do all of the above. They represent a complete about-face, a total rejection of one of the core values of Western man, and an acceptance of a new ethic in which life has only a relative value. No longer will every human have a right to live simply because he or she exists.

A human will now be allowed to exist only if he measures up to certain standards of independence, physical perfection, or utilitarian usefulness to others. This is a momentous change that strikes at the root of Western civilization.

It makes no difference to vaguely assume that human life is more human post-born than pre-born. What is critical is to judge it to be — or not to be — human life. By a measure of "more" or "less" human, one can easily and logically justify infanticide and euthanasia. By the measure of economic and/or social usefulness, the ghastly atrocities of Hitlerian mass murders came to be.

One cannot help but be reminded of the anguished comment of a condemned Nazi judge who said to an American judge after the Nuremberg trials: "I never knew it would come to this." The American judge answered simply: "It came to this the first time you condemned an innocent life."

Ponder well the words of George Santayana: "Those who do not remember the past are condemned to relive it."

Wm. Shirer, *The Rise and Fall of the Third Reich*, Simon & Schuster, 1959

Is this unborn being, growing within the mother, a human life? Does he or she have a right to live? Make this judgment with the utmost care, scientific precision, and honesty. Upon it may hinge much of the basic freedom of many human lives in the years to come.

CHAPTER 3

HOW TO TEACH
THE PRO-LIFE STORY

"Everything changes, yet everything remains the same." A wise teacher will observe the above. All pro-life activists are teachers, each in his or her own way. Public opinion and public knowledge develop and change. Methods of arguing the pro-life cause that were effective 10, 20, and 30 years ago, while still valid, nevertheless may lose some of their effectiveness. New approaches may work better. Accordingly, let us briefly explore how we have taught in the past and how we must now teach in this new century.

When abortion was first legalized in the U.S. and Canada, few people knew much about fetal development or abortion. Most objections to abortion arose from religious beliefs. Understanding this, the most effective methods of education then centered upon two major objectives, both of which were directly related to knowledge of fetal development. Education in the 70s and 80s had, as its primary goal, convincing the listener that this in fact was a fully living human from the first cell stage.

Religious Belief vs. Civil Rights

Opposition to abortion, stemming from one's religious beliefs, is a very important and effective motivating factor. It, however, applies directly only to those persons who share similar religious beliefs. The counter argument is very effective: "If you oppose abortion because you think it's against God's will, I respect that and you should live by that. However, I have a different religious belief (or non-belief), I do not think that it is against God's will and therefore you should respect my approval of abortion. You should not impose your religious belief on me."

They had a point. The answer to this was as follows: "Medical, biologic and natural science has long since proven that this is a living human from conception. Our founding fathers, in the charter of this republic, spoke clearly, stating: "We hold these truths to be self evident, that all men are created equal and that they are endowed by their Creator with certain unalienable rights — of life, liberty and the pursuit of happiness." The pro-life response, accordingly, was very direct: "Religious belief is a powerful motivator for the individual person, but this is not merely a religious issue, it is primarily a human rights issue, a civil rights issue; and our nation and other Western nations make laws to protect civil and human rights."

Fetal Development

The second major goal of teaching was equally related to the teaching of fetal development. A typical lecturer in the first 20 years of this movement would spend about half of his or her time giving a scientifically accurate presentation proving that human life began at fertilization. Typically, this was by slides, sometimes by a movie and, more recently, by video, by overheads, and by computers. It would be a just-the-facts-ma'am type of a show-and-tell presentation. If effective, those in the audience would be convinced that this was human life and from the beginning. Their logical next step in reasoning was: "Abortion obviously kills a living human. Abortion is bad. Therefore, we must stop abortion."

Accordingly, teaching placed its primary emphasis, and most of its available time, teaching fetal development. This worked beautifully. For the first two decades of our movement this method of teaching educated our nations and brought millions to a conviction that abortion was in fact a human rights issue and that it must be stopped. Being convinced that this was a living human, millions of people came to agree that — *Abortion came to us through the law, lawmakers make laws, lawmakers appoint judges, we elect lawmakers.*

This direct realization fostered what today are major political forces, both in the U.S. and Canada.

By the late 80s and early 90s, it was apparent to the pro-abortion industry that the pro-life movement was accelerating its momentum and showed definite signs of winning this battle. Accordingly, they took an entirely new look at the controversy. They did extensive and expensive market research to determine what they might do to change their approach to this issue with the goal of permanently locking in legal abortion in our time. From their research, focus groups, etc., several facts became apparent:

1) The industry renewed its commitment to never talk about the passenger inside of the woman. They realized that when they debated the fact of whether or not this is a baby, they consistently lost, and pro-life teaching was consistently effective. Ultrasound and other medical advances played a major part in confirming this. Their conclusion was to never talk about what is inside of her.

2) The second conclusion was that pro-abortion forces should quit arguing about abortion itself. They recognized that when the facts of abortion were debated, the pro-life side consistently won.

14

3) They changed the question. Unable to win debating the issue, as they saw it, on pro-life terms, they cleverly changed the question. They changed it from "Is abortion right or wrong"? to "Who decides, the woman or the government? We believe that the government should stay out of this very private matter. The real question here is about a woman's right to choose." It takes only a moment to realize that this is an entirely different question. Over a period of several years, by paid advertisements, by all pro-abortion leaders using the same party line, and by the enthusiastic cooperation of the liberal media, they largely succeeded in changing the terms of the debate.

Political Impact

Many political candidates were led to believe that the sleeping "pro-choice giant" had awakened and would now sweep all before it. Judging this to be a turning of the tide, many politicians across the country, who had been nominally pro-life, now became openly pro-abortion. They jumped to the side they perceived to be winning. With this there was a loss of pro-life political strength.

Counter Reaction

But the field of battle did not remain static. In the early 90s, largely through the newly formed Life Issues Institute, your authors and others devised a counter-strategy. Answers to the pro-choice argument were developed and disseminated. But this was not enough. A thorough-going re-evaluation of the situation was needed. This was accomplished using, as they had done, market research. What was revealed was that there had been, within a few years, a tidal change in public opinion. As noted above, the logic had been: "I am convinced that this is a living human from conception, that it is a human rights issue, and that abortion kills babies. Therefore, abortion is wrong and we must work to stop it." This had changed to: "I am convinced that this is a living human from conception, I believe that abortion is wrong, I would not support it or have one myself. But I am also convinced that a woman has the right to choose to have an abortion, and therefore I will not seek laws to abolish it."

Simply stated, the change was as follows. Only a few years ago, when a person was convinced that this was a baby, they then concluded that abortion must be stopped. Now, because of the "pro-choice" argumentation, even though they know it's a baby, that person now says that abortion should be allowed. This held potentially catastrophic effects. What was to be done?

What To Do

Our market research went on to reveal the following. About 25% of people hold strong pro-life views. A narrow 25% are weakly or strongly pro-abortion. There remains almost 50% of the general public, which, by its own admission, feels that they have not yet formed a firm conviction on the abortion issue. Almost four-fifths of this "conflicted middle" admits that this is a baby, that abortion kills a baby, and that abortion is wrong. But about two-thirds of that **same group** also believe that a woman has a right to choose to have one.

Further research demonstrated that this conflicted middle generally has a rather negative opinion of pro-life people. To take it to its extreme, they believe that we are right-wing religious zealots, that we shoot abortionists and burn down clinics, that we are fetus-lovers and care little for the woman after she delivers. Coloring everything in terms of public opinion, we discovered that a significant percent of the general public feels that pro-lifers are not compassionate to women. Because of this, many of them are turning a deaf ear and are no longer listening to us. Therein lies our challenge.

16

Compassion

Further research and educational test marketing revealed that therein also lay the solution to countering the pro-choice argumentation. Pro-lifers, far beyond others in our culture, and certainly beyond abortion proponents, **are** compassionate to women. What is needed, therefore, is to shout from the housetops the details of the pro-life movement's obvious compassion for women. When this is done, the folks in the middle will once again listen to us. Herein lies the educational strategy needed for the coming years. This has led to the title of this book. It is a one-liner that has proven its effectiveness in countering and reversing their "pro-choice" argumentation.

Love Them Both?

"Why not love them both?" has proven to be the key in the lock that is needed to counter their changing of the question. Just as their one-liner has been "a woman has the right to choose." The pro-life one-liner should be "why can't we love them both?"

Building upon the above, there has been continuing investigation into the psychodynamics of a pregnant woman's decision-making by the Caring Foundation. Its findings have shed new insight for us. This is summed up by Mr. Paul Swope. His report suggests that women do not see any "good" resulting from an unplanned pregnancy. Instead they must weigh what they perceive as three "evils," namely, motherhood, adoption, and abortion.

"Unplanned motherhood, according to the study, represents a threat so great to modern women that it is perceived as equivalent to a "death of self." While the woman may rationally understand that this is not her own literal death, her emotional, subconscious reaction to carrying the child to term is that her life will be 'over.' This is because many young women of today have developed a self-identity that simply does not include

17

being a mother. It may include going through college, getting a degree, obtaining a good job, even getting married someday; but the sudden intrusion of motherhood is perceived as a complete loss of control over their present and future selves. It shatters their sense of who they are and will become, and thereby paralyzes their ability to think more rationally or realistically.

"When these women evaluate the abortion decision, therefore, they do not, as a pro-lifer might, formulate the problem with the radically distinct options of either 'I must endure an embarrassing pregnancy' or 'I must destroy the life of an innocent child.' Instead, their perception of the choice is either 'my life is over' or 'the life of this new child is over.' Given this perspective, the choice of abortion becomes one of self-preservation, a much more defensible position, both to the woman deciding to abort and to those supporting her decision.

"Even those women who are likely to choose life rather than abortion do so, not because they better understand fetology or have a greater love for children, but because they have a broader and less fragile sense of self, and they can better incorporate motherhood into their self-identity.

"Adoption, unfortunately, is seen as the most 'evil' of the three options, as it is perceived as a kind of double death. First, the death of self, as the woman would have to accept motherhood by carrying the baby to term. Further, not only would the woman be a mother, but she would perceive herself as a bad mother, one who gave her own child away to strangers. The second death is the death of the child 'through abandonment.' A woman worries about the chance of her child being abused. She is further haunted by the uncertainty of the child's future and about the possibility of the child returning to intrude on her own life many years later. Basically, a woman desperately wants a sense of resolution to her crisis, and, in her mind, adoption leaves the

18

situation the most unresolved, with uncertainty and guilt, as far as she can see, for both herself and her child. As much as we might like to see the slogan 'Adoption, Not Abortion' embraced by women, this study suggests that, in pitting adoption against abortion, adoption will be the hands-down loser.

"The attitude of these women toward abortion is quite surprising. First, all of the scores of women involved in the study (none of whom were pro-life activists and all of whom called themselves 'pro-choice') agreed that abortion is killing. While this is something that is no doubt 'written on the human heart,' credit for driving home the reality of abortion is also due to the preserving educational work of the pro-life movement. Second, the women believe that abortion is wrong and evil, and that God will punish a woman who makes that choice. Third, however, these women feel that God will ultimately forgive the woman because He is a forgiving God, because the woman did not intend to get pregnant. Finally, because a woman in such crisis has no real choice — again the perception is that the woman's whole life is at stake.

"In fact, while abortion itself is seen as something evil, the woman who has to make that choice is perceived as being courageous because she has made a difficult, costly, but necessary decision in order to get on with her life. Basically, abortion is considered the least of the three evils because it is perceived as offering the greatest hope for a woman to preserve her own sense of self, her own life. This is why women feel protective toward the abortive woman and her 'right to choose,' and deeply resentful toward the pro-life movement, which they perceive as uncaring and judgmental.

"Note that the primary concerns in any of the three options revolve around the woman, and not the unborn child. This helps to explain the appeal of the rhetoric of 'choice.' It offers the sense that women in crisis still have some control over their future, and it allows women who may dislike abortion themselves to still seem compassionate toward other women in crisis."

Abortion, the Least of Three Evils,
The Psychologic Dynamic of
How Women Feel About Abortion,
Paul Swope The Caring Foundation,
10 Park Avenue, Derry, NH 03038

CHAPTER 4

DISCRIMINATION

*HAS DISCRIMINATION EVER BEEN LEGAL
BEFORE?
YES, SADLY SO.*

Discrimination by Race

The Nazi Holocaust was a terrifying example of legal racial discrimination. It began with the elimination of almost 300,000 Aryan German citizens who were "defective" and ended with the elimination of 6 million members of a race that was also judged to be "defective." (Add perhaps another 6 million Gypsies, war prisoners, and other nationalities, e.g., Poles.)

First, Jews were labeled subhuman through the use of names such as "vermin, garbage, subhuman, trash," etc. Then, legal personhood and equal protection by law were removed in 1936 by the Supreme Court of Germany. Finally, the killing began. Detailed documentation is available in *Assisted Suicide & Euthenasia, Past & Present* by J. Willke. (Hayes Publishing Co., Cincinnati); *A Sign For Cain*, (Wertham, 1966, MacMillin, Chapters 8 and 9); and *The Abortion Holocaust* (Brennan, Landmark Press).

Discrimination by Skin Color

In the U.S., from Colonial times, there was legal discrimination on the basis of skin color.

This ugly chapter in our history came to its legal climax with the Dred Scott Decision by the U.S. Supreme Court in 1857, three years before Lincoln's election and the U.S. Civil War. In essence, it confirmed that black people had no legal rights and were the property of their owners. The analogy to abortion is direct. Complete details are available on this analogy in *Abortion and Slavery — History Repeats* (Willke, Hayes Publishing Co., Cincinnati, 1984 [$5.50]).

Discrimination by Age

If you are conceived in France, your life is legally protected after 12 weeks. In the State of Washington, just prior to the *Roe vs. Wade* Decision, life was protected at 16 weeks; Sweden was 20. In New York, it had been 24 weeks; England was 28; and presently in the U.S., life is legally protected only after birth. Nobel prize winner, Dr. James Watson, has suggested "three days after birth."

At first glance, one is likely to comment that all of the above disagree. But look closer at the ethic, the logic, and the criteria. They all agree. They agree that you can discriminate against an entire class of living humans on the basis of age. They just don't agree on which age.

But note well that in the U.S. today there are 3.5 taxpayers for every retired person who draws Social Security or other tax-funded pensions. By the year 2040, there will only be 1.5 taxpayers to support each retired person (assuming no rise in the current birth rate).

This will be a completely impossible economic situation. The answer could be rather simple and direct. Copy the ethic, the logic, and the criteria of today's fatal discrimination on the basis of age — only start at the other end of the spectrum.

Perhaps a court could rule that everyone over 80 years of age was no longer a legal person. Or maybe it would have to be lowered to 75 — or even to . . . ?

Discrimination by Handicap

Handicap is one of the two most accepted reasons for abortion. But remember, before birth and after birth, it is the same patient and the same handicap. Is it any wonder that we are increasingly seeing the same "solution" after birth (killing by infanticide — see chapter 25) as before birth (killing by abortion)?

Since when have we given doctors the right to kill the patient to "cure" the disease?

Discrimination by Place-of-Residence

This is abortion in the U.S. It is discrimination on the basis of place-of-residence. If the child in the womb can escape from his first place-of-residence (the womb) the day before his scheduled execution, his life is protected by full force of law. As long as he remains in the womb or has not yet fully exited it during delivery, however, he can be killed at his mother's request.

CHAPTER 5

SOMETHING OLD, SOMETHING NEW

Are our old scientific studies obsolete and useless? Are our new scientific studies relevant and useful? Must we reject the old? Must we rely primarily only on the new? What is the balance here?

Some old studies need to be replaced by newer, more accurate, more detailed, more relevant studies. That is obvious. What serious students of this or any other issue have to keep in mind, however, is that certain older studies are classics and do not need repeating.

What is also obvious is that some new studies may prove to be inaccurate and will not stand the test of time.

Let us use a medical example. If a pregnant woman contracts Rubella or German Measles in her first trimester, there is a chance that her baby will be born with a fetal abnormality. In the early 1960s, there was an extensive rubella epidemic in the U.S. Many pregnant women were infected and there was a tragic harvest of fetal abnormality. Many studies were done at that time. This book includes a report on a summary of the results obtained from that rather extensive research through an article in the *Lancet*. Note that there have been no major studies on this since that time. Why not?

One reason has been that there has not been another rubella epidemic, and, with rubella vaccine, the chance for another one is not too likely. The other and quite relevant reason is that the studies done back then were thorough, well done, and came up with definitive answers. In the light of this, there is little stimulus to repeat all of those studies. Therefore, the *Lancet* article from 1964 stands as a classic. It is an "old" study, but unless there are major medical changes in this field, the studies are as valid today, as when they were first made.

What about knowledge of fetal development? When Hamblin published in the *Journal of the American Medical Association* in October of 1964, a study showing that brain waves had been recorded forty days after fertilization, it was a scientific breakthrough. We note a second study twenty years later in the *New England Journal of Medicine* confirming this information. Since that time, the threshold has not been pushed back any further. Is there need then to do repeat studies to rediscover what has already been discovered and to re-report on what has already been reported? Apparently, fetal researchers do not think so, as we find no further studies of this nature in the literature. Accordingly, we print these two studies mentioned, along with other well-researched studies on fetal development, which are "old," but factual. The reader will note that most of the information and studies in this book on fetal development are classics (i.e., old) and will remain our guides unless and until proven false.

When something new occurs, there is a flurry of excitement, and dozens, sometimes hundreds, of studies are done exploring that area. One example in recent years has been the French abortion pill, RU 486. Another has been the relationship of abortion to breast cancer. Another has been research on stem cells and on cloning. We can be confident that new studies in these areas will continue until the evidence is firm and definitive conclusions can be drawn. These demonstrate the value of new studies where new information is needed. The evidence is explored, and the newest facts gleaned from the research continue to be reported.

Conclusion:

The reader of *Love Them Both* will find many new facts between the covers, many new interpretations of previously reported facts and, in a few places, questioning of old assumptions. The reader will also find a significant number of questions and answers from previous editions of this book's predecessors, *Handbook on Abortion, Abortion: Questions & Answers,* and the first edition of this book. Some of these facts were analyzed and reported on earlier and remain unchallenged. Hence, we offer you some known facts along with some fascinating new information. We hope all of it will be of value to you.

PART II
THE LAW

Chapter

CHAPTER 6

TWO INFAMOUS DAYS IN THE U.S.A.

MARCH 6, 1857
JANUARY 22, 1973

1857:

On March 6, 1857, the U.S. Supreme Court finally decided a very vexing question which had troubled the citizens of the United States for many years. In the landmark Dred Scott Decision, the court ruled once and for all that black people were not legal "persons" according to the U.S. Constitution. A slave was the property of the owner and could be bought and sold, used, or even killed by the owner at the owner's discretion. The ruling was final. It was by the highest court in the land.

Those who opposed slavery protested, but were met with the retort: "So you oppose slavery? It is against your moral, religious, and ethical convictions? Well, you don't have to own a slave, but don't impose your morality on the slave owner. He has the right to choose to own a slave. The Supreme Court has spoken. Slavery is legal."

But not for long. It took a bloody civil war to stop

slavery. It took the 13th, 14th, and 15th Amendments to the Constitution to legally grant freedom, civil rights, and voting rights. From a socioeconomic view, we are still striving for full equality.

1973:

On January 22, 1973, the U.S. Supreme Court finally decided a very vexing question which had troubled the citizens of the United States for many years. In a landmark Decision, the court ruled, once and for all, that unborn humans were not legal "persons" according to the U.S. Constitution. An unborn baby was the property of the owner (mother), and she could have the baby killed at her request because of her "health" (social distress). This could be done at any time until birth. The ruling was final. It was by the highest court in the land.

Those who opposed abortion protested, but were met with a retort that seemed an echo of slavery days. "So you oppose abortion? It is against your moral, religious, and ethical convictions? Well, you don't have to have an abortion, but don't impose your morality on the mother (the owner). She has the right to choose to have an abortion. The Supreme Court has spoken. Abortion is legal."

The goal of a Constitutional Amendment or reversal by the Court is still ahead. But the pro-life movement continues to grow. It is now the largest grass-roots movement in the history of the U.S.A.

Then, the discrimination was on the basis of skin color. Now, it is on the basis of age and place of residence (living in the womb).

SLAVERY	ABORTION
Dred Scott, 1857 7-2 Decision	*Roe vs. Wade*, 1973 7-2 Decision
Black Non-person	Unborn Non-person
Property of owner	Property of Owner (Mother)
Choose to Buy-Sell-Kill	Choose to Keep or Kill
Abolitionists Should Not Impose Morality on Slaveowner	Pro-lifers Should Not Impose Morality on Mother
Slavery Is Legal	Abortion Is Legal

CHAPTER 7

LEGAL PRE-ROE

Were there laws against abortion in the early American colonies?

The colonies inherited English Common Law and largely operated under it until well into the 19th century. English Common Law forbade abortion. Abortion prior to quickening was a misdemeanor. Abortion after quickening (feeling life) was a felony. This bifid punishment, inherited from earlier ecclesiastic law, stemmed from earlier "knowledge" regarding human reproduction.

When did this change?

In the early 1800s it was discovered that human life did not begin when she "felt life," but rather at fertilization. As a direct result of this, the British Parliament in 1869 passed the "Offenses Against the Persons Act," eliminating the above bifid punishment and dropping the felony punishment back to fertilization. One by one, across the middle years of the 19th century, every then-present state passed its own law against abortion. By 1860, 85% of the population lived in states which had prohibited abortion with new laws. These laws, preceding and following the British example, moved the felony punishment from quickening back to conception.

J. Dellapenna, The History of Abortion:
Technology, Morality, and Law,
University of Pittsburgh Law Review, 1979

Quay, *Justifiable Abortion-Medical and Legal Foundations*,
49 Georgetown Univ., Law Review, 1960-1961

Who was punished?

Abortionists, if convicted, were sent to jail for varying lengths of time. There is no record of any having been executed.

Were women punished?

The definitive study on this gives the lie to Planned Parenthood's ads which claimed: "If you had a miscarriage, you could be prosecuted for murder."

Washington Post April 27, 1981

Studying two hundred years of legal history, the American Center for Bioethics concluded:

"No evidence was found to support the proposition that women were prosecuted for undergoing or soliciting abortions. The charge that spontaneous miscarriages could result in criminal prosecution is similarly insupportable. There are no documented instances of prosecution of such women for murder or for any other species of homicide; nor is there evidence that states that had provisions enabling them to prosecute women for procuring abortions ever applied those laws. The vast majority of the courts were reluctant to implicate women, even in a secondary fashion, through complicity and conspiracy charges. Even in those rare instances where an abortionist persuaded the court to recognize the woman as his accomplice, charges were not filed against her. In short, women were not prosecuted for abortions. Abortionists were. The charges of Planned Parenthood and other "pro-choice" proponents are without factual basis. Given the American legal system's reliance on precedent, it is unlikely that enforcement of future criminal sanctions on abortion would deviate substantially from past enforcement patterns."

Women and Abortion, Prospects of Criminal Charges
Monograph, American Center for Bioethics,
422 C St., NE, Washington, DC 20002, Spring 1983

But why were so few abortionists prosecuted?

Because there were no scientifically accurate methods in those days to diagnose early pregnancy. The only absolute diagnosis of pregnancy, medically and legally binding, was for the doctor to hear the fetal heart, and that was only possible after four and five months. Prior to that, the abortionist could claim that her menstrual period was late or that she had some other malady, and that all he did was to bring on her period.

It is all but impossible to convict a person of murder unless the body can be produced — the corpus delicti. Since they were almost never able to obtain and examine the tissue removed from the woman's body, in a court of law it was almost impossible to prove (a) that she had been pregnant and (b) that the actions of the abortionist had terminated the pregnancy.

In practice, abortionists, therefore, were typically only prosecuted when the woman had been injured or killed. It was not until the advent of x-rays in the early 1900s (fetal bones visible at three months), and later hormone tests for pregnancy in the 1940s, that pregnancy could be legally confirmed in its earlier weeks.

When did the first state legalize abortion?

In 1967 Colorado and California legalized abortion. By June, 1970, when the State of New York passed the first Abortion-on-Demand Law (24-week limit), it became the 16th state to allow abortion. Due to an extremely loose interpretation of "mental health," California also had de facto abortion-on-demand. Alaska and Hawaii had liberal laws. Laws in the other 12 states, which included Arkansas, Colorado, Delaware, Georgia, Kansas, Maryland, Mississippi, New Mexico, North Carolina, Oregon, South Carolina and Virginia, were very restrictive, typically allowing abortion only for pregnancies due to assault rape, incest and life of the mother as well as for severe fetal handicap.

No more laws passed after that?

Between the passage of New York's law in 1970 and the Supreme Court's decision of January '73, no more state legislatures voluntarily passed permissive abortion laws. Florida did because of a court order. The other 33 states debated the issue in their legislatures, and all 33 voted against permitting abortion for any reason except to save the mother's life.

In April of '72, New York State repealed its most permissive law. Governor Nelson Rockefeller vetoed the repeal, and the law remained in force. In the November '72 elections, however, so many pro-abortion legislators were swept out of office that the New York General Assembly had enough votes to override the governor's veto. Plans were made to again repeal the law when that legislature reconvened in 1973. Before it could act, however, the Supreme Court handed down the *Roe v. Wade* decision and nothing was done.

The old state laws were challenged?

Yes. Having been stopped cold in their attempts to legalize abortion in any additional states, after 1970 pro-abortion forces challenged the legality of laws in many of the other states. These challenges to the constitutionality of the laws forbidding abortion in these states met with rather consistent results. In about one-third of the states, most of which had already legalized abortion by statute, these laws were declared unconstitutional in varying degrees. Two-thirds of the federal courts in the states, however, declared existing laws to be constitutional. In general, the states on the east and west coasts were permissive, whereas the broad sweep between the Alleghenies and Rockies remained pro-life.

There were referenda?
Yes. After the pro-abortionists were stopped in the legislatures and in the courts, they tried referenda in two states to allow abortion-on-demand until 20 weeks in the November 1972 election.
- North Dakota, only 12% Catholic, voted 78% against abortion.
- Michigan, an industrial state (pre-polled at 60% pro-abortion), voted 63% against abortion.

The tide had turned?
Yes. It seemed obvious that most people did not want abortion. But, on January 22, 1973, the U.S. Supreme Court ruled and abortion was imposed from the top down.

Roe vs. Wade, U.S. Supreme Court
410 U.S. 113, 1973
Doe vs. Bolton, U.S. Supreme Court
410 U.S. 179, 1973

CHAPTER 8

POST *ROE VS. WADE*

On January 22, 1973, the U.S. Supreme Court struck down all laws in every state that in any way had protected the lives of developing unborn children. It legalized abortion in all 50 states, for the full nine months of pregnancy, for social and economic reasons.

- It created a new, basic constitutional right for women in the right to privacy which the Supreme Court had created only a few years earlier. That right to privacy was "broad enough to encompass a woman's right to terminate her pregnancy."
- It stated that the law protects only "legal persons" and that "legal personhood does not exist prenatally."
- It authorized no legal restrictions on abortion in the first three months.
- No restrictions from then until viability, except those needed to make the procedure safer for the mother.
- Abortion was allowed until birth, if one licensed physician judged it necessary for the mother's "health."

Roe vs. Wade, U.S. Supreme Court
410 U.S. 113, 1973
Doe vs. Bolton, U.S. Supreme Court
410 U.S. 179, 1973

How did this decision define "health?"

The Court said that abortion could be performed: ". . . in the light of all factors — physical, emotional, psychological, familial, and the woman's age — relevant to the well being of the patient. All these factors may relate to health."

Doe vs. Bolton, U.S. Supreme Court,
No. 70-40, IV, p. 11, Jan. 1973

"Maternity or additional offspring may force upon the woman a distressful life and future. Psychological harm may be imminent. Mental and physical health may be taxed by child care. There is also the distress for all concerned associated with the unwanted child, and there is the problem of bringing a child into a family already unable, psychologically or otherwise, to care for it. In other cases, the additional difficulties and continuing stigma of unwed motherhood may be involved. All these are factors that the woman and the responsible physician will consider in consultation."

Roe vs. Wade, U.S. Supreme Court,
No. 70-18, p. 38, Jan. 1973

But these reasons are social reasons, not health reasons.

That is the situation! The U.S. Supreme Court has specifically defined the word "health" to include a broad group of social and economic problems, as judged by the mother herself. It has further specifically forbidden any state to forbid abortion at any time prior to birth for these reasons, if the mother can find a doctor to do the abortion.

This is also true in every nation in the world. If abortion is allowed for "health," that state or nation has abortion-on-demand; e.g., in England in 1986, 132,000 of 135,000 legal abortions were due to mental health.

The Times, 26 March '88

Then the Supreme Court allowed abortion-on-demand until birth?

Yes.

Can you prove this?

The official report of the U.S. Senate Judiciary Committee, issued after extensive hearings on the Human Life Federalism Amendment (proposed by Senators Hatch and Eagleton), concluded:

"Thus, the [Judiciary] Committee observes that no significant legal barriers of any kind whatsoever exist today in the United States for a woman to obtain an abortion for any reason during any stage of her pregnancy."

Report, Committee on the Judiciary, U.S. Senate, on Senate Joint
Resolution 3, 98th Congress, 98-149, June 7, 1983, p. 6

"Our nationwide policy of abortion-on-demand through all nine months of pregnancy was neither voted on by our people nor enacted by our legislators."

R. Reagan, *Abortion & the Conscience of the Nation*,
Thomas Nelson Publishers, 1984, p. 15

Ever since 1973, many had denied that late term elective abortions were legal and/or did not exist. This was totally debunked during the debate on partial-birth abortions, when it was conclusively shown that such abortions were done even late in the third trimester. An example has been abortionist George Tiller ("the killer") in Wichita, Kansas, who specalizes in late second and third trimester abortions

What was the pro-life response to the *Roe vs. Wade* decision?

In the early years it was felt that a reversal by the Court itself was highly unlikely. Accordingly, great effort was expended in formulating and promoting an amendment to the Constitution to reverse these two decisions. There are two methods of doing this. One is through constitutional convention, and the other is through Congress and state legislatures.

What amendments have been proposed?

The original wording formulated in 1974 by the National Right to Life (NRLC) Committee was:

THE NRLC HUMAN LIFE AMENDMENT

Section 1: With respect to the right to life, the word "Person" as used in this article and in the Fifth and Fourteenth Articles of Amendment to the Constitution of the United States applies to all human beings irrespective of age, health, function, or condition of dependency, including their unborn offspring at every stage of their biologic development.

Section 2: No unborn person shall be deprived of life by any person, provided, however, that nothing in this article shall prohibit a law permitting only those medical procedures required to prevent the death of the mother.

Section 3: The Congress and the several States shall have power to enforce this article by appropriate legislation.

Later, another version was introduced which came to be called:

THE PARAMOUNT AMENDMENT

The paramount right to life is vested in each human being from the moment of fertilization without regard to age, health, or condition of dependency.

Then, in 1981, these two versions were merged into a new NRLC Amendment often called:

THE NRLC UNITY HUMAN LIFE AMENDMENT

Section 1: The right to life is a paramount and most fundamental right of a person.

Section 2: With respect to the right to life guaranteed to persons by the Fifth and Fourteenth Articles of Amendment to the Constitution, the word "person" applies to all human beings, irrespective of age, health, function, or condition of dependency, including their unborn offspring, at every state of their biological development, including fertilization.

Section 3: No unborn person shall be deprived of life by any person, provided, however, that nothing in this article shall prohibit a law allowing justification to be shown for only those medical procedures required to prevent the death of either the pregnant woman or her unborn offspring, as long as such law requires every reasonable effort be made to preserve the life of each.

Section 4: Congress and the several States shall have power to enforce this article by appropriate legislation.

Would all three reverse the Supreme Court Decision?

Yes, but they would go further. Prior to the 1973 Supreme Court Decision, the U.S. had a de facto states' rights situation under which each state could decide if it wanted to forbid or to permit abortion and to what degree. These amendments would reverse the 1973 Supreme Court Decision, but would also go further and mandate federal protection for the unborn in all 50 states.

Many legal experts had thought that such protection was already present in the 14th Amendment to the Constitution; but, in the late 1960s, 17 states passed laws to allow abortion for various reasons. Pro-life leaders do not want this to happen again. Accordingly, these amendments would revoke the pre-existing states' rights situation and mandate universal civil rights for all living humans — born or unborn.

Are these amendments likely to be passed?

In order to be reported out to the states, such an amendment must receive a two-thirds vote in both the U.S. Senate and in the U.S. House of Representatives. The three above amendments would provide federal constitutional protection in every state to all children from the time of conception. Such an amendment is not a likely possibility in the immediate foreseeable future. Accordingly, a lesser version was attempted.

That was a states' rights amendment?

Yes. This amendment was proposed, debated and voted on in the U.S. Senate in June of 1983. The vote was 49 for, 50 against. It failed, as it needed two-thirds majority. This amendment was the "Hatch-Eagleton" amendment. It simply stated "a right to abortion is not secured by this constitution."

If passed and ratified, it would have reversed the Supreme Court decisions and returned the nation to the condition prior to the 1973 Supreme Court decision when each state had the power to forbid abortion.

What was the Helms Human Life Bill?

This attempted a different route. Its goal was the passage of a congressional statute declaring that unborn humans were legal persons. This would have been challenged and gone to the Supreme Court, which at

41

that time had a strong pro-abortion majority. The bill was defeated in the Senate.

What of the Constitutional Convention method?

This method has not been used since the first constitutional convention approved the first ten amendments, the Bill of Rights. Many states have proposed such a "con-con," but the required number of states, 34, has not been reached, and since the mid-1980s there has been little public pressure to call such a convention.

The court decided subsequent cases?

Yes, and the later decisions removed all of the minimal constraints imposed by the '73 decisions.

- Spousal and parental consent was ruled unconstitutional. Prohibition of salt poisoning abortion on medical grounds was ruled unconstitutional.
  Planned Parenthood vs. Danforth, 428 U.S. 52, 1976

- Viability is what the doctor says it is.
  Colautti vs. Franklin, 429 U.S. 379, 1979

- The State is not required to fund "medically necessary" (i.e., elective) abortions for the poor.
  Harris vs McRae, 448 U.S. 297, 1980

- Informed consent is not required. A waiting period is unconstitutional. Mandatory hospitalization for second trimester abortions is unconstitutional. "Humane" disposal of fetal remains is unconstitutional.
  City of Akron vs. Akron Center for Reproductive Health, 103 S. Ct. 2481, 1983

- Informed consent is unconstitutional.
  Thornberg vs. Am. Col., OB&GYN, 106 S. Ct. 2169, 1986

The thrust of all of the above was to effectively eliminate any barriers to induced abortion for any reason throughout the nine months of pregnancy. But then a small change occurred in the Webster decision.

What was the Webster decision?

In February of '89 the Court broadened the restrictions that could be put on the use of tax money to pay for abortions. It also approved a requirement in the State of Missouri that after 20 weeks the abortionist must do viability testing on the preborn baby.

Perhaps its greatest significance was that it was the first loosening of the steady parade of decisions above, and that it held promise of more to come.

U.S. Supreme Court, Webster vs. Reproductive Health Services,
Oct. Term 1988, No. 88-605

The next major change occurred with the Casey decision.

What was the Casey decision?

In June 1992 the U.S. Supreme Court decided *Planned Parenthood of Southeast Pennsylvania vs. Casey*. In it the Court reversed some of its earlier decisions. It ruled that certain reasonable regulations of abortion could be enacted. These included parental notification of a minor daughter's scheduled abortion, informed consent, a 24-hour waiting period and confidential reporting. It struck down a spousal notification clause.

It clearly reaffirmed *Roe vs. Wade* however. In doing so, it rejected *Roe's* trimester scheme and spoke to a dividing line at viability. It essentially rejected the right of privacy as its justification and adopted a new "liberty" standard.

The above restrictions would not apply if they "unduly burdened" her right to abortion. The original definition of "health" remained, and so abortion remained legal until birth.

U.S. Supreme Court, June 29, 1992
Planned Parenthood of S.E. PA vs. Casey No. 91-744 and 91-902

Could the states pass laws?

Until the Webster and Casey decisions, the states were completely handcuffed. The only laws that the Supreme Court allowed them to pass were laws forbidding the use of public tax money for abortions.

During the 1980s, the federal Congress, by statute, had forbidden federal funding for Medicaid abortions through the famous Hyde amendment. Subsequently, abortion funding was withheld from federal employees' health insurance, the military, public health, Peace Corps and other areas administered by the federal government. Funding was withheld by executive order from overseas organizations that promoted abortion. Funding was cut off from the United Nations Fund for Population Activity and finally from the District of Columbia. During these years, where indicated and possible, most of the states followed suit by state statute or by initiative referendum.

And after the Webster and Casey decisions?

Given considerably more leeway, after the Casey decision, many states passed laws that included:
- Requiring parental notification for the abortion of a minor daughter.
- Some required consent.
- Requiring informed consent of the woman.
- Requiring abortion clinic regulations.
- Limiting fetal experimentation.
- Aid for adoption.

Partial-Birth Abortion

In 1995, Ohio passed the first law forbidding partial-birth abortion. It was declared unconstitutional.

In 1996, a reformulated law was passed by the U.S. Congress but was vetoed by President Clinton. Two years later a second passage met a similar fate.

Meanwhile, almost 30 state legislators had passed laws to forbid this method of killing babies during delivery. Such bans from Nebraska and Wisconsin were considered by the U.S. Supreme Court and struck down by a 5-4 vote in June 2000 *(Stenberg v. Cahart)*.

What of laws against "rescue"?

In response to the somewhat increase in violence against abortion facilities and the shooting of 5 abortionists and clinic staff, U.S. Congress passed the Freedom of Access to Clinics Act (FACE). In addition, the Supreme Court ruled that the RICO (Anti-Racketeering Act) did apply to peaceful abortion protesters. The sum total effect of these draconian laws sharply chilled, not just the symbolic, non-violent sit-ins, but also what had been completely legal — the common First Amendment-protected, peaceful sidewalk counseling and picketing outside of abortion chambers.

It is of interest that the FACE Act has been turned back on an abortionist. A Federal Appeals Court (11th Circuit) ruled for a woman who was forced to be aborted. This effectively criminalized forced abortion.

Jane Roe II v. Aware Women Clinic for Choice
E. Windle et al. U.S. Ct. of Appeals
11th Circuit No. 00-10231, June 8, 2001

What of Roe and Doe?

The Roe of *Roe vs. Wade* was Norma McCorvey. The Doe of Doe vs. Bolton was Sandra Cano. Both have become converts to the pro-life cause.

What are your goals now?

The ultimate human rights goal remains an amendment to the U.S. Constitution which will guarantee equal protection by law to all living humans from the time their life begins at fertilization until natural death.

The intermediate goal remains the complete reversal of the 1973 *Roe vs. Wade* and *Doe vs. Bolton* decisions by the Supreme Court. This will return to the citizens of each state a right and a responsibility that they had for the first 200 years of our nation's history. This will return the regulation of abortion to each state through its elected state officials, without interference by the federal courts.

Current immediate goals include passage of regulatory legislation at state level to eliminate at least some of the worst abuses of the abortion industry, through parental notification and consent, spousal notification, informed consent, clinic regulations, waiting periods, adequate record keeping, requiring high malpractice insurance, etc.

CHAPTER 9

HEALTH

MORE SPECIFICALLY, MENTAL HEALTH

In discussing abortion, and abortion for the mother's health, it is absolutely crucial to know what "health" means, legally and in practice, regarding abortion.

"Health" was defined in detail by the U.S. Supreme Court. The Court said that abortion could be performed: ". . . in the light of all factors — physical, emotional, psychological, familial, and the woman's age — relevant to the well being of the patient. All these factors may relate to health."

Roe vs. Wade, January 22, 1973

And in its companion decision, "Maternity or additional offspring may force upon the woman a distressful life and future. Psychological harm may be imminent. Mental and physical health may be taxed by child care. There is also the distress for all concerned, associated with the unwanted child, and there is the problem of bringing a child into a family already unable, psychologically or otherwise, to care for it."

Doe vs. Bolton, January 22, 1973

In a concurring opinion, Justice Douglas further elaborated what "health" meant when, in law, it related to abortion. He detailed if she had to: "endure the discomforts of pregnancy; to incur the pain, higher mortality rate, and aftereffects of childbirth; to abandon educational plans; to sustain loss of income; to forego the satisfactions of careers; to tax further mental and physical health in providing childcare, and, in some cases, to bear the lifelong stigma of unwed motherhood."

Roe vs. Wade, January 22, 1973

This definition of "health" has been adopted internationally. As a result, in any nation, if abortion is allowed for the woman's "health," that country permits abortion-on-demand unless other aspects of its laws add restrictions.

The World Health Organization of the United Nations defined it as including social, emotional and economic well being of the woman, as defined by the woman herself.

Let's narrow it down to mental health, in the psychological sense, and ask–are there mental health reasons for abortion?

No! The woman with mental health problems is far more likely to experience post-abortion emotional and psychological problems than a more stable woman. Four classic references here are these:

"Women with a history of psychiatric disturbance were three times as likely to have some psychiatric disturbance" after an abortion as others who had no such history."

E. Greenglass, "Abortion & Psychiatric Disturbance," *Canadian Psych. Assn. Jour.,* vol. 21, no. 7, Nov. 1976, pp. 453-459

Dr. Charles Ford and his associates at UCLA reported the same finding.

"The more serious the psychiatric diagnosis, the less

beneficial was the abortion."
C. Ford et al., "Abortion, Is It a Therapeutic Procedure in Psychiatry?" *JAMA*, vol. 218, no. 8, Nov. 22, 1971, pp. 1173-1178

"The more severely ill the psychiatric patient, the worse is her post-abortion psychiatric state."
E. Sandberg, "Psychology of Abortion" In *Comprehensive Handbook of Psychiatry*, 3rd ed. Kaplan & Friedman Publishers, 1980

All of these support the original official statement of the World Health Organization in 1970:

"Serious mental disorders arise more often in women with previous mental problems. Thus, the very women for whom legal abortion is considered justified on psychiatric grounds are the ones who have the highest risk of post-abortion psychiatric disorders."

Then "mental illness," as a reason for abortion, is just an excuse?
Precisely.

What about psychological problems after abortion?
When your authors wrote *Handbook on Abortion* in 1971, there were a few murmurings about post-abortion problems, but little was known. We then saw the negatives as mostly physical.

When we wrote *Abortion: Questions & Answers* in 1985, physical damage, while still a major problem, was given less emphasis, and negative psychological aftermath was being seriously investigated.

With the publication of this book, far more is known about what is now called Post-Abortion Syndrome which clearly is a post traumatic stress syndrome.

A Post Traumatic Stress Syndrome?
Yes. This type of problem was first seen in large numbers in Vietnam veterans, but did not manifest it-

self until a decade after they returned. The same ten-year delay has been evident with abortion.

T. Keane, Vietnam Vets Trauma
disorder level at 15%, *Am. Med. News*,
L. Abraham, Dec. 2, 1988, p. 2

What is Post-Abortion Syndrome (PAS)?

Many women are very ambivalent about being aborted but do go ahead. Those around her told her (and she told herself) that it wouldn't bother her. Then symptoms occurred. She told herself it can't be the abortion causing them, and then into play came her two major psychological defense mechanisms: **Repression** and **Denial**.

For some this works successfully. For others, it shades off to manageable distress, to severe and life-changing upset and even to suicide.

There is a delay?

Yes! Her initial response in most cases is a feeling of relief. Then, with repression and denial, she avoids the problem, usually for years — 5 years is common, 10 or 20 not unusual.

But then, for some, the negative feelings bubble up and break through. Often the precipitating event is: she has a baby, or a close friend or relative has a baby that she has close contact with. She finds out she is sterile, or other life-changing events.

What are the symptoms of PAS?

Guilt is ever-present in many guises, along with regret, remorse, shame, lowered self-esteem, insomnia, numbing of feelings, dreams and nightmares, flash-backs, anniversary reactions. There often is hostility, and even hatred, toward men. This can include her husband, and she may become sexually dysfunctional. Crying, despair and depression are usual, even at times with suicide attempts. Recourse to alcohol or drugs to mask the pain is frequent, sometimes leading to sexual promiscuity. There is also a numbing and coldness in place of more normal warmth and maternal tenderness.

Is this due to religious guilt feelings?

Perhaps, in some it is a factor, but most women reported on in the early studies were unchurched at the time.

Perhaps they had seen pictures of fetuses?

Again, not most. Most did not know "it" was a "baby" when they aborted.

But I've heard that the American Psychological Association says that PAS doesn't exist.

This group has been strongly pro-abortion, and this definitely colors its thinking. But during the past two decades, there have been dozens of national conferences on PAS. There are many professional articles and over 20 books adding more and more authentication to its existence and knowledge about it.

Further, every one of the almost 4,000 pro-life pregnancy help centers in the U.S. now has found that an increasing percentage of their time is now devoted to treating PAS women.

But so many studies deny PAS.

True, and most are invalid for two reasons:

(1) *Timing*: Most studies have investigated feelings for only a few weeks or months, post-abortion, when she is still feeling relief that her problem is gone. Since the delay before PAS symptoms intrude is often 5 years or more, these studies are invalid.

(2) *Superficiality*: Her repression and denial push this deep into her subconsciousness. If the survey is done by questionnaire or single interview, she routinely denies problems. These studies are invalid. Only by lengthy psychological testing and counseling can she

often admit to some symptoms, much less tie them to the abortion she so desperately wants to forget.

You mean most studies miss PAS?

Yes, most studies show few emotional problems — only a sense of relief, but "What women really feel at the deepest level about abortion is very different from what they say in reply to questionnaires." A Canadian study polled a group of women who had previously completed a questionnaire in which they denied having problems from an abortion. One-half of this group was randomly chosen for in-depth psychotherapy. "What emerged from psychotherapy was in sharp contrast [to the questionnaires], even when the woman had rationally considered abortion to be inevitable, the only course of action." It was demonstrated that the conscious, rationalized decision for an abortion can coexist with profound rejection of it at the deepest level. Despite surface appearances, abortion leaves behind deeper feelings "invariably of intense pain, involving bereavement and a sense of identification with the foetus."

I. Kent et al., "Emotional Sequelae of Elective Abortion,"
British College of Med. Jour., vol. 20, no. 4, April 1978
I. Kent, "Abortion Has Profound Impact,"
Family Practice News, June 1980, p. 80

Are there valid studies?

Yes, and two meta-analyses:

James Rogers, who carefully examined over 400 published studies, pointed to the almost universal use of "poor methodology and research design" and "grossly substandard power characteristics." He concluded that "the question of psychological sequelae of abortion is not closed."

J. Rogers et al., "Validity of Existing Controlled
Studies Examining the Psychological Sequelae of
Abortion," *Perspectives on Science and Christian Faith*,
vol. 39, no. 1, Mar. 1987, pp. 20-29

Another concurred that existing research is methodologically flawed and that women who abort show more negative outcomes than those who deliver their babies.

E. Posavac et al., "Some Problems . . . Psychological Effects of Abortion," *Psychology & Health*, 5, 13-23

How about specific studies?
An excellent study thoroughly explaining and documenting PAS by the team that named this entity is:

A. Speckhard & V. Rue, Post. Ab. Syndrome: An Emerging Public Health Concern, *J. of Soc. Issues*, vol. 48, no. 3, 1992

and

E.J. Angelo, Psych. Sequelae of Abortion, Linacre Quart. vol. 59:2, May 1992

and

P. Ney et al., Mental Health & Abortion, *Psychiat. Jour., U. of Ottawa*, vol. 14, no. 4, 1989

and

L. DeVeber et al., Post Abortion Grief, *Psychol. Sequel. of Ab., Humane Med.*, Vol. 7, no. 3, Aug. '91, p. 203

Two excellent monographs are:

J. Brende, Post-Trauma Sequelae..Abortion.., *Trauma Rec. Pub.*, 458 Morning Glory Dr., Sparta, GA 31087

V. Rue, Post Abortion Trauma, *Life Dynamics*, 1994, P.O. Box 185, Lewisville, TX 75067

Does it ever lead to suicide?
A well-designed, national, record-based study from Finland has shown previously unreported light on pregnancy related deaths. This studied all 15-49 year female deaths for the years 1989-94 and identified any pregnancy related events in the 12 months before death.

Women who aborted were 3.5 times more likely to
die than who carried to term.

Total Deaths

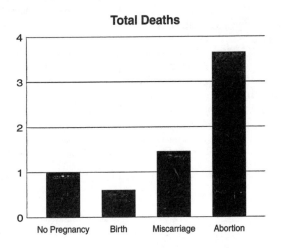

Post aborted women committed suicide seven times
more often than those who carried to term.

Deaths by Suicide

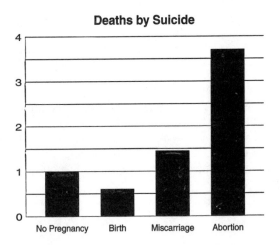

Those who aborted died in accidents four times oftener than those who carried to term.

Deaths by Accident

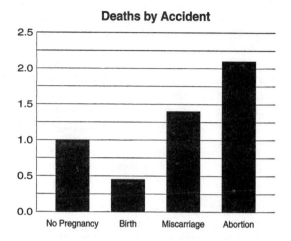

The risk of dying from homicide for post-aborted women was seven times higher than women in the general population and 13 times higher than those who delivered.

Deaths by Homicide

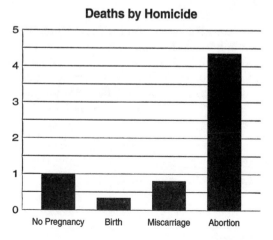

Why such dramatic differences?

Post-abortive women have consistently shown high levels of depression and suicidal ideation. Women with children may be more careful, while post-abortive women may be more prone to risk-taking, hence more accidents.

Post-abortive women are more significantly into substance abuse and have more tendencies to anger and violence, which could at times lead to homicide.

Overall, the emotionally upset post-aborted woman can engage in risk-taking behavior not engaged in by a mother with a child.

Pregnancy-associated deaths in Finland 1987-1994, M. Gissler et al, Acta obstet. Gynecal Scandi 76, 1997, p651-657.
(graphs from Elliot Institute, Dr. Reardon April 2000)

- In *Abortion: Questions and Answers*, your authors detail findings of Suicider's Anonymous that suicide, post-abortion, is several times more common than post-delivery.
- Substance abuse is five times higher after abortion. This is shown by a study by D. Reardon and P. Ney in the *American Journal of Drug and Alcohol Abuse*.

What about after abortion for fetal abnormality?
- Psychological stress has been found to be significantly higher three months later among women who terminated their pregnancies between 24 and 34 weeks in cases of fetal abnormality than it was for women who delivered such babies after 34 weeks.

Jan Hunfeld, et al., "emotional Reactions in Women Late in Pregnancy Following Ultrasound Diagnosis of Severe or Lethal Fetal Malformation," 13 Perinatal Diagnosis, pgs. 603,609, 1993.

• Protecting the child from abortion, in such cases, is better for the mother as well as for the baby. Studies of psychological complications that occur within two years of an abortion show that a disproportionate number of such complications were related to abortions for fetal abnormality.

Zolese & Blacker "The Psychological Complications of Therapeutic Abortions" 160 Br. J. Psych. Pg. 742, 1992.

Are these bad enough to elicit medical health claims?

Researchers in California, examining medical records for six years after abortion, found that post-abortive women were twice as likely to have two to nine treatments for mental health as those who delivered.

P. Coleman, D. Reardon "State funded abortions vs. Deliveries" presented at Am. Psychological Soc. 12th Annual Conv. July 26, 2000

How about an example from a non-Christian culture?

In Japan, where abortion has been legal and accepted for over four decades, a common custom is to conduct Mizuyo Kuyo services in honor of the god Jizo. This god has been made the patron saint of infants who died of starvation, abortion, or infanticide. Small baby statues, in his honor, are bought and dressed. Then, in a Buddhist Temple, rites of sorrow and reconciliation are carried out.

Does abortion have any negative effects on her other children?

In some cases, a definite "Survivor Syndrome" has been demonstrated. Children usually know that mother is pregnant. They also know when she "gets unpregnant." This may cause Survivor's Syndrome, similar to that of Jews who survived the holocaust. It is an irrational but real guilt of "why was I saved and why were they killed?" Dr. Ney has written about this.

Dr. Edward Sheridan of Georgetown University has observed also a fear and mistrust of the mother. Originally, a small child, sensing a sibling's arrival, doesn't welcome it. "When the baby suddenly disappears, the frightened child may get a warped sense of his own power to 'will people away.' Or, if he knows that his mother was an active agent in doing away with the sibling, he begins to fear her." A simple explanation of this was published in:

L. Bond, "The Surviving Sibling,"
Nat'l RTL News, Sept. 25, 1986.

It is also closely associated with child abuse: Dr. Phillip Ney, Professor of Psychiatry at the University of Christ Church, New Zealand, and later at the University of Calgary, Canada, while still at the University of British Columbia, published a widely read study of this. His analysis clearly pointed to the fact that abortion (and its acceptance of the violence of killing the unborn) lowered a parent's psychic resistance to violence and abuse of the born.

P. Ney, "Relationship Between Abortion & Child Abuse,"
Canada Jour. Psychiatry, vol. 24, 1979, pp. 610-620

Is there treatment for PAS?

Yes, but it is not easy. We first must note that only a few doctors are sensitized to the necessary dynamics of treatment. Specifically, most psychiatrists and psychologists aren't much help, nor are psychotropic drugs.

This requires a gradual healing process, and, during it, she must have ongoing close emotional support from one or several people who do not have to be trained professionals.

The place to start is your pro-life pregnancy help center. They can either work with her themselves and/or will know who can.

Basically, there are five steps to the healing process:
(1) Counter the denial. Bring this back into her consciousness and admit she was a party to killing her own baby.

(2) She must grieve over her lost child — tears, mourning — as for another loved one.

(3) Seek Divine forgiveness. This was not expected but seems essential for almost every woman.

(4) Forgive others. Difficult, again, but some of this is needed to complete the healing and get rid of her long repressed anger.

(5) Forgive herself. Not many get this far, but those who do have real inner peace.

What is absolutely crucial at every step in the above steps is compassionate empathy, support and understanding from one or more persons around her.

J. Willke, *Women Hurt*, Hayes Publishing Co. Sept., 2002

What about Men?

Everyone is aware that many men exploit and desert their pregnant partner. However, most do not. Some men desperately want the baby and when she defies him and gets an abortion, he feels it deeply.

For men, the most consistent and evident symptom is anger. There is frustration at not being able to protect his baby; he may turn to alcohol or drugs to dull the pain. He may become a workaholic, be a risk taker. This relationship almost always fails and, because of this, he may be unable to enter another. Other symptoms include nightmares, panic attacks, sexual dysfunction and other symptoms similar to those of women.

Men Hurt Too, B. Mattes, Hayes Publishing Company, Jan. 2000.

Your authors witnessed two suicides in one year of men devastated by their "baby being killed." One was a college student. The other, a 30-year-old police officer, married with children. Both left notes stating their suicide was due to their inability to cope with these abortions.

— There is healing in the mourning —

PART III
HUMAN LIFE

Chapter

CHAPTER 10

HUMAN LIFE

*Except for the pro-choice argument,
there are only two basic questions
to be answered when one considers
the abortion controversy.*

THE FIRST QUESTION IS:

When does human life begin?

The controversy swirling about the first question can be explained by the fact that different people use different standards of measurement by which to define "human life." Some would define it through a theologic or religious faith belief. Some would define "human life" using certain philosophic theories and beliefs. Others define "human life" by using biologic, scientific facts. Let us briefly explore the three methods of measurement.

THEOLOGIC
OR RELIGIOUS
FAITH BELIEF

This is best explained by considering three people who might state their respective beliefs as follows:

a) I believe in God. I believe He creates a soul. I believe the soul is created at fertilization. Therefore, I believe that human life begins at fertilization.

b) I also believe in God and a soul, but I don't believe the soul is created until birth (or some other time). Therefore, I believe that human life begins at birth (or some other time).

c) I don't believe in God or a soul.

Comment
- The above are statements of religious faith or its absence.
- None of the above religious faith beliefs can be factually proven.
- Each individual has a right to his or her own religious beliefs.

PHILOSOPHIC
THEORIES

Human life can be defined by using a wide variety of philosophic beliefs and theories. These use social or psychological rationale which can involve biologic mileposts.

Examples of philosophic definitions of when human life begins include the following: When there is consciousness; when there is movement; when there is brain function, or a heartbeat; when viable; at birth; when wanted; when there has been an exchange of love; when "humanized"; when this is a person (however "person" is defined); if mentally or physically normal, etc.

Comment

While admittedly arrived at through a certain reasoning process, all of the above remain theories.

None can be proven factually by science.

Each individual has a right to hold his own philosophic beliefs.

People of good will can and do differ completely on the correctness of any or all of the philosophic beliefs and theories mentioned.

BIOLOGIC FACTS

Biologic human life is defined by examining the scientific facts of human development. This is a field where there is no controversy, no disagreement. There is only one set of facts, only one embryology book is studied in medical school. The more scientific knowledge of fetal development that has been learned, the more science has confirmed that the beginning of any one human individual's life, biologically speaking, begins at the completion of the union of his father's sperm and his mother's ovum, a process called "conception," "fertilization" or "fecundation." This is so because this being, from fertilization, is alive, human, sexed, complete and growing.

Comment

- The above is not a religious faith belief.
- The above is not a philosophic theory.
- The above is not debatable, not questioned. It is a universally accepted scientific fact.

Note: Detailed biologic facts are in Chapters 11 and 12. Also see *Everyone Must Answer 2 Basic Questions*, J. Willke, Hayes Publishing

Must the question, "when does human life begin?" be answered?

If there is one absolutely essential function of a nation or state, it is to protect the lives of those who live within its boundaries. In order to carry out this solemn duty, it must first ask and answer when the life of its people begins.

What simple measure would you use to define Human Life?

We would ask:

Is this being alive?

Yes. He has the characteristics of life. That is, he can reproduce his own cells and develop them into a specific pattern of maturity and function. Or, more simply, he is not dead.

Is this being human?

Yes. This is a unique being, distinguishable totally from any other living organism, completely human in all of his or her characteristics, including the 46 human chromosomes, and can develop only into a fully mature human.

Is this being complete?

Yes. Nothing new will be added from the time of union of sperm and egg until the death of the old man or woman. The only changes are growth and development of what is already there at the beginning. All he needs is time to develop and mature.

But what if a person would still sincerely doubt that this is human life in the womb?

Even if a person did doubt the presence of actual

human life in the uterus at a particular time, what would be the fully human way to go? Perhaps a guide would be how we have always treated other human life when there has been a doubt that it exists. Would we not resolve a doubt in favor of life? We do not bury those who are doubtfully dead. We work frantically to help rescue entombed miners, a child lost in the mountains, or a person under a collapsed building. Doesn't a hunter withhold his shot until he knows that it is a deer and not another man? We suggest that the truly human way of thinking would be to give life the benefit of the doubt.

But isn't "conception" different from "fertilization?"

Ever since its discovery 150 years ago, both words were used to mean the union of sperm and ovum. In the 1960s, the U.S. Food and Drug Administration and the American College of OB & GYN agreed to attempt to redefine "conception" to mean implantation.

"Conception is the implantation of the blastocyst. It is not synonymous with fertilization."

> E. Hughes, ed., "*OB & GYN Terminology*,"
> Philadelphia: F. A. Davis,1972

This made it possible to call an intrauterine device a "contraceptive" even though it was an abortifacient.

But in 1982, lengthy hearings in the U.S. Senate and the two-volume report of the Human Life Bill defined "conception" and used it exclusively to mean the time of union of sperm and ovum.

> "*Human Life Bill*," U.S. Senate Common
> Judiciary, Subcommittee of Separation
> of Powers, 97th Congress, S-158,
> April-June 1982, Serial No. J-97-16

This "American" semantic distortion is not accepted in many other nations where "conception," "fertilization," and "fecundation" are all used interchangeably.

But when is it a person?

"Person" is defined in our dictionary in 14 different ways. Yellowstone Park is a person. So is General Motors. So are you. But the Supreme Court of the U.S. in 1857 ruled that black people were not persons, and in 1973 that unborn people were not persons. You answer this question by first inquiring what the questioner means by "a person."

Did Dr. Liley, the "Father of Fetology," think the tiny being was human?

Dr. Liley, who did the first fetal blood transfusion in the womb, said that seven days after fertilization:

". . . the young individual, in command of his environment and destiny, with a tenacious purpose, implants in the spongy lining and, with a display of physiological power, suppresses his mother's menstrual period. This is his home for the next 270 days, and to make it habitable, the embryo develops a placenta and a protective capsule of fluid for himself. He also solves, single-handed, the homograft problem, that dazzling feat by which foetus and mother, although immunological foreigners who could not exchange skin grafts nor safely receive blood from each other, nevertheless tolerate each other in parabiosis for nine months.

"We know that he moves with a delightful, easy grace in his buoyant world, that foetal comfort determines foetal position. He is responsive to pain and touch and cold and sound and light. He drinks his amniotic fluid, more if it is artificially sweetened, less it if is given an unpleasant taste. He gets hiccups and sucks his thumb. He wakes and sleeps. He gets bored with repetitive signals but can be taught to be alerted by a first signal for a second different one. And, finally, he determines his birthday, for, unquestionably, the onset of labour is a unilateral decision of the foetus.

"This, then, is the foetus we know and, indeed, we

66

each once were. This is the foetus we look after in modern obstetrics, the same baby we are caring for before and after birth, who, before birth, can be ill and need diagnosis and treatment just like any other patient."

A. Liley, "A Case Against Abortion," *Liberal Studies*,
Whitcombe & Tombs, Ltd., 1971

THE SECOND QUESTION IS:

Having answered the first question, we now must ask the second one. The first was a question of scientific facts. The second is one of values. It is:

Should all human life be given equal protection under the law, or can certain human lives be discriminated against, and, if so, on what basis?

The charter of the United States, the Declaration of Independence, is guiding here. "All men are created equal, that they are endowed by their creator with certain unalienable rights, that among these are the right to life, liberty and the pursuit of happiness."

The first right is "life," for, without it, there are no other rights.

But there are conflicting rights; who is to judge?

The ethical principle is that there is a hierarchy of rights, but that the right to life itself is supreme. There is a right to free speech, but not to shout "fire" in a theater. A man has a right to swing his fist, but that right stops at your nose. We all have the right to the pursuit of happiness, but we cannot achieve it by discriminating against, stealing from, injuring or killing others. Laws enforcing civil rights are of this nature. **Abortion is a civil rights, a human rights issue, and the basic right to life of all humans must be protected.**

But equal protection?

Every government has the right and duty to protect the lives of all living humans in that nation regardless of degree of dependency, degree of perfection, age, sex, or place of residence (living in or out of the womb). This protection should be guaranteed by its Constitution and should be enforced through due process of law.

The alternative to this is to allow, legislate or adjudicate a system in which there is discrimination against certain classes of living humans. In the case of abortion, there is discrimination against an entire class of living humans, on the basis of age (too young) and place of residence (still living in the womb). Such laws created by the U.S. Supreme Court and by other nations' Parliaments have granted to one living human (the woman) the legal right to kill another (her developing baby) in order to solve her own personal social problem. Should this fatal discrimination against an entire class of living humans continue? That is a question still before each nation, and one that will simply not go away.

A civilization will ultimately be judged by how it treats the smallest, the most dependent, the most innocent among its members. Did that nation cherish, protect, love and nourish them — or kill them?

But what of the pregnant woman?

It should be obvious to everyone that there are two living humans involved: the unborn child and his mother. For this nation to once again protect its unborn babies, but not to do everything humanly possible to help the mother, would be immoral. The woman with a problem pregnancy must, at the same time, be offered aid in solving her problems, to help her through that distressing time.

If, in fact, her very life is threatened physically, then the ideal is to save both. But if, in treating her, the fetal baby is lost, such may be an unfortunate result. Your authors have traveled nationally and internationally for over 3 decades lecturing on this subject, and we have yet to hear of a directly induced abortion needed to prevent her death. There are, of course, good reasons to deliver the baby and end her pregnancy in its late months, but here, hopefully the baby is saved. Never in late pregnancy is it necessary to directly kill the baby by abortion.

If her problem is something less than a threat to her life itself, then we cannot solve it by the ghastly violence of killing another innocent human life. The solutions for helping any individual woman are often many and complex, but they must be found and they must be used.

Why can't we love them both?

CHAPTER 11

THE HUMAN EMBRYO

When and where does fertilization occur?

Sperm enter the woman's vagina, swim through the cavity of her uterus and out through her Fallopian tubes. This can take as brief a time as five minutes to pass through the uterus and reach the tubes, and as brief as another 15 minutes to pass through the tubes and reach the ovaries. The egg, breaking out of the shell of her ovary, is penetrated by the head of one spermatozoa. Immediately, the ovum creates a chemical or electrical charge, or fence, preventing other sperm from entering.

The pronucleus of the sperm, containing its 23 chromosomes, in about 12 hours migrates to meet the ovum's pronucleus with its 23 chromosomes. Their fusion takes about 2 hours.

Then in another 18 hours this 46-chromosome nucleus divides into two cells.

Then into 3 cells, at which time some new opinion believes the "decision" is made to stay single or program to divide into twins.

Then to 4 cells, to 8, to 16 and on and on.

Jones and Schraeder, "The Process of Human Fertilization," *Fertility and Sterility*, vol. 48, no. 2, Aug. 1987, p. 191

Word Wars, E. Diamond, Physician, Nov. 1992, pp. 14-15

Personal Communication, J. Lejeune 1994

What is this "moment of conception" bit?

Most use the moment of sperm penetration as the "moment of conception." Others wait until their pronuclei fuse at 12-14 hours to say conception is a completed process. In either case this new human life is complete at the first cell stage.

This is then only a single cell?

Yes. But a remarkable and unique one.

This single cell is now either male or female.

This human is unique, i.e., never before in the history of the world has this exact individual human existed. Never again in history will another exactly like this human exist.

This being is complete, i.e., nothing else — no bits or pieces — will be added from this time until the old man or woman dies — nothing but nutrition and oxygen.

This being is programmed from within, moving forward in a self-controlled, ongoing process of growth, development, and replacement of his or her own dying cells.

This living being is dependent upon his or her mother for shelter and food, but in all other respects is a totally new, different, unique, and independent being.

How does it grow?

This single celled human being divides into two cells, each containing the same total and identical DNA message, the same total contents. Two becomes three, three becomes four, then eight, sixteen, etc., as it moves down the Fallopian tube. Ultimately, each human being's body contains 30 million million cells.

When sufficient cells are present, organ formation, body structure, and function begin. Cell doubling occurs only 45 times. That timing is as follows:

CELL DOUBLINGS	BY AGE	PERCENTAGE
8	by implantation	18%
30	by 8 weeks	66%
41	by birth	91%
44	by kindergarten	98%
45	by adulthood	100%

J. Lejnene & A. W. Liley, *The Tiniest Humans*
CA: Sassone Press, p. 14, 1007

I've heard that another animal also has 46 chromosomes!

True, but not 46 *human* chromosomes. Different species have different types of chromosomes.

But what of a human with 47 chromosomes, doesn't this disprove your "humans have 46" statement?

Certain humans have 12 toes. Others are born with one arm. Are they human? They certainly are, but they are humans with an abnormality. A "Triple X" or a Down's Syndrome human has an extra chromosome. Are they human? Yes, but humans with an abnormal number of chromosomes.

Give documentation:

"The intricate processes by which a baby develops from a single cell are miraculous . . . This cell, the zygote, results from the union of an oocyte (egg) and sperm. A zygote is the beginning of a new human being . . . Human development begins at fertilization."

The Developing Human, Clinically Oriented Embryology, 6th Edition,
Moore, Persaud Saunders, 1998, pages 2 & 18.

This tiny human moves down the Fallopian tube?

Yes, and at about one week of life, at the blastocyst stage of about 128 to 256 cells, it implants into the nutrient lining of the uterus. There, only three days later, this tiny male or female human sends a chemical-hormonal message into the mother's body, which stops her menstrual periods.

The new being controls her body?

Yes, for the balance of pregnancy. It is the developing baby who enlarges her breasts to prepare her for nursing and softens her pelvic bones in preparation for labor. It is even the baby who "determines his own birthday."

A. Liley, A Case Against Abortion, Liberal Studies,
Whitcombe & Tombs, 1971

Isn't the fertilized ovum only a potential human being?

No. This is not a *potential* human being; it is a human being with vast potential. One could say that the sperm and ovum, before their union, constitute a potential human being. Once their union is completed, however, they have become an actual human being.

What if this being dies soon after fertilization? Was it human then?

Human death can occur at any time during our journey through life. This could be minutes after fertilization or 95 years after fertilization. Human death is merely the end of human life.

There are those who claim that about 20% are lost in the first week. If this is so, it would mean that there is a mortality rate of almost 20% in the first week of life. This is not relevant to the question of whether or not this is human life — anymore than infant mortality is a justification for infanticide, or death in old age justifies euthanasia. All it means is that the mortality rate in the first week of life may be 20%.

Of very early pregnancies, "22% ended before pregnancy was detected clinically. The total rate of pregnancy loss after implantation, including clinically recognized spontaneous abortions, was 31%." The testing used was able to detect pregnancy accurately by day seven or eight.

Wilcox, et al., "Incidence of Early Loss of Pregnancy" *New Eng. J. Med.*, vol 319, no. 4, July 28, 1988, p. 189

Overall, from fertilization until birth, 50-60% survive past 20 weeks, and ¾ of those lost are due to failure of implantation.

Implantation & Survival of Early Pregnancy, *New England Journal of Medicine* 11-8-01, pp. 1400-1408

One reason for the apparent high percent of pre- or immediate post-implantation loss may be due to chromosome abnormalities.

Wramsby et al., "Chromosome Analysis of Human Oocytes . . ." *New Eng. J. Med.*, vol. 316, no. 3, Jan. 15, 1987, p. 121

I've heard the fertilized ovum described as only a blueprint. What of this comparison?

The blueprint of your home is merely the plan for your home. After using this instruction sheet to build your house, you can throw the blueprint away. It has not become the house. The fertilized ovum is not the blueprint, but is, in fact, the house in miniature. It, itself, will grow into the house in time. It is the house already. Your home was built piece by piece until it ultimately assumed a shape which could be identified as a house. The tiny human, who you once were, developed into the adult you now are, but you were there *totally* at conception. All you needed to become the adult you now are was nutrition, oxygen, and time.

But it is so small. How can it be human yet?

If the only scientific instruments you use are your own unaided eyes, then a common judgment that you might make would be that "it isn't human until it looks human." We do have microscopes, ultrasonic movies, stethoscopes, and genetic knowledge now, all of which go far beyond the limited knowledge obtained by sight alone. To base your opinion solely on what you see, rather than upon what science is capable of telling you, isn't very rational.

What of a cell from some part of a person's body which can be kept alive in a tissue culture, either separated from his living body or maintained after that person has died? Does this not upset the concept of the fertilized ovum as a human life?

No. Those cells were a part of a complete human body and can only reproduce themselves as a specific type of cell. The fertilized ovum is not a part of another body, but is a whole body him or herself. It (he or she) will not merely reproduce, but is, in totality, a complete human being and will grow into a full adult if given time. Any one of hundreds of millions or billions of these cells in a human's body can die and we do not say that human has died. When a single fertilized ovum cell dies, however, the entire new human being dies.

The other important difference is that the fertilized ovum, which subdivides and multiplies into many cells, moves immediately in the direction of specialized and differing parts, which are organized as a single unified complex being. Cells from parts of an adult human body in a tissue culture can only reproduce their own kind and cannot go on to develop differing specialized parts.

Wouldn't a successful human clone upset this reasoning?

At the first moment of his or her existence, it would be an intact and complete human life. He or she would be, in effect, the identical twin of the donor human, but of a different age. Being a total human, this living human would, in justice, be due the same protection of the law as the older donor human.

Can't we consider the developing embryo a form of plant or animal life which only becomes human at some later state of development?

Definitely not! The fertilized seed or ovum of a plant, or an animal, or of a human, at the time of fertilization and beginning growth, already is, in totality, that plant, animal, or human. Because of our present scientific knowledge of chromosome and gene structure, and because of the intricate genetic programming that we are now aware of, we know that a plant can only develop into what it already is — that is, a plant. An animal — a dog, for instance — can only develop into a dog and a specific species of that dog. All this is predetermined and already exists in totality when fertilization occurs. The same is true of a human.

But can you then call an acorn an oak tree?

That is like saying "can you call an infant an adult?" Rather, you must ask "are they both complete oaks?" Yes, they are. All the acorn needs to develop into an adult tree is time and nutrition.

What of twins?

Non-identical twins are two separate individuals created by the union of two eggs and two sperm. Identical twins, however, occur when one apparently splits into two, after which each of the two divided parts (each now an embryo in itself) grows independently in the very same manner toward full development and maturity, as the average single zygote will. This occurs sometime between fertilization and implantation.

Can we say, then, that one living human being (2-6 day old embryo) can split into two living human beings (identical twins)?

Scientific opinion is far from unanimous about how to consider this. One way of considering it is that the original human embryo, in splitting in half (whatever exactly happens, we don't know), can be considered, in effect, the parent of the new human being. This might be a form of parthenogenesis, or non-sexual reproduction. We know that this does occur in certain forms of plant and animal life. We could postulate this type of process to explain identical twinning in a human.

The other possibility is that the existing human being, in splitting, dies, to give new life to two new identical human beings like himself (herself).

What is crucial to either of these explanations is that, at the time when a total human being exists, he or she should be recognized as such and given all rights due other living human beings.

But the sperm has life. The ovum has life. Why is either of these lives any different than when the two join and become a fertilized ovum?

The sperm has life, but not an independent life; it shares in the life of the body of the father. The sperm is genetically identified as a cell of the father's body. It has reached the endpoint of its maturation. It cannot reproduce itself. It is destined to fertilize an ovum or to die. It is at the end of the line.

The ovum has life, but not an independent life; it shares in the life of the body of the mother. The ovum is genetically identified as a cell of the mother's body. It has reached the endpoint of its maturation. It cannot reproduce itself. Its destiny? To be fertilized or die. It, too, is at the end of the line.

But when sperm and ovum join, there is created at that time a new living being; a being who has never before existed in the history of the world and never again will exist; a being not at the end of the line, but at the dawn of existence; a being completely intact and containing within himself or herself the totality of everything that this being will ever be; a being moving forward in an orderly process of growth and maturation, destined to live inside the mother for almost nine months and for as many as a hundred years outside.

Will you cite some scientific authorities as to human life beginning at fertilization?

In 1981 the U.S. Senate considered Senate Bill #158, the "Human Life Bill." Extensive hearings (eight days, 57 witnesses) were conducted by Senator John East. National and international authorities testified. We quote from the official Senate report, 97th Congress, S-158:

> "Physicians, biologists, and other scientists agree that conception [they defined fertilization and conception to be the same] marks the beginning of the life of a human being — a being that is alive and is a member of the human species. There is overwhelming agreement on this point in countless medical, biological, and scientific writings."
>
> Report, Subcommittee on Separation of Powers
> to Senate Judiciary Committee
> S-158, 97th Congress, 1st Session 1981, p. 7

On pages 7-9, the report lists a "limited sample" of 13 medical textbooks, all of which state categorically that the life of an individual human begins at conception.

Then, on pages 9-10, the report quotes several outstanding authorities who testified personally:

- Professor J. Lejeune, Paris, discoverer of the chromosome pattern of Down's Syndrome: "Each individual has a very neat beginning, at conception."

- Professor W. Bowes, University of Colorado: Beginning of human life? — "at conception."

- Professor H. Gordon, Mayo Clinic: "It is an established fact that human life begins at conception."

- Professor M. Matthews-Roth, Harvard University: "It is scientifically correct to say that individual human life begins at conception."

But Dr. Leon Rosenberg, from Yale University, and others said otherwise!

Dr. Rosenberg did state that he knew of no scientific evidence showing when actual human life begins. But, he then defined human life in a philosophic way and spoke to a value judgment.

To quote the Senate report (on page 11):

"Those witnesses who testified that science cannot say whether unborn children are human beings were speaking in every instance to the value question rather than the scientific question. No witness raised any evidence to refute the biological fact that, from the moment of human conception there exists a distinct individual being who is alive and is of the human species."

Even though Dr. Rosenberg and others used the word, "science," they did not mean biologic science. Rather, they were speaking of their philosophic beliefs such as what Dr. Rosenberg called "the complex quality of humanness."

Hearings, S-158, 24 April at 25

This confusion of provable natural biologic science, with value judgments based upon non-provable theories and beliefs, must be shown at every opportunity to be two entirely different ways of reasoning.

How about other proof?

See the First International Symposium on Abortion, which concluded:

"The changes occurring between implantation, a six-weeks embryo, a six-months fetus, a one-week-old child, or a mature adult are merely stages of development and maturation.

"The majority of our group could find no point in time between the union of sperm and egg, or at least the blastocyst stage, and the birth of the infant, at which point we could say that this was not a human life."

Willke & Willke, *Handbook on Abortion*,
(1971, 1975, 1979 Editions),
Ch. 3, Cincinnati: Hayes Publishing Co.

What is a pre-embryo?

It is many millions of sperm swimming after an ovum. When one penetrates it, the "pre" is over and this now becomes a zygote (a fertilized egg) which, on dividing, is called an embryo.

But the term "pre-embryo" is used for the first week or two.

This is an arbitrary term recently introduced by pro-abortion people in an attempt to dehumanize this early human. "In rigorous ethical debate, such arbitrary terminology, particularly if used to assign moral values, should be avoided."

Arbitrary Partitions of Prenatal Life, Biggers,
Human Reproduction, Oxford U-Press, Vol. 5, No. 1, pp. 1-6, 1990

CHAPTER 12

FETAL DEVELOPMENT

When does implantation occur?

The tiny human implants himself or herself in the nutrient lining of the womb 8 to 10 days after fertilization.

Wilcox AJ, Baird DD, Weinberg CR.
Time of implantation of the conceptus and loss of pregnancy.
N Engl J Med. 1999;340:1796-1799.

And then?

About three days later, this tiny living human male or female sends a chemical hormonal message out into the mother's body, which stops her menstrual periods. Later, it is this tiny passenger who causes her breasts to enlarge in preparation for nursing, softens her pelvic bones to prepare for labor, and, without question, sets his or her birthday. The onset of labor is a unilateral fetal decision (see chapter 10).

Why is the primitive streak important?

It really isn't. Much is made of the fact that identical twinning cannot occur after the 14th day, when this early spinal cord can be seen. Actually, identical twinning probably happens in the first 2-4 days of life. Use of the primitive streak is a thinly veiled attempt to dehumanize the early human embryo, so that destructive embryo experimentation can proceed and that I.V.F. embryos can be killed.

When does the heart begin to beat?

At 18 days [when the mother is only four days late for her first menstrual period], and by 21 days it is pumping, through a closed circulatory system, blood whose type is different from that of the mother.

J.M. Tanner, G. R. Taylor, and the Editors of Time-Life Books, *Growth*, New York: Life Science Library, 1965, p. 64

When is the brain functioning?

Brain waves have been recorded at 40 days on the Electroencephalogram (EEG).

H. Hamlin, "Life or Death by EEG," *JAMA*, Oct. 12, 1964, p. 113

Brain function, as measured on the Electroencephalogram, "appears to be reliably present in the fetus at about eight weeks gestation," or six weeks after conception.

J. Goldenring, "Development of the Fetal Brain," *New England Jour. of Med.*, Aug. 26, 1982, p. 564

Only several generations ago, doctors used the ending of respiration to measure the end of human life. This is no longer true, for the use of artificial ventilators is common.

Only one generation ago, doctors were using the ending of the heartbeat to measure the end of human life. This is no longer true, for now the heart can be stopped and restarted for different operations. It also may stop during a heart attack and sometimes can be restarted.

Today, the definitive and final measure of the end of human life is brain death. This happens when there is irreversible cessation of total brain function. The final scientific measurement of this is the permanent ending of brain waves.

Since all authorities accept that the end of an individual's life is measured by the ending of his brain function (as measured by brain waves on the EEG), would it not be logical for them to at least agree that individual's life began with the onset of that same human brain function, as measured by brain waves recorded on that same instrument?

Early on, this being has gill slits and a tail. Isn't this proof that it is not human then?

The "gill slits" are not slits but folds of skin much like an infant's "double chin." These stretch out as he grows.

The tail isn't a tail either. The central nervous system consists of brain and spinal cord. It is the most important part of the early body and grows the fastest. The tail is really the end of the spinal cord which grows faster than the torso. The torso catches up with it, and its tip then becomes your adult "tail bone."

"The body of the unborn baby is more complex than ours. The preborn baby has several extra parts to his body which he needs only so long as he lives inside his mother. He has his own space capsule, the amniotic sac. He has his own lifeline, the umbilical cord, and he has his own root system, the placenta. These all belong to the baby himself, not to his mother. They are all developed from his original cell."

Day & Liley, *The Secret World of a Baby,*
Random House, 1968, p. 13

How early do some organs form?

The eye, ear and respiratory systems begin to form four weeks after fertilization.

K. Moore, *Before We Were Born,* 3rd ed., 1989, p. 278

And function?

Very early, e.g., glucagon, a blood sugar hormone, has been demonstrated in the fetal pancreas 6 weeks after fertilization, and insulin by 7 to 8.

F. Cunningham, "Pancreas," *William's Obstet.*, 19th ed., 1993, p. 183-4

Thumbsucking has been photographed at 7 weeks after fertilization.

W. Liley, *The Fetus As Personality, Fetal Therapy,* 1986, p. 8-17

When does the developing baby first move?

"In the sixth to seventh weeks. . . . If the area of the lips is gently stroked, the child responds by bending the upper body to one side and making a quick backward motion with his arms. This is called a 'total pattern response' because it involves most of the body, rather than a local part."

L. B. Arey, *Developmental Anatomy* (6th ed.),
Philadelphia: W. B. Sanders Co., 1954

At eight weeks, "if we tickle the baby's nose, he will flex his head backwards away from the stimulus."

A. Hellgers, M.D., "Fetal Development, 31,"
Theological Studies, vol. 3, no. 7, 1970, p. 26

Another example is from a surgical technician whose letter said, "When we opened her abdomen (for a tubal pregnancy), the tube had expelled an inch-long fetus, about 4-6 weeks old. It was still alive in the sack.

"That tiny baby was waving its little arms and kicking its little legs and even turned its whole body over."

J. Dobson, *Focus on the Family Mag.*, Aug. '91, pg. 16

But pregnant women don't "feel life" until four or five months!

The inside of the uterus has no feeling. The baby has to be almost a foot long (30 cm.) and weigh about one pound (454 gm.) before he or she is large enough to brace a shoulder against one wall and kick hard enough against the opposite wall to dent it outward. Then the mother feels it because the outside of the uterus is covered by a sensitive peritoneal surface.

What is the development at seven to eight weeks?

The baby's stomach secretes gastric juice by eight weeks. Now we can listen to the tiny one's heartbeat on an ultrasonic stethoscope. These are now common in doctors' offices and on hospital wards. They are never used in abortion facilities, however, as this information is universally withheld from mothers prior to abortion. Abortionists know that if they tell women there already is a heartbeat — and certainly if they would let her listen to the heartbeat — some mothers would change their minds. The actual sounds of an six-week-old baby's heartbeat are available on tape from Cincinnati Right to Life, 1802 W. Galbraith Rd., Cincinnati, OH 45239 ($3.00).

"Eleven years ago, while giving an anesthetic for a ruptured tubal pregnancy (at two months), I was handed what I believed to be the smallest human being ever seen. The embryo sac was intact and transparent. Within the sac was a tiny (one-third inch) human male swimming extremely vigorously in the amniotic fluid, while attached to the wall by the umbilical cord. This tiny human was perfectly developed with long, tapering fingers, feet and toes. It was almost transparent, as regards the skin, and the delicate arteries and veins were prominent to the ends of the fingers.

"The baby was extremely alive and swam about the sac approximately one time per second with a natural swimmers stroke. This tiny human did not look at all like the photos and drawings of 'embryos' which I have seen, nor did it look like the few embryos I have been able to observe since then, obviously because this one was alive.

"When the sac was opened, the tiny human immediately lost its life and took on the appearance of what is accepted as the appearance of an embryo at this stage (blunt extremities, etc.)."

P.E. Rockwell, M.D., Director of Anesthesiology,
Leonard Hospital, Troy, New York, U.S. Supreme Court.,
Markle vs. Abele, 72-56, 72-730, p. 11, 1972

When are all his body systems present?

By eight weeks (two months).

Hooker & Davenport, *The Prenatal Origin of Behavior,*
University of Kansas Press, 1952

When do teeth form?

All 20 milk-teeth buds are present at six and a half weeks.

"Life Before Birth," *Life Magazine*, Apr. 30, 1965, p. 10

And include dental lamina at 8 weeks.

Med. Embryology, Longman, 3rd Ed., 1975, p. 406

How about nine weeks?

At nine to ten weeks, he squints, swallows, moves his tongue, and if you stroke his palm, will make a tight fist.

By nine weeks he will "bend his fingers round an object in the palm of his hand."

Valman & Pearson, "What the Fetus Feels,"
British Med. Jour., Jan. 26, 1980

When does he start to breathe?

"By 11 to 12 weeks (3 months), he is breathing fluid steadily and continues so until birth. At birth, he will breathe air. He does not drown by breathing fluid within his mother, because he obtains his oxygen from his umbilical cord. This breathing develops the organs of respiration."

"Life Before Birth," *Life Magazine*, Apr. 30, 1965, p. 13

"Maternal cigarette smoking during pregnancy decreases the frequency of fetal breathing by 20%. The 'well documented' higher incidence of prematurity, stillbirth, and slower development of reading skill may be related to this decrease."

F. Manning, "Meeting of Royal College of Physicians & Surgeons,"
Family Practice News, March 15, 1976

"In the 11th week of gestation, fetal breathing is irregular and episodic. As gestation continues, the breathing movements become more vigorous and rapid."

C. Dawes, "Fetal Breathing: Indication of Well Being,"
Family Practice News, Mar. 16, 1976, p. 6

Episodic spontaneous breathing movements have been observed in the healthy human fetus as early as ten weeks gestational age.

Conners et al., "Control of Fetal Breathing in the Human Fetus,"
Am J. OB-GYN, April '89, p. 932

And 11 weeks (9 weeks post-fertilization).

Cunningham, Wm. *Obstetrics*, 1993, p. 193

When can he swallow?
At 11 weeks.

Valman & Pearson, *British Med. Jour.*,
"What the Fetus Feels," 26 Jan. 1980, p. 233

What of detailed development, like fingernails and eyelashes?
Fingernails are present by 11 to 12 weeks; eyelashes by 16 weeks. Fingerprints are completely established during the fourth month of gestation.

Hamilton et al., *Human Embryology*, Fourth Ed., 1972, p. 567

At what point are all his body systems working?
By 11 weeks.

"Life Before Birth," *Life Magazine*, Apr. 30, 1965, p. 13

How does the size of the baby increase in weight?
At 12 weeks (three months) she weighs about 30 gm (1.0 ounce); at 16 weeks about 170 gm (6 ounces); and at 20 weeks (four months), approximately 454 gm (one pound).

When is taste present?

"Taste buds are working between 13 and 15 weeks gestation" (11 to 13 weeks after conception).

Mistretta & Bradley, *Taste in Utero*, 1977, p. 62

Bradley et al., "Dev. Taste Buds . . . ,"
J. Anat. 101 (4) 1967, p. 743-752

How about hearing?

"Auditory sense is present in the infant 24 weeks before birth [14 weeks after conception]. This involves brain functioning and memory patterns."

M. Clemens, "5th International Congress Psychosomatic,"
OB & GYN, Rome: Medical Tribune, Mar. 22, 1978, p. 7

Fetal hearing and fetal learning are present at 20 weeks and perhaps as early as 16 weeks. (With controls) fetal babies remembered music played at these ages.

W. Evans, U. of Keele; R. Parncutt, U. of Bath, to
Brit. Psy. Soc. 3-26-98

Recent technology allowed a tiny microphone to be placed by the fetus's head and
"We heard almost everything, from people talking 12 feet away, to a door opening in the room, to a cart going down the hall with the door closed. The clarity was incredible. It was easy to tell who was talking."

The results showed the fetus hears everything we do, only 10 decibels less. Their earliest response to sound was at 26 weeks.

Is Noise an Intrauterine Threat, Phelan & Satt,
by R. McGuire, Med. Tribune, Nov. 30, 1989

He certainly can't cry!

Although the watery environment in which he lives presents small opportunity for crying, which does require air, the unborn knows how to cry, and given a chance to do so, he will.

A doctor

". . . injected an air bubble into the baby's amniotic sac and then took x-rays. It so happened that the air bubble covered the baby's face. The whole procedure had no doubt given the little fellow quite a bit of jostling about, and the moment that he had air to inhale and exhale they heard the clear sound of a protesting wail emitting from the uterus. Late that same night, the mother awakened her doctor with a telephone call, to report that when she lay down to sleep the air bubble got over the baby's head again, and he was crying so loudly he was keeping both her and her husband awake. The doctor advised her to prop herself upright with pillows so that the air could not reach the baby's head, which was by now in the lower part of the uterus."

Day & Liley, *Modern Motherhood*,
Random House, 1969, pp. 50-51

Does the unborn baby dream?

Using ultrasound techniques, it was first shown that REM (rapid eye movements), which are characteristic of active dream states, have been demonstrated at 23 weeks.

J. Birnhaltz, "The Development of Human Fetal Eye Movement Patterns," *Science*, 1981, vol. 213, pp. 679-681

REM have since been recorded 17 weeks after conception.

S. Levi, Brugman University of Brussels,
American Medical Association News, February 1, 1983

Since REM are characteristic of dream states after birth, researchers are asking if the unborn child also dreams.

Does he/she think?

In adults, when we contemplate a physical move or action from a resting state, our heart rate accelerates several seconds before the motion. Similarly, the fetal baby's heart rate speeds up six to ten seconds prior to fetal movement. Is this conscious thought and planning?

N. Lauerson & H. Hochberg, "Does the Fetus Think?" *JAMA*, vol. 247, no. 23, July 18, 1982

"We now know that the unborn child is an aware, reacting human being who, from the sixth month on (and perhaps earlier), leads an active emotional life.

"The fetus can, on a primitive level, even learn in utero.

"Whether he ultimately sees himself and, hence, acts as a sad or happy, aggressive or meek, secure or anxiety-ridden person depends, in part, on the messages he gets about himself in the womb."

T. Verney & J. Kelly, *The Secret Life of the Unborn Child*, Delta Books, 1981, p. 12

"At eight weeks of life a tapping stimulus on the amniotic sac results in arm movements . . . the primitive brain receives the stimulus, selects a response and transmits the response as a signal to the arm."

M. Rosen, "Learning Before Birth," *Harpers Magazine*, April 1978

You mean that the unborn baby's emotions can be affected?

This is probably true.

"We know already that even embryonic nervous tissue is 'open' to maternal communication via brain chemicals called 'neurotransmitters.' This is a finding with enormous implications. It means that the mother's emotional state can affect the unborn almost from conception onward. Even before the baby can hear in the womb, or think consciously, it is capable of sensing discord between its parents. If the mother is in constant turmoil, its own environment will be tainted by the biochemistry of fear and hostility, grief, and anger."

Shettles & Varick, *Rites of Life*,
Grand Rapids: Zondervan, 1983, pp. 87-89

At four-and-a-half months, a very bright light on a woman's abdomen will cause the baby to slowly move its hand to a position shielding the eyes.

Loud music will cause the baby to cover its ears.

A woman in an unhappy marriage has a 237% greater risk of bearing a child with physical and psychological problems than a woman in a secure relationship.

T. Verney & J. Kelly, *The Secret Life of the Unborn Child*,
Delta Books, 1981, p. 49

Agreeing with Dr. Liley, Dr. W. Freud (grandson of Sigmund Freud), observed 10,000 ultrasound visualizations and reported, "It looks as if the fetus has a lot of intentionality." He also once saw unborn twins fighting.

1st International Congress, Pre & Peri Natal Psychology,
Toronto, July 8-10, 1983

So the fetus is really the Second Patient? Can he or she be treated?

"The status of the fetus has been elevated to that of a patient who, in large measure, can be given the same meticulous care that obstetricians have long given the pregnant woman."

Cunningham, F.G., et. al, *Williams Obstetrics*, 19th ed.
(Norwalk, CT: Appleton & Lange, 1993), 165.

Diaphragmatic hernia and obstructive hydrocephalus can be corrected while still in the womb. In addition:

"Medical treatment of the fetus includes exchange transfusion, thyroid hormone replacement and administration of steroids for surfactant induction. Correction of obstructive uropathy with urinary diversion has proved successful in decreasing fetal morbidity and mortality, while other procedures are still in the experimental stage. Extrauterine fetal surgery is performed only rarely but represents an exciting new direction in the treatment of medicine's youngest patients."

Camosy, P., "Fetal Medicine: Treating the Unborn Patient," *Am. Fam. Physician*, 52 (5) (October 1995): 1385-92

Give specific examples:

In a 4-month-old fetus with a fatally weak immune system, three intrauterine bone marrow transplants were done and the baby was born healthy.

A. Flake, New England Journal of Medicine 12-12-97

A 21-week baby had a spina bifida that was compressing his brain. In a first-of-its-kind, Dr. J. Bruner at Vanderbilt University opened the uterus and repaired the defect. As he was about to close the uterine incision, the baby reached his arm out into the air and took hold of the surgeon's finger. Snapped at that second by photographer Michael Clancy, the picture is dramatic proof of the humanity of the preborn.

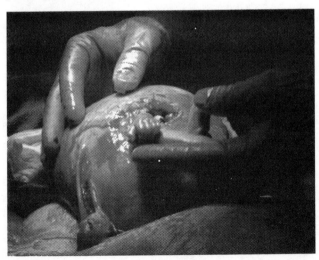

Five-year followups at Vanderbilt and at Children's Hospital in Philadelphia of 200 such intrauterine spina bidifa repairs showed no hydrocephalus, and 67% had less leg paralysis requiring postpartum surgery. In 7%, such open repairs caused premature labor and fetal death.

J. Urology, Oct. 2000, M. Johnson
2002 Meeting Soc. Maternal – Fetal Med.

How many weeks are there in a pregnancy and how do you measure them?

There are 40 weeks. We measure a pregnancy from the time the ovum begins to ripen, that is, at the start of a woman's menstrual period. After about two weeks of growth, the egg is released from the ovary. Fertilization can then occur. This is about two weeks before her next period is due. Four of the 40 weeks have already elapsed at the time she misses her first period.

Gestational age dates from the first day of the mother's last menstrual period. Actual age of the baby dates from fertilization.

What is birth?

Birth is the emergence of the infant from the mother's womb, the severing of the umbilical cord, and the beginning of the child's existence, physically detached from the mother's body. The only change that occurs at birth is a change in the external life support system of the child. The child is no different before birth than after, except that he has changed his method of feeding and obtaining oxygen. Before birth, nutrition and oxygen were obtained from the mother through the baby's umbilical cord. After birth, oxygen is obtained from his own lungs and nutrition through his own stomach, if he is mature enough to be nourished that way. If he is quite premature, nourishment would continue through our present, reasonably sophisticated external life support systems in the form of intravenous feeding, which is similar to the umbilical cord feeding from the mother.

Did you "come from" a fertilized ovum? No, you once were a fertilized ovum who grew and developed into the child or adult you are today. Nothing has been added to the fertilized ovum, who you once were, except nutrition.

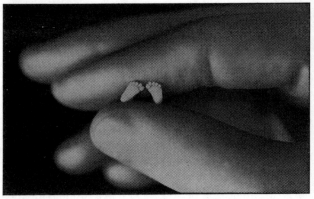

Tiny human feet at 10 weeks development.

CHAPTER 13

VIABILITY

What is viability?

It is that stage of fetal development when the baby is "potentially able to live outside the mother's womb [that is, can survive], albeit with artificial help."

Roe vs. Wade, U.S. Supreme Court, 1973, p. 45

Can you use viability as a measure of when the baby is human and therefore has the right to live?

No! To do so is completely illogical. 50 years ago viability was at 30 weeks. 25 years ago it had dropped to 25 weeks. Today we have a survivor at 20 weeks and several at 21 weeks.

But the babies haven't changed. Mothers are making the same kind of babies they always did, but they are surviving earlier.

Why?

Because of a vast increase in the sophistication of the external life support systems around the baby. Because of neonatal intensive care units. Because of greater knowledge and skill of the doctors and nurses.

So what is viability?

It is a measure of the sophistication of the external

life support systems around the baby. It is not a measure of his humanness or of his right to live.

But where did this idea come from?

From ancient times. Until the 19th century, it was assumed that the baby was not alive in the first half of pregnancy. It was also "known" that when the mother "felt life," when "the babe doth stir," that, at that time, the baby "came alive." Two examples show this:

> Abortion was always a sin in the Christian Church. A penitent confessing this sin was given a penance to perform. The penance for the sin of a late abortion was always more severe than one for an early abortion. Why? Because in the late abortion she had killed a baby who was alive.

> English Common Law succeeded ecclesiastic law and followed the same pattern. Abortion in the first half of pregnancy was a minor crime, a misdemeanor. Abortion after she felt life, after "quickening," was a felony, a serious crime.

Has that law changed?

Yes. In the early 1800s it was discovered that the baby's life began at fertilization, not at quickening (Karl Ernst Van Boar, 1827). Accordingly, in 1869 the British changed their law, dropped the felony punishment back to fertilization, and the two-tier punishment policy was eliminated.

But the old idea still lives on?

Amazingly, yes. Any lawmaker today who supports protecting babies' lives only after viability is still living in the middle ages, in pre-scientific times.

How do you measure age of survival?

The age of a premature baby at birth is measured by

age from first day of last menstrual period (LMP). Weight is also a measure when the dates are uncertain. A 20-to 22-week-old baby has an average weight of 500-600 gm (1 lb., 2 oz. to 1 lb., 5 oz.) with "normals" varying from 400 to 700 gm (14 oz. to 1 lb., 9 oz.). There are also other maturation factors that are used, such as various measurements made on ultrasound examination.

The age and weight don't always track together?

There is a variance, just as with children and adults, but a much narrower one. Dr. L. Lubchenco, University of Colorado, has been the recognized authority in preparing most of the charts used. Babies can be small for stated age or "runts," if malnourished. They can also be large for stated age, but still fall within the 90 percentile range on the charts.

Will the survival age ever drop under 20 weeks?

It seems that we have probably reached the youngest age at which the baby's lungs are well enough developed to exchange oxygen. One happy advance has been the use of surfactant in their lungs. This has meant babies under 1500 gm at birth are 30% less likely to die.

Effect of Surfactant . . . in newborn infants weighing 500-1500 gm, Schwartz et al., *N. Eng. J. Med.*, 1994; 330 (21): 1476-80

Decreasing Mortality with Surfactant . . . J.Horbar et al., *Pediatrics*, Vol.92, No.2, Aug '93, pg. 191

A further advance may be using oxygen-saturated liquid instead of air.

J.Greenspan et al., Liquid Ventilation of Preterm Baby, *Lancet*, Nov 4, '89, No. 8671,1095

C. Leach, Partial Liquid Ventilation, *N. Eng. J. Med.*, Sept. 12, '96

Beyond this, it is probably only a question of time and technology. Someday there will be artificial placentas, and then who knows how early a preemie will be able to survive?

How young can a premature baby survive?

It depends first upon the existence of a high-tech neonatal intensive care nursery. Almost all medical centers in the developed world have these.

The other factor is the baby. Some top notch medical centers just haven't yet been blessed with the birth of a child so well developed at an unusually young age that he (or she) can survive at, say, 20 to 22 weeks.

For instance?

One example is Baby Kenya King pictured below.

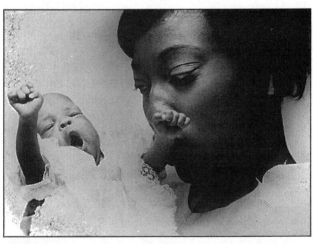

Baby Kenya King born in Plantation, Florida, 21 weeks (4 1/2 months) from the first day of her mother's last menstrual period; weighing 510 gm (18 oz) she was 10.5 inches (26.5 cm). She dropped to 370 gm (13 oz). She is shown at 2270 gm (5 lbs.) with her mother. (Miami Herald, Pam Smith photo)

Another was a 21-week baby who weighted 524 gm (1 lb., 2% oz.) born in the Persian Gulf country of Abu Dhabi

Indian Express, 2-4-0 1

But a major center such as Johns Hopkins reported the following survivors:
- at 22 weeks = none
- at 23 weeks = 15%
- at 24 weeks = 56%
- at 25 weeks = 79%

The Limit of Viability, M. Allen et al.,
N. Eng. J. Med. 11/25/93: Vol. 329, No.22, pg. 1597

Aren't a lot of preemies retarded later?

Many assume this, and there was a problem with those saved 20 years ago, but "Preterm infants of less than 1,000 gm (2 lbs.,2 oz.) do not appear to have significantly higher incidence of severe developmental abnormalities in the first 18 months of life than do 1,000 to 1,750 gm babies."

In a study of 68 babies weighing 500-750 gms at Stanford University, the overall survival rate was 35%. Of these very tiny infants, 9% had severe handicaps, 36% remedial problems, and the rest were normal.

Limiting Treatment for Preme, low wt. Infants,
E.W.Young et al., Am. J. Dis. Ch, Vol. 144, May '90, pg 549

How early can preemies survive?

In your author's files are 6 cases of 23 week (after LMP) survivors. Their weights ranged from 16 oz. (540 gm) to 24 oz. (810 gm).

We have 11 cases of survivors at 22 weeks (after LMP). These weights varied from 12 oz. (339 gm) to 22 oz. (663 gm).

We have 2 cases at 21 weeks (after LMP), including baby Kenya King above.

And 2 cases at 20 weeks (after LMP)

And how small can a baby be born and survive?

We have records of one infant born weighing 10 oz. (280 gm) at 25-26 weeks (after LMP), of an 11.5 oz. (325 gm) born at 27 weeks, and of a 12 oz. (339 gm) baby born at 23 weeks.

What of their quality of life as adults?

A study at McMaster University compared two groups: a) those born weighing less than 1,000 gms. and b) those born weighing over 2,500 gms. In adolescence, of those who were preemies, 71% "valued life highly." Those who were full term valued at 73%.

Self-perceived Health Status & Health-related
Quality of Life of Extremely Low Birth Weight
Infants at Adolescence, *JAMA*, 8/14/96, p. 453

CHAPTER 14

FETAL PAIN

YES, AND BY 8 WEEKS

By 8 weeks? Show me!

By this age, the neuro-anatomic structures are present. What is needed is (1) a sensory nerve to feel the pain and send a message to (2) the thalamus, a part of the base of the brain, and (3) motor nerves that send a message to that area. These are present at 8 weeks.

The pain impulse goes to the thalamus. It sends a signal down the motor nerves to pull away from the hurt.

PAIN

Give an example.

Try sticking an infant with a pin and you know what happens. She opens her mouth to cry and also pulls away.

Try sticking an 8-week-old human fetus in the palm of his hand. He opens his mouth and pulls his hand away.

A more technical description would add that changes in heart rate and fetal movement also suggest that intrauterine manipulations are painful to the fetus.

Volman & Pearson, "What the Fetus Feels," *British Med. Journal*, Jan. 26, 1980, pp. 233-234.

O.K., that is activity that can be observed, but is there other evidence of pain? After all, the fetal baby can't tell us he hurts.

Pain can be detected when nociceptors (pain receptors) discharge electrical impulses to the spinal cord and brain. These fire impulses outward, telling the muscles and body to react. These can be measured.

Mountcastle, *Medical Physiology*, St. Louis: C.V. Mosby, pp. 391-427

"Lip tactile response may be evoked by the end of the 7th week. At 11 weeks, the face and all parts of the upper and lower extremities are sensitive to touch. By 13 1/2 to 14 weeks, the entire body surface, except for the back and the top of the head, are sensitive to pain."

S. Reinis & J. Goldman, *The Development of the Brain* C. Thomas Pub., 1980

Give me more proof.

In 1964 President Reagan said: *"When the lives of the unborn are snuffed out, they often feel pain, pain that is long and agonizing."*

President Ronald Reagan to National Religious Broadcasters, *New York Times*, Jan. 31, 1984

This provoked a public reaction from pro-abortion circles and a response from an auspicious group of professors, including pain specialists and two past presidents of the American College of Obstetrics and Gynecology.

They strongly backed Mr. Reagan and produced substantial documentation. Excerpts of their letter (2/13/84) to him included:

"Real time ultrasonography, fetoscopy, study of the fetal EKG (electrocardiogram) and fetal EEG (electroencephalogram) have demonstrated the remarkable responsiveness of the human fetus to pain, touch, and sound. That the fetus responds to changes in light intensity within the womb, to heat, to cold, and to taste (by altering the chemical nature of the fluid swallowed by the fetus), has been exquisitely documented in the pioneering work of the late Sir William Liley — the father of fetology."

Mr. President, in drawing attention to the capability of the human fetus to feel pain, you stand on firmly established ground.

Willke, J & B, *Abortion: Questions & Answers*,
Hayes, 1991, Chpt. 10

What of *The Silent Scream*?

A *Realtime* ultrasound video tape and movie of a 12-week suction abortion is commercially available as *The Silent Scream*, narrated by Dr. B. Nathanson, a former abortionist. It dramatically, but factually, shows the pre-born baby dodging the suction instrument time after time, while its heartbeat doubles in rate. When finally caught, its body being dismembered, the baby's mouth clearly opens wide — hence, the title (available from American Portrait Films, P.O. Box 19266, Cleveland, OH 44119, 216-531-8600). Pro-abortionists have attempted to discredit this film. A well documented paper refuting their charges is available from National Right to Life, 512 10th St. NW, Washington, DC 20004, $2.00 p.p.

A short, 10-minute video showing the testimony of the doctor who did the abortion in *Silent Scream* definitely debunks any criticism of *Silent Scream's* accuracy. *The Answer*, Bernadel, Inc.

Pain? What of just comfort?

"One of the most uncomfortable ledges that the unborn can encounter is his mother's backbone. If he happens to be lying so that his own backbone is across hers [when the mother lies on her back], the unborn will wiggle around until he can get away from this highly disagreeable position."

M. Liley & B. Day, *Modern Motherhood*,
Random House, 1969, p. 42

But isn't pain mostly psychological?

There is also organic, or physiological pain which elicits a neurological response to pain.

P. Lubeskind, "Psychology & Physiology of Pain,"
Amer. Review Psychology, vol. 28, 1977, p. 42

But, early on, there is no cerebral cortex for thinking, therefore no pain?

The cortex isn't needed to feel pain. The thalamus is needed and (see above) is functioning at 8 weeks. Even complete removal of the cortex does not eliminate the sensation of pain. "Indeed there seems to be little evidence that pain information reaches the sensory cortex."

Patton et al., Intro. to Basic Neurology,
W. B. Saunders Co. 1976, p. 178

Note also that anencephalic infants (who have no cerebral cortex), definitely react to a painful stimulus, just as normal infants do.

How about during an abortion?

This really hit the fan during the 1996 debate in the U.S. Congress over a law to ban partial-birth abortions. Pro-abortionists had claimed that the anaesthetic had already killed the fetal baby. Top officials of the U.S. Society for Obstetric Anaesthesia & Perinatology vigorously denied this, explaining that usual anaesthesia did not harm the baby.

D. Gianelli, Anaesthesiologists Question Claims in Abortion Debate, *Am. Med. News*, Jan. 1, '96

This brought the issue of fetal pain into the news, and testimony was given to the Subcommittee on the Constitution of the U.S. House of Representatives.

"The fetus within this time frame of gestation, 20 weeks and beyond, is fully capable of experiencing pain. Without doubt, a partial-birth abortion is a dreadfully painful experience for any infant.

R. White, Dir. Neurosurgery & Brain Research, Case Western Univ.

Give me more research data.

Data in the British Medical Journal, *Lancet*, gave solid confirmation of such pain. It is known that the fetal umbilical cord has no pain receptors such as the rest of the fetal body. Accordingly, they tested fetal hormone stress response, comparing puncturing of the abdomen and of the cord.

They observed: "The fetus reacts to intra-hepatic (liver) needling with vigorous body and breathing movements, but not to cord needling. The levels of these hormones did not vary with fetal age."

M. Fisk, et al., Fetal Plasma Cortisol and B-endorphin Response to Intrauterine Needling, *Lancet*, Vol. 344, July 9, 1994, pg. 77

An excellent British study commented on this: "It cannot be comfortable for the fetus to have a scalp electrode implanted on his skin, to have blood taken from the scalp or to suffer the skull compression that may occur, even with spontaneous delivery. It is hardly surprising that infants delivered by difficult forceps extraction act as if they have a severe headache."

Valman & Pearson, "What the Fetus Feels,"
British Med. Jour., Jan. 26, 1980

In 1998, researchers at University College in London discovered that newborn babies feel pain longer and more sensitively than children and adults. Further, they feel it over larger areas of the body. Because some pain fibers do not function fully until soon after birth, "the preemie cannot benefit from the natural pain-killing system which, in adults, dampens down pain messages as they enter the central nervous system."

CHAPTER 15

INVITRO FERTILIZATION
— AND OTHER TECHNOLOGIES —

What is it?

It involves giving a woman drugs to induce ovulation and then harvesting (collecting) those mature eggs through a laparoscope. The man masturbates to collect the semen. Then the semen and ova are mixed in a dish, where fertilization may occur. Then the tiny, new embryonic human(s) are put into the cavity of the woman's uterus with the hope that they will plant and grow.

Is it ethical?

Many RTL groups, especially church-related ones, oppose this as "unnatural." Other RTL groups limit their official organizational policy to protecting human life already conceived, and thus have no official position on the "preliminaries." All, however, totally object to the destruction of any of these tiny human lives once they exist. All, therefore, condemn the "pick-of-the-litter" practice. This is when certain "concepti" (embryos) are discarded (killed) while others are planted.

How many get pregnant?

In 1993, the American Fertility Society reported on an aggregate of 33,000 attempts of "assisted reproductive technology." Remembering that in each attempt, 3 to 5 embryos are planted, the success per attempt (not per embryo) was:

- 24,671 cycles with I.V.F. and 15% deliveries
- 5,452 cycles with GIFT and 26% deliveries
- 2,104 cycles with ZIT and 20% deliveries
- 714 cycles with combinations and 19% deliveries

During 1998, of 82,000 cycles of treatment, 20,241 deliveries took place, less than a twenty-five percent success rate overall. However, it's routine to plant three or four human embryos in each procedure, so divide twenty-five percent by three or four. Therefore, the survive-and-delivery rate of living human embryos planted in a woman's womb is six to eight percent.

Fertility and Sterility, "Assisted Technology in the United States, 1998, 1/02, pp. 18-31.

In addition, 4,838 frozen embryo procedures were tried with one of the above methods and 11% deliveries.

What is ICSI?

It is intracytoplasmic sperm injection introduced in 1973. In it a single sperm is injected directly into the ovum in the laboratory. Its authors claim a success rate equal to I.V.F.

Z. Rosenwaks, *JAMA*, Dec. 18, 1996

What are these other methods?

GIFT is Gamet Intra-Fallopian Transfer. It brings together the egg and the husband's sperm collected from her vagina after the sex act.

LTOT is Low Tubal Ovum Transport. It enables sperm to bypass a blocked tube.

Amer. Fert. Society, Assisted Reprod. Technology, data from Registry, *Fertility & Sterility*, vol. 59, no. 5, May '93

ZIT is Zygote Intra-Fallopian Transfer. One study demonstrated only 16% survived transfer.

Bustillo et al., "Ovum Transfer in Infertile Women," *JAMA*, vol. 251, no. 9, Mar. 2, 1984

What of frozen embryos?

Of embryos frozen on day 1, 2, 3, 4 or 5, the number surviving thawing were 87%, 33%, 43%, 12% and 0, respectively.

"The chances for a surviving, frozen-thawed embryo becoming a clinically diagnosed pregnancy was 15%."

J. Testait,". . . Preg. rate . . . after embryo freezing," *Fertility & Sterility,* vol. 46, no. 2, p. 268, Aug. '86

What can I read on this?

The proceedings of the famous frozen embryo case in Marysville, Tennessee and Professor Jerome Lejeune's testimony should be required reading. Copies are available from Right to Life of Greater Cincinnati, 1802 W. Galbraith Rd., Cincinnati, Ohio 45239.

Are there any long-term bad effects on women who attempt I.V.F.?

Perhaps yes. A study in 1993 at Stanford University has suggested that women who take the fertility drugs needed for I.V.F. were three times as likely to develop ovarian cancer.

L. Gubernich et al., *Tarnished Miracle,* Forbes, Nov. 6, 1995, p. 98

Are there any problems with I.V.F. babies being abnormal?

Australia is one of the world leaders in this field. The reports are disturbing.

Multiple pregnancies occur more than 30 times more often in I.V.F. than in other pregnancies. These frequently produce low-birth-weight prematures who have more problems than full term babies.

Major congenital handicaps have been reported in 2.2% of I.V.F. births compared with 1.5% of normal conceptions.

Of 633 embryos conceived invitro by the most successful team under Dr. Alan Trounson, only 45, or 7%, lived to deliver. That is a 93% loss, or 12 out of 13 died.

A. Fisher, *I.V.F. The Critical Issue,*
Collins Dove Publishers, Melbourne, 1989

Infants from I.V.F. "have twice as high a risk of a major birth defect as naturally conceived infants — in single and multiple pregnancies."

Risk of Major Birth Defects, *N. Eng. J. Med.*, 3-7-02, pp. 725-730

Specifically, what malformations?

I.V.F. babies have six times the national average for congenital cardiac transposition and five times as many spina bifida. Stillbirths and deaths in the infant's first three months after delivery are more than three times the national average.

J. Fleming, S. Cross Bio-Ethics Institute,
from Natl. Perinatal Statis. Unit, Sidney U., Autumn 1989

For those who need further proof that a fully human life exists in the first week, we report an invitro fertilization experience.

A white couple, using invitro fertilization, had a three-day-old embryo of theirs implanted in her uterus. There was a lab mix up. Also planted was another embryo, but from another couple who were black-skinned. She delivered twins, one white, one black. She had inadvertently served as his surrogate mother. At birth he didn't look like the white lady, but rather like his black parents.

This proves that, as a single cell, he already was the son of the black parents, for all she offered him for those nine months was food and shelter.

New York Times and New York Post, 3-30-99

110

Where is all this new technology going?

No one knows, but Canada is trying to set limits by calling for a voluntary moratorium and refusing federal funding for:

"sex selection for non-medical reasons; commercial pre-conception or surrogacy arrangements; buying and selling of eggs, sperm, and embryos; egg donation in exchange for invitro fertilisation services; germ-line genetic alteration; ectogenesis; human embryo cloning; the creation of animal-human hybrids; and the retrieval of eggs from fetuses and cadavers for purposes of donation, fertilisation, or research."

D. Marleau, *"Canada Calls for Moratorium on I.V.F. Technologies,"*
The Lancet, vol. 346, Aug. 5, 1995, p. 367

CHAPTER 16

EXPERIMENTATION ON EMBRYOS, FETUSES AND NEWBORNS

Experimentation can be carried out on the living human embryo before or during his attachment to her womb, or to a fetus while he or she still lives in the womb. Experimentation can also be carried out on the living human baby after delivery. If the experiment (for example, trial of a new drug in treatment) is done for the possible benefit of this specific living human, then it is ethical if the parents approve. If, however, the experiment is done with the intention of later killing this living human to determine the effects from the experiment, then a serious crime is committed against human rights.

But if the mother has the right to abort, why not the right to consent to an experiment? The child can't live anyway.

The U.S. Supreme Court in 1973, and the parliaments in some other nations, debated the conflict of rights between mother and baby. By legalizing abortion, they granted the mother the superior right. Through the surgery of abortion, she can "become unpregnant." Once the mother and child are separated, however, if the child is born alive, there is no longer a conflict of legal rights. Besides being alive and human, the child is now separated from the mother and equally entitled to his or her human rights and protection.

The same should apply to pre-implantation embryos in a dish. Killing in abortion (by law) should not extend forward or backward outside the womb.

Under what conditions can parents give consent for experimentation?

Parents who give consent for experimentation on their children are assumed to have concern for their child's welfare, and the hope has always been that such experimentation will benefit them.

Parents who give consent to have their child in the womb killed, obviously have no such loving interest. Legal tradition through our country's history has always forbidden parents to injure or allow others to injure their child. That is what child-abuse laws are all about. If such experiment is not done to preserve the life or health of the baby, the parents should have no right to grant permission.

Let's start with embryos. Is there experimentation?

Practices and laws vary in different nations. In Germany and France it is forbidden. In England much is permitted. In China there are no limits.

In the U.S., Australia, and Britain, the push is to allow destructive, live embryo experimentation until 14 days.

And on fetuses?

Not in the U.S. with tax money, but it is legally permitted with private money, as long as the baby is inside and the mother agrees. Laws in other countries differ.

For fetal transplants, are there special needs for the tissues?

Yes, the older the baby the better; the more alive the better. Excised tissues die quickly, therefore, immediate chilling or freezing has been tried, but intact tissue or entire organs are needed. These are best taken from an abortion in one operating room and planted in the recipient in the next room.

Are fetal tissues available, even without government funds?

Read this electronic mail:

"Human embryonic and fetal tissues are available from the Central Laboratory for Human Embryology at the University of Washington. The laboratory, which is supported by the National Institutes of Health, can supply tissue from normal or abnormal embryos and fetuses of desired gestational ages between 40 days and term. Specimens are obtained within minutes of passage, and tissues are aseptically identified, staged and immediately processed according to the requirements of individual investigators. Presently, processing methods include immediate fixation, snap fixation, snap freezing in liquid nitrogen, and placement in balanced salt solutions or media designated and/or supplied by investigators. Specimens are shipped by overnight express, arriving the day following procurement. The laboratory can also supply serial sections of human embryos that have been preserved in methyl Carnoy's fixative, embedded in paraffin and sectioned at 5 microns." Inquiries are directed to Alan G. Fantel, Ph.D., Department of Pediatrics RD-20, University of Washington, Seattle, WA 98195.

copy of e-mail transmission as printed out and mailed to A.L.L.
J. Brown, *Communique,* May 13, 1994, p. 3

Where do these babies come from?

Most are from partial-birth abortions of which there are several thousand each year in the U.S. alone. This is the only method of abortion that delivers an intact body (except the brain). Sometimes these infants are delivered alive, drowned, and then even the brain is recoverable. An entire industry has grown up around "selling baby parts."

A commercial industry?

Yes, price lists are available. One eyeball is $100.00. A hind quarter is $450.00. A liver is $150.00. An intact brain is $950.00. For details on this, contact Life Dynamics, P.O. Box 2226, Denton TX 76202.

Is it ever ethical to use fetal tissues?

Yes, but if done, transplantation of fetal organs into the body of a born person should observe the same ethical norms as for organs from born persons. These include:

- Proper permission, i.e., from parents who have loved and offered proper care to keep the unborn baby alive and well. If the parent is part of the killing team, she surrenders any moral right to give such permission.
- The newly developed baby must be dead (there are definition-of-death laws in most states) before any organs are removed.
- One cannot kill a baby (in or out of the uterus) to get an organ.

What about using the placenta?

After the child is born, he or she no longer needs their placenta. For many years, hospitals have frozen and sold placentas to drug companies to extract hormones and other substances. More recently, placentas have also been sold to cosmetic manufacturing companies. This may be distasteful or even revolting to many people.

There is, however, no major ethical problem in such use.

Can fetal transplants cure Parkinson's Disease?

About every two years for the last two decades we've seen a major media splash reporting on a cure. Usually this comes with pictures of a wheel chair patient now walking. What has not been given publicity is reporting a year later. In all of these cases, the improvement was temporary and the patient relapsed.

In March, 2000 a report received world wide publicity. It recounted a major problem in some patients with Parkinsonism who had received fetal transplants in their brains. These patients developed severe, continuous, involuntary movements of face and body. This could not be controlled and was judged to be permanent. The medical name for this is tardive dyskinesia. "They chew constantly, their fingers go up and down and then wrists flex and extend. They writhe and twist, jerk their heads, fling their arms about. It is tragic, catastrophic, a real nightmare. And we cannot selectively turn it off."

P. Areen New England Journal of Medicine March 2001

"It is unlikely, for both practical and biological reasons, that transplantation of fragments of embryonic tissue will be therapy of the future.

editorial, ibid.

A similar attempt to seed embryonic tissue into a Parkinson's patient's brain in China also had tragic consequences. A 52-year-old man died two years after such surgery. Autopsy revealed that the implanted tissue had grown wildly into hair follicles, bone, skin, cartilage, and other debris.

Citizen Magazine, Jan. 2000
Journal of Neurology, May 1966

Theoretically, transplanting fetal brains should help such patients. In practice, this has failed.

How about Diabetes?

Transplanting islet cells from the pancreas of fetal babies has given temporary help. There are 1,500,000 diabetics in the U.S. For each patient, early experiments used cells from 8 aborted babies, 14-20 weeks old. To "cure" all diabetics would require 12 million, but only 120,000 such babies are aborted annually.

A Russian experiment reported using 3 fetuses with 12 newborn rabbits. Some preliminary improvement was reported.

T. Maugh, *Transplant Cells Aided Diabetics,* Los Angeles Times, 4/12/95

What about using newborn anencephalic babies as organ donors?

After he or she dies, the above rules apply. These are live babies and they should not be killed for their organs.

Loma Linda University experimented with such babies but quit when it became evident that by the time of brain death (including brain stem death), the other organs were not usable.

"Providing anencephalic newborns with intensive care will tend to preserve their brain stems as effectively as the other organs, rendering the occurrence of brain death [ahead of other organs] unlikely."

D. Shewmon et al., *Anencephalic Infants as Organ Donors,*
JAMA, Vol. 261, No. 12, 3/24/89

A detailed investigation of the use of anencephalic infants as transplant donors was reported from Loma Linda University. Dr. Joyce Peabody studied 12 such infants. With intensive care, only two demonstrated total brain death after one week, and their organs were then unsuitable.

J. Peabody et al., *Anencephalic Infants as Prospective
Donors,* N. Eng. Jour. Med., 321:344-50, 8/10/89

Dr. Peabody abandoned her study and announced she will not pursue any further such investigation.

When asked about a law to permit such transplants, she stated, "If you're going to call these infants dead, you're going to have to call them dead — period.

"So the anencephalic infant would be born — and what would you do? Would you write a birth certificate and then immediately write a death certificate? Would there be no legal distinction between a stillborn anencephalic infant and an anencephalic infant who was breathing? Would there be no distinction between an anencephalic infant whose parents wanted to donate and an anencephalic infant whose parents didn't want to donate? Would the anencephalic infant whose parents didn't want to donate be 'alive' and the anencephalic infant whose parents wanted to donate be 'dead'?

"Two anencephalic infants, lying side by side with exactly the same vital signs and exactly the same appearance: Would you call one alive and one dead? I think, legally, with all the rules of discrimination, and so forth, you'd have to call them both the same.

"And, as dramatic as it sounds, if you were to declare anencephalic infants dead for purposes of organ donation, it would mean that you would be removing hearts from babies that breathe, suck, kick and cry. I would need to have the individuals who passed that law feel that, if it were not for organ donation, they would be equally comfortable in burying a baby who was breathing, sucking, kicking and crying."

She was asked:

Q: Could you do that?

A: "Absolutely not."

J. Peabody *AMA News*, June 29, 1992

Do doctors agree with using living anencephalics as donors?

Most medical societies in most countries condemn it. In 1994,p the USAMA Ethics Council approved it. After a full year of turbulent objections, it reversed its opinion.

What is your answer?

We would follow the example of a pediatrician couple in Cincinnati who now speak publicly about this issue. They took their anencephalic child home who lived a few days. They fitted him with a little skull cap to hide the defect. They and their children loved this little infant for the few days that they had him. He was baptized, named and photographed with various members of the family. Other family members visited. The children came to know, in those few short days, their little brother, who now is permanently enshrined in photographs on their mantel. They describe a completely heartwarming and touching experience that they feel has been a profound learning and maturing experience for them and their children. They see the experience as a great blessing to them all. The baby was buried, has a headstone, and lives now in the family memories.

Personal communication, Dr. & Mrs. J. Molnar

Compare this memory with that of a couple who killed their baby by a late abortion.

Incidentally, a mid-term abortion is far more dangerous for the mother than delivering at full term.

CHAPTER 17

STEM CELLS & CLONING

What is a clone?
- This is called somatic cell nuclear transfer.
- You start with an egg or ovum cell that has not been fertilized.
- Remove its nucleus.
- Take a cell from the body to be cloned and put its nucleus into the enucleated ovum.
- Pass an electric current through it.
- Hopefully, it (he or she) will act like a fertilized egg and begin to develop.

This is not easy?
The failure rate is horrific. Before Dolly the sheep was finally born in 1996, there were 276 failures.

"The Issue of Human Cloning is Born" Ross, Washington Times, Aug. 14, 2000

In 2001, the Whitehead Institute cloned 613 mice embryos. Five were born, all abnormal.

One cloned kitten has been born (*Nature*, 2002). It took 87 embryos and 8 surrogate mothers. Several other types of mammals, including cows, pigs, goats, and other animals have been cloned.

Can a Human be Cloned?

Humans are mammals but very complicated ones. Since Dolly the sheep showed that a mammal can be successfully cloned, some scientists have been attempting to clone a human.

What is a "failure"?

This is a clone that just doesn't develop. It is one that doesn't implant. It is a miscarriage. It is a premature birth and death. It is a fetal deformity that dies. It is a fetal deformity that is killed after delivery. Finally, some clones suddenly die. Others age prematurely.

Dolly the sheep developed arthritis at the early age of 5 years. Of 12 cloned mice who were born, 10 died prematurely at Japan's National Institute of Infectious Diseases.

Nature Genetics, 2-11-02

The *Journal of Science* (July 2001) and many other sources report success rates as low as 1-2%. Additional abnormalities included enlarged tongues, squashed faces, bad kidneys, livers, and hearts, blocked intestines, diabetes, shortened tendons, and the "large offspring syndrome" with oversized umbilical cords.

Jan Wilmut (Who cloned Dolly the sheep)
H. Griffin, Roslin Institute, Edinburg
J. Robl, Hamatech, Mass., M. West,
Advanced Cell Tech., Mass.

Even apparently normal clones can have genetic instability too subtle to detect.

R. Jaenisch, Whitehead Inst. MA Inst. of Tech. Aug. 2000

A scientist's worst nightmare would be to have a cloned child with serious malformation turn up on CNN.

There are two types of cloning?

Scientists have arbitrarily categorized:

• Research or Therapeutic cloning, in which this embryo is killed at 4 or 5 days (for his stem cells). In this type of cloning, the donor kills his/her own twin brother or sister.

• Reproductive cloning, more accurately, "live birth" cloning, in which this human is allowed to grow and be born.

Actually there is no difference. They have hung a separate name on the one so as to hide the fact that this is a "clone to kill" method.

Why Research Cloning?

To allow research that might lead to treatment and cure of diseases.

Why object?

Because it kills one living human in an attempt to help another.

It violates the Nuremberg Code. It forbids experimentation on a human when it is known beforehand that death or disabling injury will result.

Have Governments spoken?

President Bush's Bioethics Council on 7-11-02 called for a total ban on live birth cloning.

Most nations object to live birth cloning, but many would permit the research type. However, pro-life critics say that if you permit research cloning, you cannot prevent implantation and birth. To do so would create the ridiculous requirement that if she **does not kill** her developing baby, she is guilty of a felony.

What are stem cells?

The single cell zygote or fertilized egg is called omnipotent because it develops into an entire human.

After cell division, in the first few days of a human's life, some of the cells making up this embryo are pluripotent. This means that at this stage of development, these cells are still undifferentiated but will, in time, develop into specific organs such as heart and liver. These are called embryonic stem cells.

Much research is being done on the possibility of "using" these stem cells to repair or replace the organs of another human. Such cells can be obtained from human embryos but also can be obtained from born humans.

What is the difference between adult and embryonic cells?

Embryonic stem cells can only be obtained by cutting open a 5-day-old embryo and removing these stem cells from his or her interior. This kills this living embryonic human.

Adult stem cells can be obtained from cord blood, placentas, bone marrow, skin, fat, and other organs. Originally, it was assumed that these stem cells were multipotent, i.e., not as versatile as embryonic stem cells. Research, however, is increasingly demonstrating that adult stem cells may be "tweaked" into developing into the same organs as the more primitive embryonic ones can.

What are the advantages of embryonic stem cells?

They are plastic, i.e., can possibly grow into any adult cell or organ. They are relatively non-immunogenic, that is, will not be rejected by the recipient's body. They can be reproduced in a cell culture, endlessly replicating themselves. If kept in a certain biochemical culture media, they reproduce but remain undifferentiated. When this "control" is removed, they proceed to differentiate.

What have embryonic stem cells cured?

Nothing yet, but there are some hints of success. According to the proceedings of the Natl. Academy of Science (3-26-02), they can develop into blood vessels. Also, the Natl. Institute of Neurological Diseases (*Nature*, 6-20-02) grew neurons in rats.

But disadvantages?

They can also be too "plastic," as they can develop into all kinds of tissue, desirable or not, and have grown into cancerous tumors, e.g., a report in Jan. 2002 using embryonic stem cells in rats with Parkinson's resulted in 20% developing brain tumors.

Another problem is that, while such very primitive cells are usually considered to be non-immunogenic, this may not always be true and the host may reject them. If so, they could require life-long administration of drugs to prevent this.

"You can't make a clone of you until you get an egg cell from someone else. But even after the nucleus is removed from the egg, it still retains the mitochondria of the mother. (mitochondria generate energy for the cell). These can cause trouble. The only way to get a true clone is to get the egg from your mother."

Congressman D. Weldon, M.D.
Human Events, 3-12-02

Finally, there is the problem of infection. If the egg donor has HIV infection, she will pass it on.

How about Adult Stem Cells?

Adult stem cells offer no ethical problem, for, in obtaining them, the donor human is not injured. Also, because they can be taken from the same human into whom they are retransplanted, there is no problem of organ rejection. And there have been many successes.

• Adult pancreatic islet cell transplants have helped 9 of 15 diabetic patients remain insulin-free for over two years.

Am. Diabetes Assn. Report, 6-24-01

• Bone marrow transplants have been done for 20 years. In the patient, the marrow cells die off. The stem cells survive and repopulate the recipient's marrow and cure him.

J. Science in Dallas Morning News, 6-28-02

• Olfactory ensheathing cells (nose lining) continue to regenerate. If injected into an injured spine, they may stimulate nerve growth.

Griffith Univ. Brisbane Australia

• Adult stem cells have helped delay multiple sclerosis symptoms in patients who had been rapidly deteriorating.

Denver Conference, 4-18-02
Univ. of Wash. Med. Center

• Bone marrow stem cells have been "coaxed" into becoming liver-like cells.

C. Verfaillie, *J. Clinical Invest.*, 2-25-02 and 5-15-02

• She also took adult rodent stem cells as was able to change them into many types of tissue.

C. Verfaillie, *Brit. J. Nature*, 6-20-02

And More?

Yes. Dr. David Prentice of Indiana State University has prepared the following chart showing adult stem cell potential:

• **Adult stem cells (and other non-embryonic stem cells) are successfully being used clinically**
  Cancer (Including leukemia, lymphoma, multiple myeloma, breast cancer, brain tumors, retinoblastoma, ovarian cancer, testicular cancer)

Autoimmune Diseases – Multiple sclerosis, Systemic Lupus, Rheumatoid arthritis, Juvenile rheumatoid arthritis

Immunodeficiencies (Including first successful human gene therapy)

Anemias (Including sickle cell anemia)

Cartilage and bone diseases in children

Stroke – first report using cultured cells to treat stroke; 6 of 12 patients improved.

Heart damage after heart attack

Skin – for grafts; growth from hair follicle stem cells, after plucking a few hairs from patient

Cornea scarring – growing new corneas to restore sight to legally blind patients

- **Adult stem cells show great success in animal models of disease**
  Diabetes – reversed diabetes in mice
  Stroke – repaired brain damage; improved mobility
  Heart attack – repaired heart damage; increased heart output
  Spinal cord damage – repaired, improved mobility
  Muscular dystrophy – increased muscle mass
  Retinal damage – repair of damage
  Liver disease – repair of damage

- **Adult stem sells show the ability to home in on damaged tissue**
  They can target and repair damaged tissue and attack tumors.

  Probably one of the best sources of stem cells is human fat, easily obtainable by liposuction.

  Zuk, et al., Multilineage Cells from Human Adipose Tissue: Implications for Cell-Based therapies, Tissue Emergency, 7(2):211-228, April 2001

But either will work?

There have been multiple successes with adult stem cells but not a singe one with embryonic stem cells to date. Early on, as this research developed, it was assumed that embryonic stem cells had almost unlimited potential. As time passes, however, adult stem cells from an increasing number of organs are being shown to have more and more potential.

But an analysis by Maureen Condic in the respected periodical *First Things* commented (Sept. 2002):

"Proponents of embryonic stem cell research and human cloning have not succeeded in garnering public support on the basis of the scientific evidence, largely because there is no compelling evidence in support of their assertions. Even if strong scientific evidence existed, the equally strong moral objections to this research would undoubtedly persist. Advocates have also not succeeded in defining the matter solely in terms of scientific freedom and the pursuit of knowledge; the history of the last century amply illustrates the need to restrict scientific inquiry in some circumstances. In the face of these failures to recruit the public to their cause, advocates of human cloning and embryonic stem cell research have attempted to recast the issue as one of compassion and hope by marshaling the ranks of the desperate. The strategy appears to be: when you can't win on legitimate grounds, win by any means possible. Such a strategy does not preclude outright deceit and emotional manipulation, all in the name of 'hope.' "To offer false hope to the desperate as a means of advancing a political, social, or economic agenda is worse than merely cruel, it is objectively evil."

No Public Support?

From pro-abortion politicians, non-moralistic scientists, the biotech industry and anti-life organizations, yes, but the financial world offers an interesting perspective.

Financial analysis of which has more promise is probably reflected in which has attracted more venture capital funding. According to *Forbes Magazine* (9-1-01, Pg. 32) and the *Wall Street Journal* (R. Miniter, Sept., 01) of 15 funded projects, 13 were with adult and 2 with embryonic stem cells.

Since there is so little private investment, we presume this accounts for the almost desperate efforts to get government funding for research cloning and embryonic stem cell research.

Any other problems?

If human cloning is legalized, it will require huge numbers of womens' eggs. To obtain these, she must be first stimulated to produce multiple ovulation. Then she needs a general anesthetic and laparoscopic surgery. The surgeon then scrapes the egg cells off the surface of the ovary.

Where will these women come from? Depend on it, they will exploit Third World women as guinea pigs.

PART IV
ABORTION

Chapter

CHAPTER 18

HOW MANY?

How many abortions are there?

In the U.S. there are 2 reporting agencies. The U.S. Center for Disease Control is a passive recipient of reports voluntarily sent to it by the states. Since all states don't report, and many report inaccurately, these totals are under-reported. The CDC does do a meticulous job of breaking down the categories, and so these are the percentages everyone uses.

The Alan Guttmacher Institute, a branch of Planned Parenthood, aggressively contacts hospitals and known abortionists, and the result is a more accurate and larger figure, which we use.

How many? During the 1980s and 1990s, total abortions stayed about 1,550,000 annually, slowly decreasing in the 1990s. Note that the Guttmacher Institute reported that 10% of known abortion providers did not report. Adding 10% to its 1,550,000 equals 1,700,000. When the unreported abortions are added (income tax evasion, cover-up for privacy, etc.), a figure of 1,800,000 may have been more realistic. Live births have hovered just under 4 million. Therefore: *Until the early and mid 90s, almost every third baby conceived in America was killed by abortion.*

Then these began a steady decrease in total numbers in almost every state:

	Guttmacher	CDC
1975	1,034,200	854,853
1980	1,553,900	1,297,606
1990	1,608,600	1,429,577
1995	1,363,690	1,210,883
1998	1,328,000	1,162,318

The 1998 report is from Alan Guttmacher Institute and released by the CDC and the National Center for Health Statistics.

Report 6-6-2002

Final figures always lag years behind, but the decrease continues so that, with births holding at 4 million, the head count is now closer to 1 in 4.

Note must be taken of Missouri, South Carolina, Wisconsin, and several other states where the decrease is 40-50%.

What's the story on numbers of abortion providers?

In 1973 half of all abortions in the U.S. were done in hospitals. Twenty years later it was down to 7%.

Most are done in 440 large free-standing abortion chambers which did 70% of all abortions. The rest are done in doctors' offices or in clinics that do less than half of their "business" in abortion.

S. Henshaw et al., Ab. Service in U.S.
Fam. Plan Persp., June '94

How far along in pregnancy were they?

Using a 1,500,000 figure, in 1992:
- 1.2% or 18,000 were 22 weeks or older
- 10.0% or 150,000 were 13-20 weeks
- 88.8% or 1,332,000 were 12 and under

Center for Disease Control, MWWR, Dec. '94

How many are repeaters?

Repeat abortions were 20% in 1973 but rose to 44% in 1987. In the U.S., by 2000, 47% of all abortions were repeats. This has plateaued since then.

S. Henshaw et al., Ab. Characteristics, 1994-95, Fam. Plan. Persp., Vol. 28, No. 4, July '96, p. 143

Thirty-five percent of abortions in the U.S. are performed on African-American women, while they represent only 12% of the female population.

US. C.D.C./U.S. Census 2000

In 1982 there were 2,908 facilities doing abortions. Fifteen years later it was 2,042. The decline has occurred almost entirely in facilities that did fewer than 400 abortions a year. It would appear that local public opinion has been substantially responsible for the closing of these smaller facilities that could not stand up against the opposition of their communities, as a significant percent of their income was derived from other medical practice, which is vulnerable to boycotting. Full-time abortion chambers are less vulnerable to this kind of pressure.

What are the leading causes of death in the U.S.?

Clearly, abortion is, as shown below.:

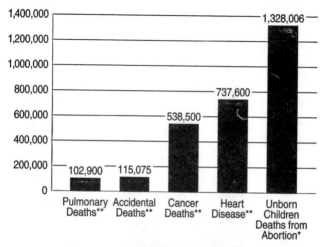

*1997 Alan Guttmacher Institute figures
**1997 U.S. National Centar for Health Statistics,
Statistical Abstract of the United States: 1998
1997 is the latest year a statistical breakdown on deaths is available

But the impact on the Black community is nothing less than black genocide.

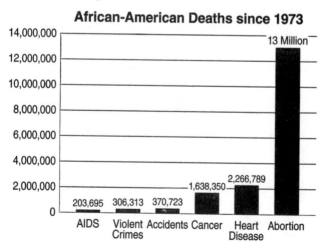

1997 figures, see above

New York City is the worst example. More black babies are aborted there than are born — 49,235 abortions and 40,481 births. In Brooklyn it was 31,500 to 23,700.

NY State Dept Health, 1997 (2001 report)

Abortion of Babies in Brooklyn

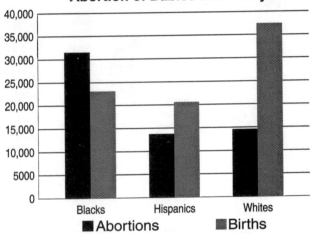

How many in 3rd trimester?

The official figures in the U.S. stop at 22 weeks, but Dr. Wm. Swartz reported on inserting laminaria in 700 women for *third* trimester abortions.

Swartz, *OB/GYN News,* vol. 21, no.11, p. 23, Jan. '87

The partial-birth abortion technique has certainly increased late second and early third trimester abortions. One center in New Jersey was reported doing 1,500 yearly.

Testimony, Congressman C. Smith

How many abortions are there in Canada?

In Canada, in 1984, there were 64,449 abortions, which is 17.5% of their birth rate (11.7% were late abortions). In 1993 there were 104,403 abortions.

In 1997, there were 114,848, which is one killed for every 4 births.

Statistics Canada

The 1969 Canadian law was struck down in 1988. Since then, many free-standing abortion chambers have been set up. The result has been a steady increase in the numbers of abortions.

How about sex selection?
Few abortionists admit to doing this and so there are few reports. When reported, it is girls who are killed, except for a few males known to carry or have genetic diseases.

Is abortion done for sex selection?
Selective abortion of multi-fetal pregnancies is a good example. Doctors faced with quadruplets (4) will at times selectively kill two in the womb on the supposition that survival of two has better odds than four. But if the sex can be determined, which ones are killed? "Ninety-nine percent of the requests are to keep the boys."

M. Evans, Progress in Fetal Studies . . . Thorny Ethical Issues, *OB, Gyn News,* Oct. 1, 1990, p. 3

In a series of 8,000 amniocenteses done for sex selection in Bombay, India, 7,999 unborn girl babies and one boy baby were killed.

But think of the additional welfare costs for all these babies born to teenagers.
Planned Parenthood's own figures are that there will be welfare costs of $13,900 for each first birth to a teenager (married and unmarried), and $8,400 cost for each first birth to her if she is 20 years or older. Compare this with the average of nearly $50,000 each will ultimately pay in taxes as an adult.

M.Burt, "Public Cost of Teen Childbearing,"
Family Planning Perspectives, vol.18, no. 5, Sept. 1986

What about Informed Consent?

This is one of the most tragic abuses associated with the abortion industry. In any other type of surgery, the doctor is required to explain in detail what the procedure is, its possible complications, etc. Only then does the patient give "informed" consent.

Abortion is unique in that, while it is surgery that is potentially dangerous to the mother, it also destroys the living being within her. To be fully informed, she should be given full factual information on the surgery, its possible complications (immediate and long-term), and, also, full details about "what she carries."

What is done? Very little factual information is given at all, and what is given is often false. The complications are ignored, glossed over, or given on a paper in fine print. Her passenger is referred to as "pregnancy tissue," "not alive yet," "not a baby yet," "just a bunch of cells," "only a glob." These descriptions are given at a stage of development when the baby already sucks her thumb and feels pain, and when we can listen to her tiny heartbeat on an office ultrasonic stethoscope.

Such deception of the mother and planned railroading of her into an abortion is never more evident than when the so-called "counselor" asks her, "Do you want your menstrual period re-established? If so, just sign up for this procedure." Abortion is not mentioned, nor anything about the baby.

There is no better example of the exploitation of women than this continuing, commercialized, and almost universal deception.

How are abortions different in practice in clinics compared to other surgery?

Abortions are unique among all types of surgery. The chart below reflects the situation in free standing abortion facilities in the U.S. To a greater or less extent, in every nation, abortion procedures are commonly exempt from the sanitary and professional rules required of other surgery.

	ABORTION	ETHICAL SURGERY
Payment	Cash at door	Pay later
Pathologic exam	Seldom	Routine
Advertising	Routine	Rare
Counseling	Usually a farce	Done if needed
Second opinion	Never	If needed
Informed consent	Legally not required	Always
Kickbacks	Sometimes	Never
Record Keeping	Sketchy	In detail
Pre-op exam	Often not done until she is on the table	Mandatory and detailed
Follow-up exam	None	Mandatory and detailed
Correct Diagnosis	10-15% done on non-pregnant women	Surgeon is disciplined if he does many wrong operations
Husband's consent	Not needed	Expected
Husband informed	Not necessary	Always
Consent of parents of minor	Not needed	Legally required
Parents informed	Seldom	Legally required
Tissue disposal	In garbage	In humane and dignified manner
Burial	In garbage	Yes, if large enough
Surgical training	Not required	Absolutely required
Non-medical reasons	99%	About 1%
Cash "kick-backs"	common	forbidden

Any reasons why abortions are declining while the population is increasing?

We are convinced that abortion contains within itself the seeds of its own demise. The experience of many women has been very negative, and this is being passed on to their daughters — "Don't do it, Sue. I did and it's the worst mistake I ever made."

The Supreme Courts in the U.S. and Canada have not allowed any direct bans on abortion but peripheral legislation has certainly cut the numbers. Such laws

include:
- Parental notification and consent laws
- Women's Right to Know laws
- Abortion clinic regulations
- Fetal homicide laws
- Partial-birth abortion bans
- Safe Haven for Abandoned Infants Act
- Ban on tax money for abortion
- Child Custody Protection Acts

And there will be more, if the courts allow it.

Right to Know laws require the abortionist to see the patient and mandate a waiting or "cooling off" period. Most require that an information booklet be given her. The best such book is from the Ohio Department of Health and was approved by the Ohio Medical & Hospital Associations. For a copy, send $3.00 to Cincinnati Right to Life at 1802 W. Galbraith Rd., Cincinnati, Ohio, 45239, USA.

CHAPTER 19

WHAT KIND AND HOW?

Spontaneous abortions are usually called miscarriages. Most occur at home with little danger to the mother. There is sometimes excessive bleeding, however, or incomplete emptying of the uterus requiring hospitalization, during which the surgeon must gently tease the rotting remnants of the placenta (afterbirth) from the inside walls of the womb with a blunt instrument. Even when this procedure (called a D&C) is needed, there is rarely damage to the mother because the cervix (womb opening) is already softened and partly opened. Infection is rare. Baby parts are seldom found.

What kind of induced abortions are there?

In the first week there are micro-abortions caused by "contraceptive" drugs and devices.

After implantation, there are those induced by drugs such as RU 486, Methotrexate, and prostaglandins.

In the first trimester there are surgical abortions like suction and D&C.

In the second and third trimesters there are instillation types, D&E, intracardiac injections and partial-birth abortions.

What are the first trimester surgical ones?

There are several types:

- **Menstrual extraction:** This is a very early suction abortion, often done before the pregnancy test is positive.
- **Suction-aspiration:** In this method, the abortionist must first paralyze the cervical muscle ring (womb opening) and then stretch it open. This is difficult because it is hard or "green" and not ready to open. He then inserts a hollow plastic tube, which has a knife-like edge on the tip, into the uterus. The suction tears the baby's body into pieces. He then cuts the deeply rooted placenta from the inner wall of the uterus. The scraps are sucked out into a bottle (see color photo in back of book). The suction is 29 times more powerful than a home vacuum cleaner.
- **Dilatation & Curettage (D&C):** This is similar to the suction procedure except that the abortionist inserts a curette, a loop-shaped steel knife, up into the uterus. With this, he cuts the placenta and baby into pieces and scrapes them out into a basin. Bleeding is usually profuse.

What are second trimester ones?

In the 1970s and '80s the most common type was saline amniocentesis, or salt poisoning abortions. These are not used much anymore because of danger to the mother. These are done after the 16th week. A large needle is inserted through the abdominal wall of the mother and into the baby's amniotic sac. A concentrated salt solution is injected into the amniotic fluid. The baby breathes and swallows it, is poisoned, struggles, and sometimes convulses. It takes over an hour to kill the baby. When successful, the mother goes into labor about one day later and delivers a dead baby.

Is it actually poisoning?

Yes. The mechanism of death is acute hypernatremia, or acute salt poisoning, with development of widespread vasodilatation, edema, congestion, hemorrhage, shock, and death.

Galen et al., "Fetal Pathology and Mechanism of Death in Saline Abortion, *Amer. Jour. of OB&GYN,*1974, vol. 120, pp. 347-355

And other methods?

In the '70s and '80s, prostaglandin drugs were used to induce violent premature labor and delivery. When used alone, there was: ". . . a large complication rate (42.6%) associated with its use. Few risks in obstetrics are more certain than that which occurs to a pregnant woman undergoing abortion after the 14th week of pregnancy."

Duenhoelter & Grant, "Complications Following Prostaglandin F-2 Alpha Induced Mid-trimester Abortion." *Jour. of OB & GYN,* Sept. 1975

Because of these problems, the D&E, or Dilatation & Evacuation method, was developed and largely replaced the above. It involves the live dismemberment of the baby and piecemeal removal from below.

A pliers-like instrument is used because the baby's bones are calcified, as is the skull. There is no anesthetic for the baby. The abortionist inserts the instrument up into the uterus, seizes a leg or other part of the body, and, with a twisting motion, tears it from the baby's body. This is repeated again and again. The spine must be snapped, and the skull crushed to remove them. The nurse's job is to reassemble the body parts to be sure that all are removed.

This sounds dangerous.

It is, but a report from the U.S. Center for Disease Control, Dept. HEW, stated that it is still safer for the mother than the salt-poisoning or Prostaglandin methods.

"Comparative Risks of Three Methods of Midtrimester Abortion,"
Morbidity and Mortality Weekly Report,
Center for Disease Control, HEW, Nov. 26, 1976

It is reported that every year about 100,000 women are aborted by the D&E method, between 13 and 24 weeks' gestation. Of this, 500 have "serious complications." This was still judged to have a "lower risk of morbidity and mortality than the infusion procedures."

MacKay et al., "Safety of Local vs General
Anesthesia for Second Trimester D&E Abortions"
OB-GYN, vol. 66, no. 5, Nov.1985, p. 661

Any new methods?

Yes, intracardiac injections. Since the advent of fertility drugs, multi-fetal pregnancies have become common. "The frequency of triplet and higher pregnancies . . . has increased 200% since the early 1970s." Since these are usually born prematurely and some have other problems, a new method has been developed.

Assisted Repro. Techniques . . . , L. Wilcox,
Fertl. & Sterility, vol. 65, #2, Feb. '96, pg. 361

At about 4 months a needle is inserted through the mother's abdomen, into the chest and heart of one of the fetal babies and a poison injected to kill him or her. This is "pregnancy reduction." It is done to reduce the number or to kill a handicapped baby, if such is identified. If successful, the dead baby's body is absorbed. Sometimes, however, this method results in the loss of all of the babies.

Are there 3rd trimester abortions?

Yes, there are, and as late as 8 months or more. These are done by intracardiac injection. A more recently developed method is the partial-birth abortion, also called "brain suction," "D&X," or intact dilitation and evacuation methods.

• These are done after 4 or 5 months.

- 80% of babies are normal.
- Most babies are viable.

This is like a breech delivery. The entire infant is delivered out into the air, except the head which is held in the external birth canal. A scissors is jammed into the base of the skull. A tube is inserted into the skull, and the brain is sucked out. The now-dead infant is pulled out. The drawings illustrate this:

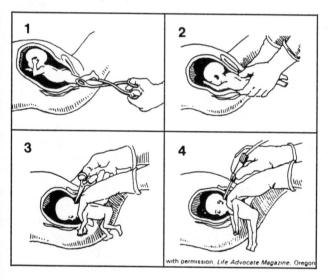

with permission, *Life Advocate Magazine*, Oregon

Perhaps it's her only choice.
"There are no medical circumstances in which a partial-birth abortion is the only safe alternative. We take care of pregnant women who are very sick, and babies who are very sick, and we never perform partial-birth abortions. . . . There are plenty of alternatives. . . . This is clearly a procedure no obstetrician needs to do."

F. Boehm, Dr. OB, Vanderbilt U. Med.
The Washington Times, May 6, 1966, p. A1

But isn't it the safest?

To do this was called a "version & breech delivery." This was abandoned decades ago as it was too dangerous. Instead today the much safer Cesarean Section is used.

Dr. Warren Hern, author of *the* late term abortion medical text, said, "I would dispute any statement that this is the safest procedure to use. The procedure can cause amniotic fluid embolism or placental abruption."

AMA News, Nov. 20, 1995, p. 3

Dr. Pamela Smith, Director of Medical Education, Dept. of Ob-Gyn at Mt. Sinai Hospital in Chicago, has stated: "There are absolutely no obstetrical situations encountered in this country which would require partial-birth abortion to preserve the life or health of the mother." And she adds two more risks: cervical incompetence in subsequent pregnancies caused by three days of forceful dilation of the cervix, and uterine rupture caused by rotating the fetus in the womb.

Joseph DeCook, Fellow, Am. Col., Ob/Gyn, founder of PHACT (Physicians Ad Hoc Coalition for Truth), stated: "There is no literature that testifies to the safety of partial-birth abortions. It's a maverick procedure devised by maverick doctors who wish to deliver a dead fetus. Such abortions could lead to infection causing sterility." Also, "Drawing out the baby in breech position is a very dangerous procedure and could tear the uterus. Such a ruptured uterus could cause the mother to bleed to death in ten minutes. The puncturing of the child's skull produces bone shards that could puncture the uterus." (Congressman Charles Canady (R-FL), 7/23/02).

Weren't there laws passed to forbid this gruesome method?

Yes. In the U.S., over half of the states passed laws to stop it. These were challenged in court. The U.S.

Supreme Court struck down all of these laws.

Stenberg v. Carhart, US Supreme Court, June 2000

But why kill the infant?

You've said it! Obviously the mother wants to get unpregnant. Even if this is accepted, we must still ask, why kill? Most of these babies are viable. They are only 3 or 4 inches (10 cm) from complete delivery. One gentle pull and the head will come out. Then the cord could be cut, and the infant given to the nurse to take to the intensive care nursery.

There is absolutely no medical reason to kill the baby except that the mother wants him dead.

Are there videos?

Two excellent videos are "The Procedure" by Dan Donahey on partial-birth abortion and "Eclipse of Reason" by B. Nathanson, both obtainable through a Right to Life Office.

What about toxemia, serious diabetes, etc., in late pregnancy?

In these cases the pregnancy may have to be terminated to save the mother's life. But left alone, both might die. Treatment here is not abortion but premature delivery. This attempts to save both lives.

Is surgery on an ectopic pregnancy an abortion?

Some do define this as an abortion, and this is one reason why Right to Life people usually accept a "life of the mother" exception to laws that would forbid abortion.

Until recent years, this required surgical removal of the tube, which at times contained a live human embryo which then would die.

By the time most ectopic surgery is done, the developing baby is dead and often destroyed by the hemorrhage. In any case, such surgery is done primarily to prevent the death of the mother. This is good medical practice because there is no chance for the baby to survive.

If medical technology were advanced enough to allow transplanting the baby from its pathological location, and placing it into the uterus, then most ethicists would say this should be done. Since this is not possible with present technology, the tiny new baby's life today is lost.

The newest approach is laparoscopic. Through an operating laparoscope, the lump in the tube can be seen. It is now possible to cut this open and suck out the contents. Recent reports tell that, 80% of the time, what is removed is not (no longer?) human life. But it is possible to do what amounts to an intra-abdominal "suction-abortion." This would be a direct attack on the baby and is very disturbing to moralists. This will continue to be debated.

But, for now, the embryonic baby has a zero chance of survival. Without the procedure, both would die. The surgery will save her life, and so, for now, the Right to Life Movement will allow this.

How about removal or treatment of a cancerous or of a traumatized pregnant uterus, or of some other organ while the mother is pregnant?
The same applies. Surgery is done or treatment is given to prevent the death of the mother. The death of the baby, if it occurs, would be an unfortunate and undesired secondary effect. If at all possible, the baby should also be saved.

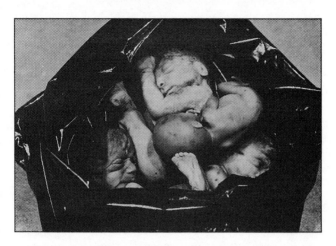

This was the result of one morning's work in a Canadian teaching hospital. These babies had attained fetal ages of 18-24 weeks (4-5 months) before being killed by abortion.

"In times past, abortion took the life of one, for otherwise two would die. Today, abortion takes the life of one, where otherwise two would live."

H. Ratner, M.D.

CHAPTER 20

VERY EARLY ABORTIONS

These fall into two general categories: those that prevent implantation at one week of life and those which kill a developing baby days or weeks after implantation.

Before Implantation:

Which methods do this? In varying degree, the methods that prevent implantation, and therefore kill a baby at one week of life, include the intra-uterine device (IUD), Norplant, Depo Provera, Progesterone-only pills, low-dose contraceptive combination pills, and the morning-after pills. Let's take them one at a time.

How about Norplant?

This is an implant under the skin of her forearm that lasts five years. In the first half of that time, its effect is to almost always suppress ovulation. In the last half of that time, break-through ovulation is the rule. However, very few pregnancies survive. Clearly, this second half is commonly effective through micro-abortions and prevention of implantation.

What about Depo Provera?

As with Norplant, there is some variance from woman to woman, but in a far higher percent of cases Depo Provera suppresses ovulation. Break-through ovulation, however, does occur as attested to by full-term pregnancies recorded with women who were receiving this shot every three months.

What of the IUD?

The intrauterine device, commonly referred to as an IUD or coil (in Europe), is a small plastic or metal device that is inserted through the vagina and into the cavity of the uterus. The purpose of this is to "prevent" pregnancy.

Is an IUD a contraceptive or an abortive agent?

Until recently, almost all scientific papers had agreed that its effect was to prevent the implantation of the tiny new human being into the nutrient lining of the uterus; an abortive action.

The U.S. Food and Drug Administration stated in an official report that its effectiveness is "in direct proportion to the quantity and quality of the inflammatory reaction to various types of IUDs"...and states that there "is one common thread . . . " They all "interfere in some manner with the implantation of the embryo in the uterine cavity."

Second Report on IUDs, Dec. 1978, U.S. Dept. of HEW,
Food & Drug Administration Document 017-012-00276-5

"The inhibition of implanation of the embryo remains a major, if not the dominant, mechanism of action of IUDs"

J. Spinnato, "Mechanism of Action of IUDs . . ."
Am. J. OB & GYN, 3/97, Vol. 176, No. 3, pp. 503-6

A detailed report in a Planned Parenthood publication in 1989 claimed that a high percentage of its action was the prevention of fertilization.

IUDs are Contraceptives, not Abortifacients:
A Comment on Research and Belief, I. Sivin, Studies in Family Planning,
Vol. 20, No. 6, Dec. '89

The above report, however, has not been duplicated and therefore has not presented enough evidence to change the conventional wisdom that the IUD is almost always an abortive agent.

What of Progesterone-only pills?
These fall into the same category as the Progesterone-only implant, Norplant, and the Progesterone-only injection, Depo Provera.

How does the morning-after pill work?
This medication has an antinidatory effect on the endometrium (that is, a hardening of the lining of the uterus), which prevents implantation of the tiny new human being (blastocyst stage).

If, for example, a rape victim had ovulated just before the assault and fertilization had occurred, then the use of such medication after the event would clearly be abortive.

There is a possibility that it can act in a sterilizing fashion. The large hormone dose could rapidly affect the ovary and prevent an ovulation that might have occurred one to three days after the intercourse. If sperm were still present and active in the woman's genital tract, she might be fertilized one to three days after the event. In this case, some have suggested that such treatment (as for an assault rape victim) might actually prevent a pregnancy, but this has not been proven.

Kahlenborn, Larimore, and Stanford
The Annuals of Pharmacotherapy
"Effective Hormone Emergency Contraception"
March 2002, Volume 36, Number 3 Page 465-470

Kahlenborn, et al., amply document that the so-called emergency contraceptive pill would more logically be termed, emergency abortion pill. We had always known that if she ovulated before she had intercourse, and the next day took this pill, that it was ridiculous to think that it could prevent a fertilization that had occurred 12 hours earlier. This study shows that even if it's taken prior to ovulation, it has a significant failure rate.

They also thoroughly document the abortive effect, that while ovulation and fertilization can occur, this pill prevents implantation at one week of life and therefore is legitimately called an abortifacient.

ibid.

What about the standard contraceptive pill?

There are over 30 "contraceptive" pills on the market, each differing a little from the others. They "prevent" pregnancy through three separate functions.

1. They thicken the mucous plug at the cervix. If this is the primary effect, then it truly is contraceptive because it prevents sperm from entering.

2. They prevent release of the ovum. If this is the primary effect, then the function is "temporary" sterilization.

3. They render the lining of the womb hostile to the implantation of the tiny new human at one week of life. This effect is abortifacient.

The earlier high-estrogen pills largely prevented ovulation. The newer low-estrogen pills allow "breakthrough" ovulation in up to 20% or more of the months used. Such a released ovum is fertilized 10% or more of the time. Most of these tiny new lives which result do not survive. The reason is that, at one week of life, this tiny new boy or girl cannot implant in the womb lining (see number 3 above) and dies. These are micro-abortions.

The pill, then, can have a contraceptive or temporary sterilization effect (by far the most common), or it can be an abortifacient.

C. Kahlenbam "Breast Cancer,
Its Link to Abortion and the Birth Control Pill,"
One More Soul Publ, 2000, p. 315-324

You mean the effect is to abort?

Yes! "The morphological changes observed in the endometrium of oral contraceptive users have functional significance and provide evidence that reduced endometrial receptivity does indeed contribute to the contraceptive efficacy of OCs." In other words, because the endometrial lining is not receptive to the human being, who must implant in order to continue living, the human being will die.

Somkuti, et al., "The Effect of Oral Contraceptive Pills on
Markers of Endometrial Receptivity," *Fertility and Sterility,*
Vol. 65, #3, 3/96, p. 488

W. Larimore, et al. Post Fertilization Effects of
Oral Contraceptives and Their Relationship to Informed Consent,
Arch. Fam. Med., Vol. 9, Feb. 2000, pg. 126-133.

Post-Implantation:

The best known example of this is the French abortion pill, RU 486 (Mifepristone).

How does RU 486 work?

RU 486 kills a developing baby after his or her heart has begun to beat.

It blocks a vital nutrient hormone, Progesterone. The embryonic baby, who had implanted into the nutrient lining of the mother's womb at least two weeks earlier, can be compared to a grape on a vine. If the stem is pinched, preventing the nourishing sap from reaching the grape, it will wither, die and drop off. Just so, if this drug is used, it causes the embryonic baby to wither and die. A second drug, prostaglandin, is used to expel the dead baby from her womb.

Counting from the first day of her last normal menstrual period, it is effective only from the fifth through the seventh week. Some claim success, but with decreasing effectiveness, into the 9th week.

RU 486 alone is effective from 60 to 80% of the time. If Prostaglandin is added, the abortion rate rises to 95%.

Couzinet et al., "Termination of Early Pregnancy
by RU-486 (Mifepristone), *New Eng. J. of Med.*,
vol. 315, no. 25, Dec. 18, 1986
O. Ylikorkala et al., *Outpatient Abortion With*
RU-486, *OB-GYN*, vol 74, no. 4, Oct. 1989
M. Rodger et al., Blood Loss . . . After RU-486 and
Prostaglandin...," *Contraception*, vol. 40, no. 4, Oct. 1989.
Science Magazine, Sept. 1989

How is it used?

During the US clinical trials on RU 486, women who had one of the following conditions or diseases were prohibited from taking the drug:

Under 18 years of age, more than 35 years of age, smoked over 10 cigarettes a day and had another cardiovascular risk factor, liver disease, respiratory disease, kidney disease, adrenal disease, cardiovascular disease, blood clots, hypertension (high blood pressure), anemia, insulin-dependent diabetes, known allergy to prostaglandins (Cytotec), using an intrauterine device (IUD), breast-feeding, receiving anticoagulation therapy, receiving long-term cortisone therapy, masses or cysts in female organs, infection in female organs, ectopic (tubal) pregnancies, signs that she might abort spontaneously

These patient precautions were also followed during the clinical trials on RU 466 in France.

First Visit: She must have a thorough history, physical exam and blood count. She needs an ultrasound exam to confirm the age of her baby and to rule out a tubal pregnancy. She must sign permission and, in some states or nations, wait 1 or more days.

Second Visit: She takes the pills.

Third Visit: She is given the prostaglandin drug. This produces hard labor. Usually the baby parts are passed that day.

Fourth Visit: If she has not aborted, or if there is still bleeding, she will need an ultrasound to determine if the uterus is empty. If not, she needs a D&C. The French Ministry of Health requires that the abortion facility be equipped with an EKG, IV equipment, and a "crash cart" with a defibrillator in the event of a heart attack resulting from the drugs.

There are complications?

Yes. Bleeding is the most common. In the controlled testing reported, one woman in a hundred bled so profusely she either needed a D&C (surgical scraping out of her womb) and/or a blood transfusion. In an underdeveloped country, such a treatment would normally not be available and, very likely, some of these women would bleed to death.

e.g., In a controlled trial in the state of Iowa, one woman took the pills and went home. She bled so badly, she needed four emergency blood transfusions to save her life.

Interruption of Preg. with RU-486 & Prostaglandin, Silvestre et al., *N. Eng. J. Med.,* Vol. 322, 3/8/90, No. 10
Efficacy of Mifepristone & Prostaglandin in 1st Trimester Abortion, UK Multicentre Trial, *Br. J. OB/Gyn,* June '90, Vol. 97, pp. 480-486

Other complications include substantial pain, tubal pregnancies, incomplete abortion, uterine rupture, e.g., an 18-week abortion with RU 486 and prostaglandin produced rupture of the uterus and a near fatality.

Uterine Rupt.-Ab.-Second Trimester: J. Norman, *Br. J. Ob/Gyn,* vol. 102, Apr. '95, p. 332

And psychological upset, ranging from mild to serious, post-abortion syndrome and, in a few cases, death of the woman.

In April, 2002, the FDA required the drug company to report that four women developed "serious illnesses" and that two more died after taking RU 486. These problems included ruptured tubal pregnancies, infections, and a heart attack.

Danco Labs. April 17, 2002

Are there problems with the baby?

RU 486 and a prostaglandin will produce an abortion 95% of the time. The rest will be advised to have a surgical abortion. But there will be some who will refuse surgery and carry to term. These babies will have a significant possibility of fetal deformity. Why?

Two poisonous drugs were given when the heart, limbs, etc., were being formed. This didn't quite kill, but the effect can be to cause severe structural deformities as a direct toxic effect, similar to those from Thalidomide.

In the tightly controlled French experience, there has been one such tragedy. Under the far looser private care in North America, the number of deformed babies should be greater.

Two French researchers report on two women who continued their pregnancies after their RU 486 failed to cause abortion. One delivered a normal baby. "The second pregnancy was terminated because of malformations (sirenomelia)" [fusion of lower extremities].

J.C. Pons et al., letter to Lancet, Scrip, Sept. 26, 1991

Aren't there therapeutic uses?

To date, there are *no* proven uses of RU 486 to treat any human illness. Research is underway testing whether it will have any beneficial effect on one type of breast cancer, on meningioma (brain tumor), Cushing's Syndrome or endometriosis. No serious research is projected for any other conditions.

Note that pro-life groups have never opposed research with RU 486 to find therapeutic uses. To date all studies of this drug were paid for by, or associated with, the manufacturer.

Where can I find more details?

A pamphlet, "RU 486, A Human Pesticide," is available from Hayes Publishing Company in Cincinnati – Phone (513) 681-7559.

A detailed scientific description of function, effects, efficacy, complications, etc. is available.

J. Willke, "Mifepristone – A Boom or a Bust,"
Ann. Pharmacotherapy, Vol. 35, No. 3, Mar. 2002, pp 376-381

What about Methotrexate?

This also works to kill a baby after his or her heart has begun to beat. It works roughly within the same timeframe, but in a different fashion. The RU 486 essentially starves the baby which then dies and is lost. Methotrexate is a direct poison and kills the developing baby.

Methothrexate & Misoprostol, M. Creinin et al., JAMA, Oct. 19, 1994

Methotrexate & Misoprostol to Terminate Early Pregnancy,
R. Hausknecht, N. Eng. J.M., Vol. 333, No. 9, 8/31/95, pg. 537

Is Methotrexate safe?

Definitely not. It is a cellular toxin and has been used for years to kill cancer cells. The object of cancer treatment is to kill cancer cells before the drug kills the patient. This is a commonly used chemotherapeutic agent. Most readers have known loved ones who have had chemotherapy. There are some serious side-effects at times -loss of hair, inability to digest food, diarrhea, anemia and even death. All of these have been caused by methotrexate. The trick is to use a dose just large enough to kill the sensitive embryonic baby but not large enough to do any serious damage to the mother.

It works alone?

No. It also needs a follow up dose of prostaglandin to empty the uterus.

What of Prostaglandin alone?

A pill form, Cytotec or Misoprostol, has been used alone in concomitant oral and vaginal doses. Its "effectiveness" is in question. Used without medical supervision in Brazil, it has frequently failed to produce abortions and has caused fetal deformity.

"The most striking manifestations . . . were growth retardation, underdeveloped bones, short equinovarus feet, joint rigidity and webs, hypoplasia or atrophy of limb muscles . . ."

Other researchers report cranial nerve deficiency, hydrocephalus, delayed motor and mental development and mobius anomaly.

Coelho, et al. "Misoprostol Embryotoxicity Evaluation of 15 Patients with Arthrogryposis," *Am. J. Med., Genetics*, 95, 2000, pp 297-301

The maker approves?

Absolutely not. The maker of Cytotec, the Searle Co., sent a drug warning to physicians stating, "Cytotec administration, by any route, is contraindicated in women who are pregnant . . . Serious adverse effects reported following its use in pregnant women include maternal or fetal death, uterine hyperstimulation, rupture or perforation requiring surgical repair, hysterectomy, amniotic fluid embolism, severe vaginal bleeding, retained placenta, shock . . ."

Searle Co., M. Cullen, 23 Aug. 2000

This drug is being used for induction of labor at term. But the USFDA reports over 50 cases of uterine rupture and other serious complications, some with neonatal and maternal deaths.

Misoprostol and the Politics of Convenience, *The Lancet*, p 2142, 6-30-01

Label Change:
The Searle Co. (above) refused to change the label. Then, in July, 2002, the FDA itself changed it, changing Searle's warning to merely stating that women taking it should not get pregnant.

CHAPTER 21

MATERNAL COMPLICATIONS
Immediate

*Scientific reports on maternal complications
from induced abortion are grossly inaccurate.*

Why?

Published reports from scientific studies all come
from university medical centers. Surgery in them is
done by highly qualified surgeons. Further, they have
immediate access to topnotch care if a mishap occurs.
But less than 10% of U.S. abortions are done in such
elite institutions. Consequently, the published reports of
safety hazards do not in any way reflect the actual situation "out there" where over 90% of abortions are done
in free-standing, for-profit abortion facilities or in doctors' offices.

Aren't there any reports on those "out there"?

The typical abortion mill will rarely report any complications. If the problem is acute, the injured woman
is taken by van (never an ambulance — that's bad publicity) to the nearest emergency room and left there.

More commonly, she'll be sent home. If she bleeds,
gets septic, etc., she must seek help elsewhere, as the
abortion mills rarely give any follow-up care.

But aren't there state or federal reports?

There are reporting regulations in most states, but these are largely voluntary, and most private clinics simply don't report complications. Many don't even report the abortions done which means that in some states abortion reporting is highly inaccurate. A glaring example of this was Ohio, 1988. This was the last year of Gov. Richard Celeste's term. Celeste was pro-abortion and had apparently not adequately funded the health department reporting mechanism. In that year, the total number of induced abortions reported from Hamilton County (Greater Cincinnati) was 3,218. In an entirely separate report, Planned Parenthood, which runs one of the four busy abortion mills in Cincinnati, in its national reporting stated that its abortion mill alone had done 3,144. Subtracting the two, left only 74 abortions done in the other three busy abortion mills in the city of Cincinnati. Obviously, this is absurd. Just as obviously, those three abortion facilities were simply not reporting.

The next governor (George Voinovich) was pro-life, and when this was called to his attention, a major change occurred, and it is felt that abortion reporting now is probably accurate. (In 2000, there were 6,941 reported from Cincinnati.) This lack of supervision in the field of reporting is very typical of the entire issue of abortion when reporting complications, deaths, etc. Abortion reporting is different. It stands by itself. It cannot be compared to any other medical procedure.

Be advised, if these places do not even report how many they perform, guess how many surgical complications they *voluntarily* report.

So the U.S. Center for Disease Control reports don't really reflect the actual situation?

Correct – and for two reasons. One is that few abortion complications are reported to them. The other is that this official government bureau has been shown to be consistently under-reporting the abortion complications sent to it while over-exaggerating complications of pregnancy and delivery.

M. Crutcher, Lime 5-Exploited by Choice,
Genesis Pub. 1996, Chapter 4, "Cooking the Books"

Isn't there any accurate source?

A landmark expose has peeled back some of the curtain of silence here. It is *must* reading for anyone who wants the true picture of the abortion industry in the U.S., e.g.:

- It gives brief documented case histories of several hundred women badly injured or killed by abortion, only a percentage of whom were reported.
- It details for the first time sordid details of sexual abuse and assault in these clinics.

"During our research for this book, our observation was that a woman probably is less likely to be injured, raped or killed at a Planned Parenthood facility than at a non-Planned Parenthood one." But . . . "the difference is insignificant. About the best they could claim to be is the cream of a rotten crop."

ibid., Chapter 3, p. 117

- It devotes 50 pages to detailing the psychic problems, nightmares and breakdowns of those whose business is doing abortions, another chapter to the total silence of the industry of the breast cancer connection, and finally details the extreme difficulty of getting legal redress for her injuries.

ibid., Chapters 3, 4, 5

Well, let's look at reported complications, even if some are only the tip of the iceberg:

Before and after legalization in the '70s and '80s, there were many studies done. Few have been repeated in the '90s. Rather, studies have moved to new areas such as invitro, chemical abortions, fetal reduction, chorionic villi and genetic testing, ultrasound, laparoscopic surgery, etc.

Accordingly, we present mostly older, classical studies, e.g.:

A study of 11,057 pregnancies in Jerusalem, of whom 752 had had previous abortions, showed that those with abortions were more likely to report bleeding in the first 3 months of this pregnancy, less able to have a normal delivery, and more needed manual removal of the placenta or other intervention in the third stage of labor. There was a significant increase in low birth weight, a 3 to 4 times increase in neonatal deaths, and an increase in fetal malformations.

S. Harlap et al., "Late Sequelae of Induced Abortion,"
Am. J. of Epid. (1975) 102, p. 217

Sterility is the most feared long-term complication of induced abortion. This can result from scarring due to infection caused by the abortion. It can also result from the surgical procedure itself. If the suction curette scrapes and cuts too deeply across the tube opening, these can scar shut, and she is sterile.

Are there any studies?

"The relative risk of secondary infertility among women with at least one induced abortion and no spontaneous miscarriages was 3-4 times that among non-aborted women."

D. Trichopoulos et al, "Induced Abortion & Secondary Infertility,"
British Jour. OB/GYN, vol. 83, Aug. 1976, pp. 645-650

In 1974 Dr. Bohumil Stipal, Czechoslovakia's deputy minister of health, stated: "Roughly 25% of the women who interrupt their first pregnancy have remained permanently childless."

Do miscarriages occur more frequently after induced abortions?

A Boston study by a group who have aggressively done abortions denied any increase after one abortion, but, after two or more abortions, they did find a "two- to three-fold increase in risk of first trimester spontaneous abortions [miscarriages]," as well as "losses up to 28 weeks gestation."

Levin et al., "Association of Induced Abortion with Subsequent Pregnancy Loss," JAMA, vol. 243, no. 24, June 27, 1980, pp. 2495-2499

Of a group of 50 women who had induced abortions 10-15 years previously and who were followed very closely during that length of time, it was found that one-half (27) had no problem with subsequent pregnancies. There was one ectopic pregnancy, eight subsequent — but long-delayed — conceptions, and three women with permanently blocked tubes. Of the remaining 11 women, there were 33 pregnancies with 14 early and 3 midtrimester losses, 6 premature deliveries, and only 10 full-term births.

Hilgers et al., "Fertility Problems Following an Aborted First Pregnancy." In New Perspectives on Human Abortion, edited by S. Lembrych. University Publications of America, 1981, pp. 128-134

A high incidence of cervical incompetence resultant from abortion has raised the incidence of spontaneous abortions to 30-40%.

A. Kodasek, "Artificial Termination of Pregnancy in Czechoslovakia," Internat'l Jour. of GYN & OB, vol. 9, no. 3, 1971

Women who had one induced abortion had a 17.5% miscarriage rate in subsequent pregnancies, as compared to a 7.5% rate in a non-aborted group.

Richardson & Dickson, "Effects of Legal Termination on Subsequent Pregnancy," British Med. Jour., vol. 1, 1976, pp. 1303-4

Women who had delivered their first pregnancy had (in the second pregnancy) the "best reproductive performance." Those who had a spontaneous miscarriage on the first had "the highest frequency of an early loss." Those with induced abortion on their first had "the highest frequency of late spontaneous abortion and premature delivery."

Koller & Eikham, "Late Sequelae of Induced Abortion in Primagravida" Acta OB-GYN *Scand*, 56 (1977) p. 311.

What about second trimester losses?

There was a doubled incidence of midtrimester spontaneous losses.

Herlap, *New England Jour. of Med.*, no. 301, 1979, pp. 677-681

"In a series of 520 patients who had previously been aborted, 8.1% suffered a mid-trimester loss (compared to 2.4% controls)."

G. Ratter et al., "Effect of Abortion on Maturity of Subsequent Pregnancy," *Med. Jour. of Australia*, June 1979, pp. 479-480

"There was a tenfold increase in the number of second trimester miscarriages in pregnancies which followed a vaginal abortion."

Wright et al., "Second Trimester Abortion after Vaginal Termination of Pregnancy," *The Lancet*, June 10, 1972

"It is concluded that a relationship, presumably a cause-effect relationship, exists between an induced abortion and a second trimester abortion in a subsequent pregnancy." There also was a four-fold increase in prematurity.

Puyenbeck and Stolte, Relationship Between Spontaneous and Induced Abortion, and Second Trimester Abortion Subsequently, Europ. J. OB-GYN, Reprod. Biol. 14, 1983, 299-309.

What of uterine rupture?

This condition occurs during labor in almost 1% of cases when women have had earlier first trimester abortions.

D. Nemec et al., "Medical Abortion Complications,"
OB & GYN, vol. 51, no. 4, April 1978, pp. 433-436

Uterine rupture (1%) is also one of the feared and sometimes fatal complications from prostaglandin abortions.

Duenhalter & Gant, "Complications Following Prostaglandin
Mid-Trimester Abortion," *OB & GYN,* vol. 46, no. 3,
Sept. 1975, pp. 247-250

And urinary incontinence?

The major study here showed twice the amount of urinary incontinence, 23.7%, after induced abortion as the incidence seen, 12.6%, after term pregnancy.

Slunsky, "Urinary Incontinence in Pregnancy,"
Z. Geburt, *Perinatology* 165:329-35, 1966.

Do menstrual symptoms change after abortion?

"Women with prior abortions consistently reported an excess of symptoms in all age groups."

L. Roth et al., "Increased Menstrual Symptoms Among Women
Who Used Induced Abortion," *Amer. Jour. OB/GYN,*
vol. 127, Feb. 15, 1977, p. 356

What about synechia?

"The frequency of uterine adhesions [synechia] is especially high among patients who have had two or more curettages. . . . Dr. J. G. Asherman, for whom the syndrome is named, has reported intrauterine adhesions in 44 of 65 women who had two or more curettages."

"Abortion Risks: Getting the Picture,"
Medical World News, Oct. 20, 1972

And blood clots?

This is discussed in the next chapter. Here let's note that "ovarian vein thrombosis can occur after first trimester abortion . . . Significant morbidity and mortality is associated with it."

"Ovarian Vein Thrombosis after Elective Abortion",
Obst. & Gyn., Nov. 2000, pp. 828-829

What about endometriosis?

This can develop along the needle or catheter tract from the midtrimester puncture.

Ferrare et al., "Abdominal Wall Endometriosis Following Saline Abortion," *JAMA*, vol. 238, no. 1, July 4, 1977, pp. 56-57

Do abortions affect Rh sensitization?

"Even in very early suction abortions done prior to eight weeks, fetal-maternal hemorrhage can occur, thereby sensitizing Rh-negative women."

M. Leong, "Rh Therapy Recommended in Very Early Abortion," *OB-GYN Observer*, June 1978

This means that in later pregnancies, babies of these mothers will have Rh problems, need transfusions, and occasionally are born dead or die after birth. This can be tested for prior to the abortion and largely prevented by giving the mother a medication called RhoGAM. If not done, the number who become sensitized varies from "3% to 17%." Unfortunately, many abortion chambers do not take this expensive precaution.

J. Queenan, Cornell University
Medical World News, April 30, 1971, p. 36G

What of placenta previa?

Placenta previa is when the afterbirth (placenta) covers part or all of the cervix, the womb's opening into the birth canal. It can be very serious and usually requires a Cesarean section, sometimes with loss of the baby.

Doctor Barrett and others did a study at Vanderbilt University in which they evaluated over 5,000 deliveries and found that those who had prior induced abortions in the first trimester had a "seven-to-fifteen fold increased prevalence of placenta previa." They linked it to scarring of the lining of the womb from the currettage or suction aspiration "predisposing to the abnormal site of placental implantation and an increased placental surface area." They also found that the changes occurred with the first induced abortion and were permanent. Neither the time elapsed nor the number of induced abortions changed this.

Barrett et al., "Induced Abortion, A Risk Factor for
Placenta Previa," Amer. Jour. *OB/GYN,*
Dec. 1981, pp. 769-772

Women who report one or more spontaneous or induced abortions are 30% more likely to have a subsequent pregnancy complicated by placenta previa than those without such a history.

V. Taylor et al., Placenta Previa Related
to Abortion; *OB&GYN,* 1993; 82:88-91

"We cannot exclude the possibility that the large number of induced abortions plays a role in the remarkable increase in cases of placenta previa."

Z. Bognar, "Mortality and Morbidity Associated with
Legal Abortions in Hungary, 1961-1973"
Amer. Jour. Public Health, 1976, pp. 568-575

What is the incidence of ectopic pregnancies?
In 1970 the incidence was 4.5 per 1,000 live births, for a total of 17,800. By 1980 it was 14.5, for a total of 52,200. By 1992 it totaled 108,800, and 28 women died.

The thin-walled tube cannot support this life, and it soon ruptures, causing internal bleeding and requiring emergency surgery.

Some of these deaths were *after* induced abortions. The mothers had their wombs emptied by "abortion," when, in reality, the tiny baby was lodged in the tube. Later, the tube ruptured and the women died.

Rubin et al., "Fatal Ectopic Pregnancy After
Attempted Induced Abortion," *JAMA,*
vol. 244, no. 15, Oct. 10, 1980

H. Atrash et al., "Ectopic Preg. Concurrent With
Induced Abortion"; *Am. J. OB-GYN,* Mar. '90, p. 726

ECTOPIC PREGNANCIES IN THE UNITED STATES

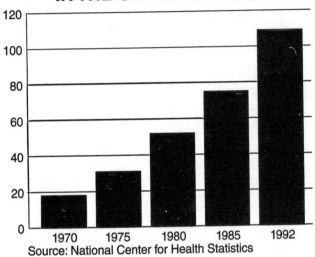

Source: National Center for Health Statistics

How many of these were related to previous abortions?

A French study of women with no prior ectopic pregnancies reported "prior induced abortion was associated with an increased risk of ectopic pregnancy . . . 1.4 for one abortion and 1.9 for two abortions."

"Risk of Ectopic Pregnancy and Previous Induced Abortion
C. Thoraux-Deneux, et al.,
Am. J. Public Health, Mar. 1998, Vol. 88, No. 3, pp. 401-406

Daling, et al., also reported increases of 1.4 and 1.8.
"Ectopic Pregnancy in Relation to Previous Induced Abortion"
JAMA, Feb. 15, 1985: 253 No. 7, 1005-1008

Regarding elective abortion and the increased ectopic pregnancy rate . . . "both have increased in parallel since the Supreme Court made abortion legal."
G. Huggins, Meeting Am. Col OB & Gyn, News Jan. 1-14, 1985, p. 3.

In Athens, half of ectopic pregnancies may be attributed to previous abortions — a ten-fold relative risk.

Panayotou et al., "Induced Abortion
& Ectopic Preg." *Am J. OB-GYN,*
1972 114:507

Tubal pregnancy increased 30% after one abortion and 160% after two or more abortions.

Am. J. Public Health, 72:253-6, 1982

Why is this?

"The increased incidence of PID (Pelvic Inflammatory Disease) — especially Chlamydia — and induced abortion appear to play leading roles in the dramatic rise in ectopic pregnancies."

H. Barber, "Ectopic Pregnancy, a Diagnostic Challenge,"
The Female Patient, vol. 9, Sept. 1984, pp. 10-18

Women with chlamydia have more than twice as many ectopic pregnancies.

JAMA, June 1990

How does abortion cause tubal pregnancy?

If the abortionist's curette scrapes or cuts too deeply across the opening of the tubes, there is scar formation. When partial blockage is a result of this procedure, the microscopic sperm can still travel through the tube to fertilize the ovum as it breaks out of the ovary. After fertilization, this new human life, many hundred times larger than the sperm, may not be able to get back through the tube if it has been partly scarred closed. Then the tiny baby nests in the tube, and the mother has an ectopic pregnancy.

What of premature births?

A history of prior induced abortion was associated with a modest increase in risk for a spontaneous preterm delivery, which increased with increasing numbers of induced abortions.

I. Haas, et al., "Spontaneous Preterm Birth:
A Case-Control Study," *Am. J. OB-GYN,* 1991; 165:1290-6

Researchers at the Danish Epidemiology Science Center report that women who abort are twice as likely to have either a pre-term or a post-term delivery. They followed 61,753 women for 12 to 14 years. Of these, 15,727 had a first-trimester-induced abortion. The women who had abortions were from 1.9 to 2.6 times more likely to have a subsequent pre-term delivery and 1.9 to 2.6 times more likely to have a post-term delivery.

J. of OB and GYN. Dec. 1999

CHAPTER 22

MATERNAL DEATHS AND LONG-TERM COMPLICATIONS

— *ABORTION – CHILDBIRTH* —

*It is claimed by abortion proponents that abortion
is safer than childbirth. They claim 1 death per
100,000 abortions compared to 10 deaths per
100,000 deliveries . . .*

Not True

What is the maternal mortality from childbirth?

The reported average maternal mortality 1982-1996
had declined to 7.5 deaths for every 100,000 live births.
Broken down racially, it was 5 to 6 for white women
and 18-22 for black women.

Morbidity & Mortality Report
1991; 47; pp. 705-707

If all causes of maternal death, other than those associated with live birth, i.e., abortion, tubal pregnancy,
molar pregnancy, etc., were excluded. . . . "the maternal mortality for 1985 would be 4.7 deaths per 100,000
live births."

"Induced Termination of Preg . . . ," Council on Scientific
Affairs, AMA; *JAMA*, Dec. 9, '92, Vol. 268, No. 22, p. 3231

But some mothers do die?

In developed nations, almost never. The National Maternity Hospital in Dublin, Ireland, receives many complicated cases from around that nation and delivers 10% of all births in Ireland. In 10 years (1970-79) it delivered 74,317 births at more than 28 weeks gestation, with only one woman dying from a cause related to her pregnancy.

J. Murphy et al., Therapeutic Ab., The Medical Argument,
Irish Med. J., Aug. '82, Vol. 75, No. 8

Ed. note: And this report was from two decades ago. Since then medical care has improved substantially.

Abortion Deaths

These have been grossly under-reported. The exposé on this is detailed in *Lime 5* published by Life Dynamics. The author and his staff have verified 23 deaths from induced abortion in 1992-93. All were reported to state agencies. There is documentation from state health departments that 18 were reported to the Federal Center for Disease Control. However, the official report of the CDC listed only 2 deaths.

"At Life Dynamics we knew abortion complications were grotesquely under-reported, but attributed it to garden-variety bureaucratic incompetence." But after continuing research, they documented that "the flawed abortion data from the CDC was not from ineptitude but of dishonesty and manipulation." After finding that "a large percentage of CDC employees had direct ties to the abortion industry," they retitled the CDC to stand for "Center for Damage Control. They concluded that the CDC doesn't oversee abortion, it justifies it.

M. Crutcher, Lime 5-Exploited by Choice,
Genesis Pub., Chapter 4, "Cooking the Books," p. 135.

The claim that relevant statistics can be collected from the place where the abortion was performed "is little short of science fiction."

"Complications following abortions performed in free-standing clinics is one of the most frequent gynecologic emergencies . . . encountered. Even life-endangering complications rarely come to the attention of the physician who performed the abortion unless the incident entails litigation. The statistics presented by Cates represent substantial under-reporting and disregard women's reluctance to return to a clinic, where, in their mind, they received inadequate treatment."

L. Iffy, "Second Trimester Abortions," *JAMA,* vol. 249, no. 5, Feb. 4, 1983, p. 588.

What can cause her death?

The main causes are infection, hemorrhage and uterine perforation.

How often do women get infection as a consequence of induced abortion?

A study from one of the most prestigious medical centers in the world, John Hopkins University, reported:

"Occurrence of genital tract infection following elective abortion is a well-known complication." This institution reports rates up to 5.2% for first trimester abortions and up to 18.5% in midtrimester.

Burkman et al., "Culture and Treatment Results in Endometritis Following Elective Abortion," *Amer. Jour. OB/GYN,* vol. 128, no. 5, 1977, pp. 556-559.

For the local, freestanding abortion facility in your community, with far inferior quality of care, the number of such infections will be at least double that of such a medical center.

"One sequel to abortion can be a killer. This is pelvic abscess, almost always from a perforation of the uterus and sometimes also of the bowel,"

173

said two professors from UCLA, in reporting on four such cases.

C. Gassner & C. Ballard, Amer. Jour. *OB/GYN*, vol. 48, p. 716 as reported in *Emerg. Med. After Abortion-Abscess*, vol. 19, no. 4, Apr. 1977

In an underdeveloped country, complications are more frequent and treatment is usually less available and effective.

Can infection cause damage?

Infection in the womb and tubes often does permanent damage. The Fallopian tube is a fragile organ, a very tiny bore tube. If infection injures it, it often seals shut. The typical infection involving these organs is pelvic inflammatory disease (PID).

Patients with Chlamydia Trachomatis infection of the cervix (13% in this series) who get induced abortion "run a 23% risk of developing PID."

E. Quigstad et al., *British Jour. of Venereal Disease*, June 1982, p. 182

"Pelvic Inflammatory Disease (PID) is difficult to manage and often leads to infertility, even with prompt treatment . . . Approximately 10% of women will develop tubal adhesions leading to infertility after one episode of PID, 30% after two episodes, and more than 60% after three episodes."

M. Spence, "PID: Detection & Treatment," *Sexually Transmitted Disease Bulletin*, John Hopkins Univ., vol. 3, no. 1, Feb. 1983

"Acute inflammatory conditions occur in 5% of the cases, whereas permanent complications, such as chronic inflammatory conditions of the female organs, sterility, and ectopic [tubal] pregnancies, are registered in 20-30% of all women . . . these are definitely higher in primigravidas [aborted for first pregnancy]."

A. Kodasek, "Artificial Termination of Pregnancy in Czechoslovakia," *Internat'l Jour. GYN/OB*, vol. 9, no. 3, 1971

Venereal disease, usually Gonorrhea or Chlamydia, causes PID. This, if present, vastly complicates an induced abortion.

"Chlamydia Trachomatis was cultured from the cervix in 70 of 557 women admitted for therapeutic abortion. Among the 70, 22 developed acute PID postoperatively (4% of the total)."

E. Quigstad et al., "PID Associated with C. Trachomatous Infection, A Prospective Study," *British Jour. of Venereal Disease,* vol. 59, no. 3, 1982, pp. 189-192

Another study revealed a 17% incidence of post-abortal Chlamydia infection.

Barbacci et al., "Post Abortal Endometritis and Chlamydia," *OB & GYN,* 68:686, 1986.

In a classic English study at a university hospital which reported on four years' experience, "there was a 27% complication rate from infection."

J.A. Stallworthy et al., "Legal Abortion: A Critical Assessment of its Risks," *The Lancet,* Dec. 4, 1971

What of bleeding?

Bleeding is common. Most get by, but some need blood transfusions. The Stallworthy study (above) reported that 9.5% needed transfusions. Most recent studies are reporting smaller percentages.

Are blood transfusions a cause of death in abortions?

Yes, and these deaths are never associated directly with, nor reported as statistics related to abortions. Here is how this works:

First, we must know how many women need blood transfusions after getting induced abortions. These figures are hard to come by. The only controlled studies are from university medical centers, which do only a small fraction of all abortions. Over 90% of abortions in the U.S., and varying percentages in other nations, are done in free-standing abortion chambers where the medical care is only a faint shadow of the competence of those medical centers. Women who hemorrhage from these abortions are sent to "real" hospitals for transfusions and surgery. The percentage who need transfusions then must remain an estimate, as these commercial establishments do not report this.

How many then? Let's be conservative and say that one in every hundred needs a blood transfusion. If there are 1,400,000 abortions annually in the United States, this means that 1%, or 14,000 women were transfused.

Viral hepatitis is transmitted in up to 10% of patients transfused. Ten percent of 14,000 is 1,400 women.

Amer. Assn. Blood Banks and Amer. Red Cross,
Circular Information, 1984, p. 6

An analysis of 300,000 cases of Hepatitis virus infection showed that deaths occurred from three causes: 322 from acute disease, 5,100 from cirrhosis, and 1,200 from liver cancer. This mortality rate is over 2%.

R. Voelker, Hepatitis B: Planned Standard, Am.
Med. News, Oct. 13, '89, pg 2.

Two percent of 1,400 women means that ultimately 28 deaths result annually from abortions for this reason.

AIDS is another threat. Two percent of AIDS had been acquired by blood transfusions. With recent careful screening techniques, this is now much less. Even so, 200-400 people in developed countries, per year, are still being exposed via blood transfusions.

Noyes, "Transfusions Risk Despite Screening,"
Family Practice News, May 15, 1987.

In underdeveloped nations, the AIDS threat ranges from seldom to common.

Are blood clots ever a problem?

Blood clots are one of the causes of death to mothers

who deliver babies normally. They are also a cause of death in healthy young women who have abortions performed.

Embolism (floating objects in the blood that go to the lungs) is another problem. Childbirth is a normal process, and the body is well prepared for the birth of the child and the separation and expulsion of the placenta. Surgical abortion is an abnormal process. It slices the unripe placenta from the wall of the uterus into which its roots have grown. This sometimes causes the fluid around the baby, or other pieces of tissue or blood clots, to be forced into the mother's circulation. These then travel to her lungs, causing damage and occasional death. This is also a major cause of maternal deaths from the salt poisoning method of abortion.

For instance, pulmonary thromboembolism (blood clots to the lungs) was the cause of eight mothers dying from abortions, as reported to the U.S. Center for Disease Control.

W. Cates et al., *Amer. Jour. OB/GYN,* vol. 132, p. 169

And this can occur in those as young as 14 years old.
Pediatrics, vol. 68, no. 4, Oct. 1971

Also, amniotic fluid embolism has "emerged as an important cause of death from legally induced abortion." Of 15 cases, the risk seems to be greater after three months. Treatment is ineffective."

R. Guidotti et al., Amer. Jour. OB/GYN,
vol. 41, 1981, p. 257

And has an 80% mortality rate.
S. Clark, Amniotic Fluid Embolism, the Female Patient,
vol. 14, Aug. '89, p. 50

What is Disseminated Intravascular Coagulation?

This is a sudden drop in blood clotting ability which causes extensive internal bleeding and sometimes death. The classic paper was on hypertonic saline (salt poisoning) abortions (see reference below).

H. Glueck et al., "Hypertonic Saline Abortion, Correlation with D.I.C.," *JAMA*, vol. 225, no. 1, July 2, 1973, pp. 28-29

"Saline-induced abortion is now the first or second most common cause of obstetric hypofibrinogenemia." [Same as D.I.C. above].

L. Talbert, Univ. of NC, "DIC More Common Threat with Use of Saline Abortion," *Family Practice News,* vol. 5, no. 19, Oct. 1975

In recent years this method has been seldom used. However, D.I.C. has also been caused by D&E and Prostaglandin abortions.

White et al., ""D.I.C. Following Three Mid-Trimester Abortions," *Anaesthesiology*, vol. 58, 1983, pp. 99-100

But many are mis-reported on the original death certificate and are not quite innocent.

- The kindhearted surgeon, unable to save the life of an abortion victim, feels that she and her family have been punished enough. He doesn't want to ruin her and her family's reputation in the community — so he forgets to mention abortion on the death certificate.
- If the abortionist does the follow-up care, and the patient dies from the abortion, the abortionist doesn't want the reputation of being a butcher, so another cause is listed.
- Usually, however, a different doctor sees a patient who dies from the damage done from an abortion, but she and her family hotly deny the abortion. The abortion connection cannot be absolutely proven, and the new doctor fears a suit for malpractice or for defamation of character, so he lists another cause.

Apart from deliberate mis-reporting to mask abortion death, are there others innocently missed?

Yes. For instance:

- Consider the mother who hemorrhaged, was transfused, got hepatitis, and died months later. Official cause of death, Hepatitis. Actual cause, abortion.
- A perforated uterus leads to pelvic abscess, sepsis (blood poisoning), and death. The official report of the cause of death may list pelvic abscess and septicemia. Abortion will not be listed.
- Abortion causes tubal pathology. She has an ectopic pregnancy years later and dies. The cause listed will be ectopic pregnancy. The actual cause, abortion.
- Deep depression and guilt following an abortion lead to suicide. The cause listed, suicide! Actual cause, abortion.

You mean all maternal deaths from abortion are not reported?

That's exactly correct. The official reporting agency for the U.S. government is the Center for Disease Control in Atlanta, Georgia. Listen to this:

During the two-year stretch of 1991 and '92, the CDC officially reported only one mother each year dying from induced abortion. In fact, there are 20 documented deaths. Of these, 14 were reported directly to the CDC from state health agencies. The CDC only listed two of them. Mr. Crutcher's book, *Lime 5*, which accuses this agency of gross dishonesty and malfeasance in its reporting, is extremely convincing.

M. Crutcher, Life Dynamics, personal communication, July '96

Even so, the situation today is better than the "5,000 to 10,000 women who died annually in the U.S.A. from back-alley abortions," isn't it?

These figures, often cited by pro-abortionists, are simply false. During the debate on the floor of the U.S.

Senate on the Hatch-Eagleton Pro-Life Amendment in 1983, the U.S. Bureau of Vital Statistics provided the data on such deaths.

Its reports showed that you must go back to the pre-Penicillin era to find more than 1,000 maternal deaths per year from illegal and legal abortions combined. The precipitous drop in maternal deaths in the 1950s and '60s occurred while abortions were still illegal. Before the first state legalized abortions in 1966, the total deaths were down to 120 per year. By 1972, before the Supreme Court legalized abortion in all 50 states, it was down to 39 per year in the entire U.S. Since legalization, the slow decline has continued, so that now the only difference is that more mothers are dying from legal, rather than illegal abortions.

U.S. BUREAU OF VITAL STATISTICS
CENTER FOR DISEASE CONTROL

YEAR	Reported Maternal Deaths from Illegal Abortion in U.S.
1940	1,679
1950	316
1960	289
1966	120 First State Legalized in 1967
1970	128
1972	39 Supreme Court Decision in 1973
1977	21
1981	8

Taken from U.S. Senate graph
See also:
Never Was, Nerer Again Pamphlet,
Hayes Pub.Co., 2002
and
Poland, No Back Alley Abortions,
Hayes Pub.Co., 2002

What of pregnancy and abortion in teenagers?

Early on, it was thought that pregnancy in young teenagers was more risky than in older women, but recent studies have shown that teenage mothers have no more risks during pregnancy and labor, and their babies fare just as well as their more mature sisters' babies, if they have had good prenatal care.

"We have found that teenage mothers, given proper care, have the least complications in childbirth. The younger the mother, the better the birth. If there are more problems, society makes it so, not biology."

B. Sutton-Smith, *Jour. of Youth and Adolescence*
As reported in the *New York Times,* April 24, 1979

"No relationship between mother's physical growth and maturation and adverse pregnancy course or outcome was demonstrated."

Sukanich et al., "Physical Maturity and Pregnancy
Outcome Under 16 Years," *Pediatrics,*
vol. 78, no. 1, July 1986, p. 31

Dr. Jerome Johnson of Johns Hopkins University and Dr. Felix Heald, Professor of Pediatrics, University of Maryland, agree that the fact that teenage mothers often have low birth weight babies is not due to "a pregnant teen-ager's biologic destiny." They pointed to the fact that the cause for this almost invariably is due to the lack of adequate prenatal care. "With optimal care, the outcome of an adolescent pregnancy can be as successful as the outcome of a non-adolescent pregnancy."

Family Practice News, Dec. 15, 1975

"The overall incidence of pregnancy complications among adolescents 16 years and younger is similar to that reported for older women."

E. Hopkins, "Pregnancy Complications Not Higher in Teens,"
OB-GYN News, vol. 15, no. 10, May 1980

"Obstetric and neonatal risks for teenagers over 15 are no greater than for women in their twenties, provided they receive adequate care."

There is evidence that in 15- to 17-year-old women, pregnancy may even be healthier than in older ages.

E. McAnarney, "Pregnancy May Be Safer,"
OB-GYN News, Jan. 1978

Pediatrics, vol. 6, no. 2, Feb. 1978, pp. 199-205

F. Avey, Canada Col. Family Physicians,
"Pregnant Teens . . ." *Family Practice
News,* Jan. 15, 1987, p. 14

But the abortion picture is different, particularly in regard to cervical damage.

After years of legalized abortion experience, a pro-abortion professor of OB/GYN at the University of Newcastle-on-Tyne reported on his follow-up, ranging from two to twelve years, of 50 teenage mothers who had been aborted by him. He noted that "the cervix of the young teenager, pregnant for the first time, is invariably small and tightly closed and especially liable to damage on dilatation." He reported on the "rather dismal" results of their 53 subsequent pregnancies:

Six had another induced abortion.

Nineteen had spontaneous miscarriages.

One delivered a stillborn baby at 6 months.

Six babies died between birth and 2 years.

Twenty-one babies survived

J. Russell, "Sexual Activity and Its Consequences in the Teenager."
Clinics in OB, GYN, vol. 1, no. 3, Dec. 1974, pp. 683-698

"Physical and emotional damage from abortion is greater in a young girl. Adolescent abortion candidates differ from their sexually mature counterparts, and these differences contribute to high morbidity." They have immature cervixes and "run the risk of a difficult, potentially traumatic dilatation." The use of laminaria "in no way mitigates our present concern over the problems of abortion."

C. Cowell, *Problems of Adolescent Abortion,*
Ortho Panel 14, Toronto General Hospital

"The younger the patient, the greater the gestation (age of the unborn), the higher the complication rate. . . . Some of the most catastrophic complications occur in teenagers."

"Eighty-seven percent (87%) of 486 obstetricians and gynecologists had to hospitalize at least one patient this year due to complications of legal abortions."

M. Bulfin, M.D., *OB-GYN Observer,* Oct.-Nov. 1975

**Abortions May Be Legal
But
They Are Not Always Safe**

CHAPTER 23

NEONATAL AND
CHILDHOOD SEQUELAE

— RELATED TO ABORTION —

What is the main problem?

Premature birth and earlier losses. The main reason for this is cervical incompetence. This can result from the too-early, forceful dilatation (stretching open) of the cervix (mouth of the womb).

During an abortion procedure, the cervical muscle must be stretched open to allow the surgeon to enter the uterus. There is no harm to the muscle in a D&C performed because of a spontaneous miscarriage, as the cervix is usually soft and often open. Also, there is rarely any damage caused by a D&C done on a woman for excessive menstruation, etc. When, however, a normal, well-rooted placenta and growing baby are scraped out of a firmly closed uterus, protected by a long, "green" (unripe) cervix, this "donut" muscle can be and often is torn. If enough muscle fibers are torn, the cervix is permanently weakened, the most damage being done if this is her first pregnancy.

Why is this a problem?

Let's look at a woman's first labor and delivery. Her labor is often 12 to 20 hours. The nurse, as she checks the mother's progress, uses the terms "two fingers" (or cm) — "four fingers" — then "complete." These terms refer to measuring the slow dilatation of the cervix. Only when it is wide open ("complete") can the baby begin the journey through the birth canal.

Before birth, nature opens this "door" very slowly. In a miscarriage, all those cramps do the same thing. After emptying the uterus, this strong donut-like muscle closes tight again.

The lowest part of a woman's uterus is the cervix, and, when a woman is pregnant and stands upright, the baby's head rests on it — in effect, bouncing up and down on the "door" throughout the pregnancy. The muscle must be intact and strong in order to keep the cervix closed. If it is weak, or "incompetent," it may not stay closed and may result in premature opening and miscarriage, or premature birth.

"The main risk of induced abortion is . . . permanent cervical incompetence."

L. Iffy, "Second-Trimester Abortions,"
JAMA, vol. 249, no. 5, Feb. 4, 1983, p. 588

Second trimester miscarriage and premature birth frequently follow induced abortions.

A. Arvay et al., "Relation of Abortion to Premature Birth,"
Review French GYN-OB,
vol. 62, no. 81, 1967

Levin et al.,
JAMA, vol. 243, 1982, p. 2495

A. Jakobovits & L. Iffy, "Perinatal Implications of Therapeutic Abortion." *Principals and Practice of OB & Perinatalogy,*
New York, J. Wiley & Sons, 1981, p. 603

C. Madore et al., "Effects of Induce Abortion on Subsequent Pregnancy Outcome," *Amer. Jour. OB/GYN,*
vol. 139, 1981, pp. 516-521

"In a series of 520 patients who had previously been aborted, 8.6% had premature labor compared to 4.4% of [non-aborted] controls."

G. Ratten et al., "Effect of Abortion on Maturity of Subsequent Pregnancy," *Med. Jour. of Australia,* June 1979, pp. 479-480

"The induced abortion group had the highest incidence of late spontaneous abortion and premature delivery."

O. Kaller et al., "Late Sequelae of Induced Abortion in Primigravidae," *Acta OB GYN Scandinavia,* vol. 56, 1977, pp. 311-317

Can this damage be prevented?

Using laminaria is an attempt to lessen such damage. This is a small bit of dehydrated material which is inserted into the cervix one day before the abortion. It absorbs water and swells to many times its size and, in the process, dilates the cervix.

Laminaria, incidentally, are seldom used in most freestanding abortion chambers because it means two visits, smaller volume, and smaller cash flow.

The use of laminaria reduces, but does not eliminate, cervical incompetence.

S. Harlap et al., "Spontaneous Fetal Losses After Induced Abortions," *New England Jour. Med.,* vol. 8, Sept. 1971, p. 691

Have premature births increased?

In the early years of legalized, wide-open abortion, there was ample evidence of the fact that induced abortion caused a sharp increase of premature births and their unfortunate aftermaths. Some of the major original studies included:

• After one legal abortion, premature births increase by 14%; after two abortions, it is 18%, after three, it increases to 24%.

Klinger, "Demographic Consequences of the Legalization of Abortion in Eastern Europe," *Internat'l Jour. GYN & OB,*

• "Previous induced abortion was associated with an increased risk of preterm birth." It was 1.4 times after one abortion and "increased with the number of abortions."

L. Henreit, *Br. J. OB&Gyn*, Oct 2001
Vol. 108, pp. 1036-1042

• Women who have had abortions have twice the chance of delivering a premature baby later.

G. Papaevangelou, U. Hospital, Athens, Greece,
Jour. OB-GYN British Commonwealth,
vol. 80, 1973, pp. 418-422

• In Czechoslovakia, premature births resulting from abortions are so frequent that a woman who has had several abortions, and who becomes pregnant, is examined, and:

• "If the physicians can see scar tissue, they will sew the cervix closed in the 12th or 13th week of pregnancy. The patient stays in the hospital as long as necessary, which, in some cases, means many months."

"Czechs Tighten Reins on Abortion,"
Medical World News, 106J, 1973

• Among others, Dr. Zedowsky reported a higher percent of brain injuries at birth. His report cited "a growing number of children requiring special education because of mental deficits related to pre-maturity."

ibid.

• A very large study, by the World Health Organization, of 7,228 women in eight European countries, showed that previously-aborted women had significantly higher midtrimester pregnancy loss, premature delivery and low birth weight babies.

Collaborative Study, Lancet 1979
20 Jan; 1 (8108): 142-5

Are there any comprehensive studies on premature births?

In New York State, a major prospective study was done between 1975 and 1979 which compared over 40,000 women, half of whom had an abortion and half of whom had a live birth. An analysis of the subsequent reproductive history of these women found a definite pattern of increased complications for those who had abortions (see chart below).

	Study Group had an abortion	Control Group had a live birth	Difference
Spontaneous fetal deaths All subsequent pregnancies	8.7%	5.3%	1.65 times more
Spontaneous fetal deaths First subsequent pregnancies	8.7%	4.7%	1.85 times more
Low Birthweight (less than 2500 gms) white non-white	7.0% 13.4%	4.7% 8.4%	1.5 times more 1.5 times more
Premature Birth (less than 33 weeks)	2.3%	1.3%	1.8 times more
Labor Complications	13.0%	4.3%	3.0 times more
Congenital Malformations	- - - - - - - -	- - same - - -	- - - - - - - -
Newborn Death			1.4 times more

V. Logrillo et al., "Effect of Induced Abortion on Subsequent Reproductive Function,"
N.Y. State Dept. of Health,
Contract #1-HD-6-2802, 1975-78

More preemies die?

Yes. A study of 26,000 consecutive deliveries at UCLA was done to determine if previous abortions (and premature births) had increased the number of stillborn babies and neonatal (after birth) deaths. The findings were that the death rate "increased more than threefold."

S. Funderburk et al., "Suboptimal Pregnancy Outcome
with Prior Abortions and Premature Births,"
Amer. Jour. OB/GYN, Sept. 1, 1976, pp. 55-60

Why does the U.S. rate about 20th in the world in its infant mortality rate?

There are five major reasons:

(1) Because, in some cases, we're comparing apples with oranges. Rated #1 is Japan. But they do not count deaths until 72 hours after birth. If the U.S. did this, it would be almost first too.

(2) Some nations, like Sweden, do not have large numbers of low socio-economic people. Therefore, you could more realistically compare Sweden to Minnesota than to the entire U.S.

(3) When asked, many blame it on "poor" prenatal care, particularly in the groups with the highest rates, i.e., teens and low socio-economic groups. But good prenatal care is almost universally obtainable. The problem is that mothers in these groups often don't avail themselves of it.

(4) The big one is the trio — alcohol, smoking and drugs — often associated with illegitimacy. Bluntly speaking, many newborns die because of their parents' unhealthy behavior. Even good prenatal care cannot compensate for the mother's smoking, drinking and drug use.

Nicholas Eberstadt of the American Enterprise Institute has studied illegitimacy. He points to an eight-state study that found a higher infant mortality among unmarried college graduates than among married grade school dropouts.

M. Charen, Inst. Mort., "Deeper Than Health Care,"
Feb. 2, 1992

(5) Prematurity as a result of earlier induced abor-

tion. More preemies die than full term babies.

With increasing technology, more ought to survive?

As detailed in the viability chapter, this is true, but technology has also brought a new way for them to die. Through Invitro fertilization, multiple pregnancies are common. The technique of "pregnancy reduction" (see chapter on Abortions) sometimes results in the loss of all the fetal babies.

L. Wilcox et al., "Assisted Repro. Tech . . . & Multiple Births . . ."
Fert. & Ster., vol. 65 #2, Feb. '96, p. 361

U.S. Infant Mortality

Deaths per 1,000 live births

• in 1980 = 12.6

• in 2000 = 6.9

CDC, M&M Report, 9-12-02

CHAPTER 24

BREAST CANCER

*There is an ominous relationship
between abortion and later
development of breast cancer.*

Is this proven?

No, but there is a very close correlation that has been demonstrated in a large number of scientific studies. If further studies continue to demonstrate this, and no other definitive cause is found, it is highly likely that this will some day be seen as a cause and effect.

Is breast cancer increasing?

According to the American Cancer Society, in 1962 there were 63,000 cases.

In 1972, 90,000
In 1982, 120,000
In 1992, 180,000

Since then, the numbers have not increased.

Perhaps some of the above is attributable to better diagnoses with mammograms, etc. Even so, the increase is dramatic. In 1960, one woman in fourteen developed breast cancer. Today, it is almost one in eight.

There are certain other risk factors, are there not?

Major risk factors that are well recognized are:
• family history in first degree relatives
• early onset and late cessation of menstruation
• being female (male breast cancer, while rare, has not increased)
• nulliparity, i.e., not being pregnant.

There are other suspected risk factors?

Yes, diet is one. It is postulated that a high fat diet may contribute. Toxic chemicals, pesticides and pollutants have been suggested, as have lack of anti-oxidants in the diet. Alcohol, smoking and drugs may be implicated. Electromagnetic fields, such as living under high tension wires or being exposed to electronic display boards have been suspected. Certain genes may predispose. None of these, however, has been proven.

Contraceptive pills have been implicated. In the overall, however, 60% to 70% of all breast cancer occurs in women who do not have any of the classic risk factors.

Does pregnancy protect?

Yes, definitely. Women who have never been pregnant have twice the risk of breast cancer compared to those who have had children. Women who delay their first pregnancy into their thirties have almost a doubled risk of breast cancer compared to those who have babies in their late teens or early twenties. It is also possible that breast feeding may add another protective effect, but there is no real proof of this.

B. MacMahon et al., 1970
Bull. Wld. Halth. Org., 43:209-21

J. Brind et al., *"Induced Abortion as an Independent Risk Factor For Breast Cancer A Comprehensive Review & Meta Analysis"*
J. Epidemol Community Health, 1996

When was abortion first suspected as a cause?

Dr. M. C. Pike, at the University of Southern California in 1981, published the first serious scientific study that demonstrated a direct association of induced abortion with later breast cancer. He studied 163 women who developed breast cancer before age 33 and compared them with 272 controls. He showed that if a woman had aborted her first pregnancy, her chance for developing breast cancer was increased by a factor of 2.4 times.

Pike MC, Henderson BE, Casagrande JT, Rosario I,
Gray CE (1981) *Brit. J. Cancer,* 43:72-6.

Give me other definitive studies.

Certainly one of *the* definitive studies was by H. L. Howe. Her study was done in upstate New York using official statistics from the New York State Health Department. This was an excellent study by epidemiologic standards and was not subject to any kind of recall memory bias from people asked in questionnaires. It used only hard data. She investigated all the women in this area who developed breast cancer under age 40 and checked to see whether or not they had had abortions. The conclusion was that women who had aborted their first pregnancy had a 1.7 times increased risk of breast cancer. Those who had gone on to abort their second and/or third pregnancy had a 4.0 times increased risk.

Howe HL, Senie RT, Bzduch H, Herzfeld P (1989) et al.,
Int. J. Epidemiol. 18:300-4.

Another was in Washington State: Few studies on this issue receive media attention. This went worldwide and broke the de-facto embargo on reporting the abortion-breast cancer link. Janet Daling did a very professional study that could not be discounted. It found:

- An induced abortion raises a woman's chance of getting breast cancer before age 45 by 50%. If done

before age 18, it increases 150%; if after age 30, it's up 110%.
- A woman with a family member with breast cancer who had her first abortion after 30 years increased her risk 270%.
- All 12 women in the study with a family history of breast cancer, who aborted before age 18 — *all 12* — got breast cancer before age 45.

J. Daling, Risk of Breast Cancer Among Young Women, J. Nat. Ca. Inst., Vol. 86, No. 21, 11/2/94, pg. 1584

How much abortion increases a women's risk of developing breast cancer.

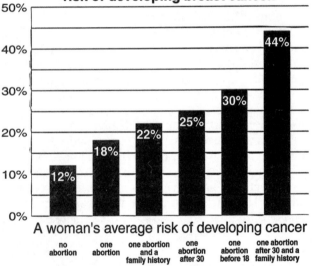

A woman's average risk of developing cancer

| no abortion | one abortion | one abortion and a family history | one abortion after 30 | one abortion before 18 | one abortion after 30 and a family history |

Other studies done since then include:

Greece: An overall increased risk of 51% was reported in women who had abortions, compared to those who did not. It involved 850 patients in Athens.

L. Lipworth, *Int. J. of Cancer,* April '95

U.S.A.: A statistically significant increased risk for breast cancer of 23% was shown to be attributable to induced abortion. For women over 60 years, the risk was 80%.

P. Newcomb et al., *Preg. Termination & Risk of Breast Cancer,*
JAMA 1/24/96, Vol. 275, No. 4, pg. 283

For a thorough explanation of the Newcomb study above, see *Natl. RTL News,* 2/6/96, by J. Brind.

Paris: "Having at least two abortions is associated with an increased breast cancer risk of 2.1 times."

N. Andrieu, *Role of Genetic & Repro. Factors in Br. Ca.,*
Genetic Spidem. 11 (3): 285, 1994

By mid 2002, "out of 37 independently published studies, 28 show a causal connection, Of these, 17 provide positive associations that reach statistical significant, a 95% certainty."

Joel Brind, Breast Cancer Prevention Institute

Has anyone investigated recurrences of previously treated breast cancer?

Yes, Dr. H. Ownby did this in 1983. This was a study of women who had breast cancer that had been treated and gone into remission. Ownby studied how many of these developed a recurrence of their cancer. His research showed that among women who had carried their first pregnancy to term, 10% had a recurrence of their cancer within three years. Of those women who had aborted their first pregnancy, 20% had a recurrence. Among those who had aborted their second and/or third pregnancy also, 30% had recurrences.

H. Ownby, *Interrupted Pregnancy Poor Prognosis . . . in Breast Cancer,* 1983
Breast Cancer Res. Treat. 3:339-344

How about the aggressiveness of the tumor?

In 1991, H. Olsson studied the aggressiveness of, and the propensity to metastasize of diagnosed breast cancer. His study showed that if she had aborted her first pregnancy and later developed breast cancer, her cancer was more aggressive and more quickly lethal than cancers among women who had carried their first pregnancy to term.

A marker gene associated with breast cancer, *INT2*, was shown to be eighteen times higher among those who had aborted than among normal women.

H. Olsson et al., Cancer 67:1285-90.

Are there ethnic differences?

Two studies have investigated this. In 1978, Choi investigated the difference between groups of Protestant and Catholic women in Canada and found that the Protestant women had more breast cancer. Helmrich, in 1981, investigated the difference between Jewish and Catholic women and found that there was more breast cancer among the Jews. Does this mean a difference due to ethnicity? Or could it be that the Catholic women had fewer abortions? Certainly no conclusions can be drawn, but this may be a bit of circumstantial evidence.

N. Choi, An Epidem. Study of Br. Ca.,
Am. J. Epidemal. 107:510, 1978
S. Helmrich, Risk Factors for Br. Ca.,
Am. J. Epidemal. 117, 35-45

Are there differences in economic classes?

There were two studies done in the state of Washington that are suggestive but again offer no hard proof. That state legalized abortion in 1969 by state referendum. For the first 5 years it did not pay for welfare abortions, then, in 1974, the state began to pay for welfare abortions. Bearing this in mind, the following has been shown.

Women of higher social economic status who were aborted had an increase in breast cancer which then leveled off. Poor women did not experience a similar rise in breast cancer until 5 years later when their incidence rose up to the plateau earlier achieved by the rich.

There was a similar study by Krieger in 1990 in California showing similar results.

Choi '78, Denesa '80, Kelsey '81, Lowe '70, Krieger '90

If induced abortion is a problem, does spontaneous loss carry the same risk?

Early on, some thought yes, but more recent studies have shown dramatically lower levels of female hormone in those who miscarried, as compared to those who had induced abortions. Among these studies were ones by B. Witt, Tulane Med. Sch., in 1990; a study in the *Br. J. OBGyn.* in 1976; one by D. Stewart, U. of CA Davis in 1993; one by A. Guilloume in NY City, and the well known one by Janet Daling in '94. All have shown that miscarriages are not associated with an increased risk.

What of breast feeding? If pregnancy is protective, does it add further protection?

It would seem logical that this would be so. If maturation of the breast is what causes the protection, and if lactation in any way completes the maturing of the milk glands, then logically breast feeding should be an additive protective factor. In fact, sufficient studies have not been done on this, so we cannot draw any firm conclusions. But a collaborative re-analysis from 47 studies in 30 countries was done with 50,302 women with breast cancer and 96,973 without. It concluded: "If women in developed countries had 2 to 5 children, on average, but breast fed each child for 6 months longer than they currently do, about 25,000 (5%) breast cancers would be prevented. If each child were breast fed for an additional 12 months, about 50,000 (11%) might be prevented."

Collaborative . . .on Breast Cancer . . ."
the *Lancet* Vol. 360, No. 9328, 20 July, 2002

What about differences between the African-American and white races?

There have been two studies out of Howard University in Washington, DC that have addressed this issue. They are the first ones to compare races. Laing found that black women who had aborted had an increased incidence of breast cancer, the increase centering largely among women over 50 years old. He also found an increase in breast cancer among black women who used birth control pills, but not after spontaneous miscarriage, which was called a "protective factor."

A. Laing, *Br. Ca. Risk Factors in African-American Women,*
J. Nat. Med. Assn., Dec. '93, Vol. 85, No. 12, pg. 931

Is this a genetic ethnic difference, or might there be another explanation? It is difficult to ignore the fact that black women in the United States, where this study was done, have three abortions for every one that their white counterparts have. A high percent of these abortions cluster in the teen years which, by definition, means many of them are first pregnancies. If abortion is a causative factor, and if black women have three times as many abortions as white women, then it would seem logical that they should have a higher incidence of breast cancer, which in fact they do.

Sadly, black women die almost twice as often from breast cancer as whites.

Eley et al., *Racial Differences in Survival,*
JAMA 9/28/94, Vol. 272, No. 12, pg. 947

This study found a relatively increased risk of 50% up to age 40, increasing during the 40s to 180%, and to 370% to women over 50 years of age.

What about diet? It has been suggested as a causative factor.

Yes it has. *Time* magazine, in 1994, devoted the major subject matter of one issue to this, strongly suggesting that a high intake of fat and red meat might increase the incidence of breast cancer. It is a fact that the female hormone implicated in breast cancer, estrogen, is stored in fatty tissue. Therefore, obese women may be at greater risk. The concern, however, is not about obesity, as such, but rather about dietary intake.

Again, there is no proof. But it is interesting to note that the breast cancer rate in Japan has gone up sharply, and it has been suggested that, with their increased standard of living, it is due to their increasing consumption of red meat and fatty foods. In the U.S. the breast cancer rate has also gone up sharply, and this has continued during the last decade or two during which time the intake of red meat and fat has decreased sharply. We could compare to a third nation, the Soviet Union before its opening to the West. There the abortion rate rose even faster, but there the intake of red meat and of fat was minimal. To draw a conclusion is unscientific, as other factors undoubtedly play a part, but, if fat is causative, one might surmise that it has gone up in Japan because they have increased such dietary intake; that it has gone up in the U.S. because of a decrease in this dietary intake, and that it went up even higher in the former Soviet Union because of a near deficiency of these dietary factors.

Can stress cause breast cancer?

Investigators at the University of Wisconsin have found no link at all. "Although women with breast cancer often attribute it to stress or depression, we found no evidence of such an association." They followed 617 without and 258 with cancer for 5 years.

P. Carbone, Relationship . . . Refuted,
Primary Care & Cancer, July '96, Vol. 16, No. 7, p. 11

These studies on the association of abortion with breast cancer are rather convincing. But if they are true, how do you explain the mechanism of the development of this cancer?

This is best understood by looking at the female breast in three different phases of maturity:

Immature Phase: This is the 5-year-old girl whose breast, under the microscope, is indistinguishable from that of her 6-year-old brother. Her brother's breast never matures. Hers will.

Nulliparous Adult Stage: During adolescence there is a flood of female hormones which cause her breast to grow in size and shape. To external appearances her breast is mature but it cannot yet produce milk, and the internal structure remains relatively undeveloped.

Parous Breast: This is the third stage, the breast after being pregnant. Most women who have been pregnant remember that their breasts became swollen and tender very soon after missing their period. Also, by about 3 months, they no longer felt this very much. What happened was the last phase of growth and maturation of her breasts. During this phase, the internal milk glands completed their development and readied her to produce milk.

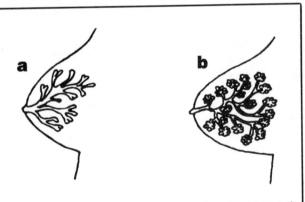

Schematic representation of tissue structure of: **a.** mature breast of a never-pregnant woman; **b.** breast at end of full-term pregnancy

So what has this to do with later cancer?

Perhaps a lot. We don't know all the causes that trigger the growth of cancer but we call such causes carcinogenic agents. We know that the immature breast cells are relatively resistant to such agents. We know that, after the first phase of growth, the cells are more susceptible and that, after a pregnancy and full maturation, the cells are again more resistant.

In early pregnancy there is a rapid growth and change of these cells. If this is suddenly interrupted, the breast is left with many transitional cells in a state of change, half-way between immature and mature cells in intermediate stages. It is thought that these cells are more unstable and less resistant to carcinogenic insult — to the triggering of cancer.

What if she has a baby and then aborts the next one?

Studies show an increased risk — but a lesser one.

If all of this is true, how many women will actually die of breast cancer?

There are approximately 1.4 million induced abortions annually in the United States. Over half, or 750,000 of these, are first pregnancies. At a conservative estimate, one in ten of these women will get breast cancer — this is 75,000 cases. About one-fourth of those who develop breast cancer, that's 18,750 women, will die from the disease.

If, in fact, abortion of her first pregnancy increases her chance of breast cancer from 1.0 to 1.5, then we should see, not 75,000 but 112,500 cases of cancer among this target population. If the death rate among them remains at 25 percent, (and it could be higher), then not 18,750, but over 28,000 women will die.

Among this group, however, if, instead of aborting their first pregnancy, these 750,000 women would have carried to term and delivered, they would have reduced their chance for breast cancer from 1.0 to .75. Accordingly, the 75,000 expected cases would be reduced to three-fourths of that, or about 56,000 cases, and the 18,750 deaths would have been reduced to 14,000 deaths.

A major study that refutes your thesis is the Linde-ford-Harris study from Sweden. What of it?

It is poorly done, from a scientific standpoint, and its authors' conclusions do not accurately reflect some of its actual findings. Dr. Brind, mentioned above, has called it the "Swedish data massage." It compared Swedish women with breast cancer to the entire Swedish population, which contains all of the same Swedish women who have breast cancer. Therefore, this comparison to the control group is invalid.

Even in this study, however, there is proof of the very thing its authors deny. In their article's conclusion, the authors state that there is no overall risk of breast cancer from abortion. However, within the report, a table of results shows that women who aborted *after* having a live birth had 58% of the average risk of breast cancer, while women who aborted *before* their first live birth had 109% of the average risk. This is an 88% increase in breast cancer, and it is clearly shown in the heart of this study, a study that is routinely held up as proving exactly the opposite.

B. M. Lindefors-Harris et al.,
Response Bias. . . . Abortions. . . . Two Swedish Studies,
Am. J. Epidemal. 1991, Vol. 134, No. 9, pg. 1003

But there are many other studies that tend to disprove your claims.

So they claim, but, with few exceptions, these were flawed by: inappropriately crude age matching or adjusting of controls (the main problem); interpreting as statistically insignificant some retrospective case controls with low statistical power; minimizing the actual results obtained in their conclusions; and attributing results to patients' "recall bias," even though a close exam refutes such a claim.

But I haven't seen such criticisms in any public reports.

There has been a true conspiracy of silence by the media and also by many researchers who, like the Swedish study, bury actual findings and conclude otherwise, e.g., editorials in journals, listing exhaustively multiple possible causes of breast cancer and never even listing abortion, e.g., *JAMA*, July 21, 1993, and *New England Journal of Medicine,* Jan. 1994, as well as *Time* magazine on Jan. 14, 1991.

Dr. Remennick concluded "an initial attitude of researchers toward abortion usually determines the way they interpret results."

[10]Remennick LI (1989) *Int. J. Epidemiol.* 18:498-510.

Has anyone compared all the studies?

Yes, happily, a comprehensive meta-analysis examined 61 published studies and subjected them to critical comparative analysis. Its conclusion was:

"The results support the inclusion of induced abortion among significant independent risk factors for breast cancer, regardless of parity or timing of abortion relative to the first term pregnancy. Although the increase in risk was relatively low, the high incidence of both breast cancer and induced abortion suggest a substantial impact of thousands of excess cases per year, currently, and a potentially much greater impact in the next century, as the first cohort of women exposed to legal induced abortion continues to age."

J. Brind et al., "Induced abortion as an independent risk factor for breast cancer: a comprehensive review and meta-analysis," Hershey Med. Center, *J. Epidemol. Community Health,* 1996

In the review of 23 legitimate studies, 18 found increased risk. By 2002. of 37 world-wide studies published since 1957, 28 found increased risk.

What about the contraceptive pill? Certainly many who take the pill also get abortions. Could it be that the pill causes the cancer and not the abortion?

There are three major studies, from Russia, Estonia, and Soviet Georgia, that were done prior to Russia's opening to the West. During those years there were almost no contraceptive pills used in those nations. During those years abortion was the method of birth control. And what happened to breast cancer? It increased by approximately 300 percent.

L. Remennick, Reprod... & Cancer Incidence in USSR, Intl. J. Epidemal., 18:498-5 12,1989

Incidentally, the above reasoning, such as it is, would also apply to the suggestion that food additives and street drugs are part of the cause of the increase in breast cancer. Prior to the lowering of the Iron Curtain, there were essentially no food additives used in the Soviet Union and neither were there many street drugs. The breast cancer rate however, as noted, sky-rocketed in these countries. This would seem to implicate abortion as a cause and to see such additives as only aggravating factors, if indeed they are implicated at all.

Aside from abortion, does the pill cause breast cancer?

By far the best analysis of this is by Chris Kahlenbom, M.D. in his book, *Breast Cancer, Its Link to Abortion and the Birth Control Pill.*

New Hope, KY 2002, One More Soul Publisher, 381pp.

Eleven of its seventeen chapters examine the cancer risks of the "pill." It shows that women who used the "pill" for four or more years before their first pregnancy had a 72% increased risk of cancer.

The pill decreases the risk of uterine and ovarian cancer but increases the risk of breast, liver and cervical cancer. The estimate is that there are 40,000 - 80,000 additional cases of cancer with a 25% mortality.

Which is the worst?
Women given Depo Provera for at least two years before age 25 have a triple increased risk.

Give me at least one study.
A meta-analysis showed that 18 of 21 studies done since 1980 showed the 72% increased risk (above).

Romien, et al. "Oral Contraceptives and Breast Cancer, Review and Meta Analysis. *Cancer*, 1990; 66:2253-2263

Summary and meta-analysis of epidemiological evidence of the abortion–breast cancer link

AUTHORS	YEAR	NATION
Segi et al.	1957	Japan
Watanabe & Hirayama	1988	Japan
Dvoirin & Medvedev	1978	Russia
Burany	1979	Yugoslavia
Pike et al.	1981	USA
Nishiyama	1902	Japan
Brinton et al.	1983	USA
Lé et al.	1984	France
Hirohata et al.	1985	Japan
Rosenberg et al.	1988	USA
Luporsi	1988(95)	France
Rohan et al.	1988(95)	Australia
Ewertz & Duffy	1988	Denmark
Howe et al.	1989	USA
Adami/Harris et al.	1989-90	Sweden/Norway
La Vecchia et al.	1993	Italy
Moseson et al.	1993	USA
Laing et al.	1993	USA
Laing et al.	1994	USA
Andrieu et al.	1994	France
White/Daling et al.	1994	USA
Lipworth et al.	1995	Greece
Zaridze et al.	1995	Russia
Bu et al.	1995	China
Newcomb et al.	1998	USA
Rookus & van Leeuwen	1998	Netherlands
Daling et al.	1996	USA
Talamini et al.	1996	Italy
Wu et al.	1996	USA
Meltye et al.	1997	Denmark
Palmer et al.	1997	USA
Marcus et al.	1999	USA
Lazovich et al.	2000	USA

Weighted Average (weight = 1/variance; random effects model)
Unweighted Average

ODDS RATIO (RELATIVE RISK) & 95% CONFIDENCE INTERVAL

0.3 0.5 1.0 1.5 2.0 3.0 4.0 8.0

PART V
INFANTICIDE &
EUTHANASIA

Chapter

CHAPTER 25

FETAL HANDICAP AND INFANTICIDE

Over the years, in most nations, the only reasons receiving consistent majority support for abortion have been life of mother-90%, assault rape and incest-75%, and fetal handicap-60%.

but

Abortion Leads to Infanticide
Like Night Follows Day

Why?

Because it's completely logical. Follow this example. Let's assume that a mother has the amniocentesis test to be sure that she is not carrying a Down's syndrome baby. If it is positive, she definitely intends to have the unborn baby killed by abortion. In this instance, the test is normal.

But, when the baby is born, he turns out to have Down's syndrome. The test was mistaken. Now what? If she had identified the baby's condition before birth, she would have "solved" the problem by killing the tiny patient.

Now the baby is breathing air. Now the diagnosis is

definite. Now there is also no danger to the mother as a result of the "procedure."

Why not kill the baby now?

> Same Patient
> Same Problem
> Same Solution

But who could justify such killing?

The Australian ethicist, now at Princeton University, Peter Singer, wrote that the sanctity-of-life view, the "religious mumbo-jumbo," should be stripped away. "Species membership in *Homo-sapiens* is not morally relevant." If we "compare a dog or a pig to a severely defective infant," he said, "we often find the non-human to have superior capacities." To Singer, quality of life is the only guide.

P. Singer, "Sanctity of Life or Quality of Life?" *Pediatrics,* vol. 73, no. 1, July 1983, pp. 128-129

- Joseph Fletcher suggested using the I.Q. measurement and allow those with an I.Q. under 20, or perhaps 40, to be declared non-human.
- They followed Nobel Laureate, James Watson, the man who cracked the genetic code:

> "Because of the present limits of such detection methods, most birth defects are not discovered until birth.
>
> "If a child were not declared alive until three days after birth, then all parents could be allowed the choice . . . the doctor could allow the child to die, if the parents so choose, and save a lot of misery and suffering."

"Children from the Laboratory," J. Watson, *AMA Prism,* Ch. 3, p. 2, May 1973

But isn't it cruel to allow a handicapped child to be born — to a miserable life?

The assumption that handicapped people enjoy life

less than "normal" persons has been shown to be false. A well-documented investigation has shown that there is no difference between handicapped and normal persons in their degree of life satisfaction, outlook of what lies immediately ahead, and vulnerability to frustration.

In a series of 150 unselected spina bifida patients questioned as older children, all were asked whether their handicaps made life not worth living, and should they have been "allowed to die" after birth. Their unanimous response was forceful. Of course they wanted to live! In fact, they thought the question was ridiculous.

W. Peacock, Pers. Comm. to D. Shewmon in
"Active Voluntary Euthanasia," *Issues in
Law & Medicine,* 1987.

Dr. C. Everett Koop, prior to becoming Surgeon General of the U.S., spent his life as a pediatric surgeon repairing "nature's mistakes." For some children this meant 30 or more operations. At one reunion of the "kids" he repaired (with all the pain and disability these entailed), he asked if they had to start over, would they want the surgery again? These young people unanimously said "yes."

Personal communication to author

But is such expensive care worth the cost?

Do you treat, care for, and help a sick or disabled person, or do you kill him? Do you measure the value of a person's life in money? Or in utilitarian usefulness?

The cost to society to care for all the physically and mentally handicapped among us is but a tiny fraction of the cost to society for the morally deformed among us.

Professor Jerome Lejeune, discoverer of the chromosomal pattern of Down's Syndrome, once related to us a story he had heard from a geneticist colleague which illustrates this well:

"Many years ago, my father was a Jewish physician

210

in Braunau, Austria. On one particular day, two babies had been delivered by one of his colleagues. One was a fine, healthy boy with a strong cry. His parents were extremely proud and happy. The other was a little girl, but her parents were extremely sad, for she was a Mongoloid baby. I followed them both for almost fifty years. The girl grew up, living at home, and was finally destined to be the one who nursed her mother through a very long and lingering illness after a stroke. I do not remember her name. I do, however, remember the boy's name. He died in a bunker in Berlin. His name was Adolf Hitler."

What about spina bifida?

Dr. D. McLone & Colleagues reported on a series of almost 1,000 unselected cases of spina bifida which they had aggressively treated.

- 75% had normal intelligence
- 80% were walking by school age
- 90% had bowel and bladder control by school age
- 99% of parents were satisfied with the treatment

D. McLone et al., "Concepts in the Management of "Spina Bifida," *Concepts in Pediatric Neuro- surgery* 33 (1986): 359-370

And if the parents don't want such an infant, there are organizations like the Spina Bifida Association of America, with over 100 couples on its waiting list, wanting to adopt an infant with spina bifida. (Write J. Grafstron, 1955 Florida Ave., Xenia, OH 45385.) The Michael Fund, 400 Penn Center, Pittsburgh, PA 15146 can give you a similar waiting list.

Little Sam's Hand:

Vanderbilt University has been a pioneer in intra-uterine fetal surgery. In August, 1999, while having his spina bifida repaired, little Sam reached his arm out of the incision and grabbed the surgeon's finger. (See the colored plates in the back of this book for this remarkable photo.)

What of Down's Syndrome?

"Upwards of 80% of Down's babies will occur to younger mothers" under 35.

Adams et al., "Down's Syndrome, Recent Trends," *JAMA*, vol. 246, no. 7, Aug. 14, 1981, pp. 758-760

The mother is not solely the cause. "In about 30% of the cases, the father has been responsible for the extra 21st chromosome in Down's Syndrome." The older the father, the higher the percent.

Roberts et al., "Midtrimester Amniocentesis," *Jour. of Repro. Med.,* vol. 28, no. 3, Mar. 1983, p. 168

Even so:

at a maternal age of 30, 99.9% of babies do not have it,
at a maternal age of 36, 99.6% of babies do not have it,
at a maternal age of 40, 99.1% of babies do not have it.

There is a list of waiting adoptive parents for any Down's baby (see Michael Fund above).

One of the truly gratifying developments in the last half-century has been the mainstreaming of Down's people.

These pleasant and functional people now have an average life expectancy of 55 years. Only 2% are born with fatal heart defects, and less than 5% with severe mental retardation. Most now can lead semi or completely independent lives and enter the workforce in some type of supported employment. Others are competitively employed.

Are birth defects inherited?

Norway maintains a national registry of birth defects. It examined 460,000 females born 1967-1982. In the general population the rate was 2.4% In women with handicaps, it was 3.8%.

New Eng J. Med. April 8,1999

How many handicapped babies are born?

Every year in the U.S. about 4 million babies are born. Of these, 5,000 have Down's Syndrome, 1,500 have Spina Bifida and 2,000 have Cystic Fibrosis.

JAMA, Apr. 10, 1991, Vol. 265, No. 14, pp. 1797-8
CDC -MMWR, Apr. 21, 1989, Vol. 38, No. 15, p. 264
Med. Tribune, May 15, 1989, Vol. 30, No. 14, p. 1

What about Rubella defects?

The classic studies on this were done during a major Rubella epidemic. Of the 16.9% of children who developed defects when their mothers got Rubella while pregnant:

- 50% had hearing loss, most correctable by hearing aids.
- 50% had heart defects, almost all surgically correctable.
- 30% had cataracts, often one-sided. Most had fair vision.
- Mental retardation was 1.5% compared to 1% in a non-affected population.

Rendle-Short, *Lancet,* vol. 2, 1964, p. 373

What if a woman receives Rubella vaccine while pregnant?

There are no reported cases of significant damage to the babies who were born after such vaccination. For example, "none of the live-born infants had serologic or clinical evidence of congenital rubella."

S. Wyall & K. Herrmann, "Inadvertent Rubella Vaccination of Pregnant Women," *Jour. Amer. Med. Assn.,* vol. 225, 1973, p. 1472

Rubella Vaccine probably poses no threat to fetuses whose mothers are vaccinated around the time of conception. All newborns tested in this study were negative.

S. Sheppard, "Rubella Vaccine," *Br. Med J.* 292:727, 1986.

The U.S. Center for Disease Control, U.S. Public Health Services, in a report covering 1971 through 1982, reported on 959 pregnant women who were vaccinated while pregnant. They reported no evidence of Rubella-induced defects. The very few abnormalities found were "expected" in such a large number.

Morbidity & Mortality Weekly Report, vol. 32, no. 33, Aug. 26, 1983

What about AIDS?

Only about 25% of babies born of HIV-infected mothers are born infected. It the pregnant women is given anti-AIDS medication, the incidence of infection is only 2-5%. Sadly, there is no cure.

Does her age increase other birth defects?

Happily not, with the one exception of Down's. A major study of 27,000 cases of birth defects demonstrated clearly that older women (over 35) have no greater risk than younger women. This survey looked at 43 defects, including spina bifida, cleft palate, heart defects and limb deformities. It even showed that hypertrophic pyloric stenosis, patent ductus arteriosis and dislocated hips decline after age 30.

P. Baird, U. of Brit. Columbia, *Lancet,* Mar. 2, 1991

Is it possible to "cleanse the gene pool?"

Any talk about breeding out genetic diseases is a lot of nonsense. Seriously affected persons are unlikely to marry and have children; the genes are passed along by carriers. For instance, there are 40 carriers for every person with sickle cell anemia. If every victim of this disease were eliminated, it would require 750 years just to cut the incidence in half; to stamp it out altogether would require 200,000 abortions for every 500,000 couples. Because each "normal" person is the carrier of three or four bad genes, the only way to eliminate genetic diseases would be to sterilize or abort everybody.

Dr. Hymie Gordon, Professor of Genetics, Mayo Clinic

Will maternal X-rays harm the baby?

"Interruption of pregnancy is never justified because of the radiation risk to the embryo/fetus from a diagnostic X-ray exam, abdominal or peripheral."

Policy Statement, Amer. College of Radiology,
AMA News, Nov. 1976, p. 12

How about ultrasound?

"We could not detect any association between exposure to ultrasound during pregnancy and leukemia." This conclusion was reported by the Karalinska Institute in the *British Medical J.* (1-28-00) after comparing all children born in Sweden born between 1973 and 1989.

How do parents emotionally handle the abortion of a handicapped baby?

Very poorly. One study reported maternal depression of 92% and paternal depression of 82%, plus a 30% incidence of marital separation after the abortion.

Blumberg et al., "Psychiatric Sequelae of Abortion for
Genetic Indication," Amer. Jour. OB/GYN,
vol. 122, no. 7, Aug. 1975, pp. 799-780

How are unborn babies tested for genetic defects?

By amniocentesis, the alpha-fetoprotein test, and chorionic villi sampling. And later in pregnancy by ultrasound exams.

What is amniocentesis?

It involves taking a small amount of fluid from the baby's amniotic sac through a needle inserted into the mother's abdomen and uterine wall. The cells in the fluid are cultured and examined a month later. Certain chemicals in the fluid can also be measured. It is done in the midtrimester to diagnose certain conditions.

What fetal conditions can be treated in the midtrimester?

Both Methylmalonic Acidemia and Biotin deficiency can be discovered in mid-pregnancy. Neither, however, is treatable until later in the third trimester.

Toxoplasmosis infection of the mother can infect her fetal baby. Treatment in late pregnancy (after the 5th month) can protect the baby.

J. Bishara et al., Toxoplasmosis, *Pediatrics in Review,*
vol. 12, no. 8, Feb. 1991

Also see AIDS above.

What about third trimester amniocentesis?

This is quite different. These are safe, and they are done to help treat and save the lives of both baby and mother. Then it is done for Rh disease, diabetes, fetal lung maturity, etc.

Is amniocentesis safe?

In England and other countries the test itself kills upwards of 1% of the babies tested.

Opinions differ. A very reputable, large English study found that there were 14 fetal deaths in the amniocentesis groups compared to 5 in the control group; severe maternal bleeding in 37 compared to 12; ruptured membranes in 0.5% compared to none; subsequent spontaneous abortion in 2.7% compared to 1.4%, and Rh antibodies developed in 9 compared to 2. Severe postpartum respiratory distress occurred after birth in 30 compared to 9, with 24 major orthopedic abnormalities compared to 1. The overall increased risk to the baby was 300% and the cumulative overall risk of all negative factors to both mother and child was 9.2% compared to 3.3% in the control group.

Royal College of OB/GYN, "An Assessment of Hazards of
Amniocentesis," *British Jour. OB/GYN,*
vol. 85, Supplement N.2., 1978

In a large follow-up study eight years later, "spontaneous abortion rate was 1.7% in the group with amnio-centesis, and 0.7% in the control group."

"Randomized Trial of Amniocentesis in 4606
Low Risk Women" *Lancet,* 1287, June 7, 1986

In 2001, researchers at the St. Bartholomew's Medical School, London, reviewed 40,000 women who had amniocentesis. One hundred cases of Down's were found, but 400 normal babies miscarried after the test.

In Greece, of 500 pregnant women who had amnio-centesis among those 35-39 years, 3.4% miscarried after the test. On the over-40 ages, it was 5.1%.

Bit. J. OB&Gyn, Papantoniou. U. Athens,
Reuters Health, 28 Nov. '01

Your author has a daily radio commentary. Every time he has discussed this problem, we receive a number of letters recounting the needless loss of normal babies from the test.

What is Alpha-Fetoprotein testing, and why is it done?

It tests the mother's blood and can reveal that she is probably carrying a child with either an open spine (spina bifida) or anencephaly.

It must be done on blood drawn between her 16th and 18th week of pregnancy. Of 1,000 women, 50 will have positive results. The blood test must then be repeated. This time, only 30 will be positive. An ultrasound test will then be done and will clear 15, leaving 15 still positive. Then these mothers must have an amniocentesis (1% of babies die from the test). After the necessary four-week wait, the results will pinpoint 1 or 2 babies who have the handicaps, who are 20-22 weeks old, and who weigh 1 to 1½ pounds each.

Even after all of this testing, some of the babies aborted will be normal, and some of the "normals" will be born with the handicap, for the test is not always correct. The test is available, however, is being used, and is required by law in some places. The main problem, even for those who favor abortion, is the level of anxiety created as the elimination process continues. Many who are "cleared" still don't believe they are "OK" and get abortions on the suspicion that the tests were wrong.

Another report found false positive and negative results varying from 4% to 17.5%.

Bradley, et al., *N. Eng. J. Med.*, vol. 315, no. 3, p. 193, July 17, 1986.

What is chorionic villi sampling?

This sampling, or biopsy, is an exam which involves passing a small instrument through the cervix, in early pregnancy, to cut away a very small piece of the edge of the tissue surrounding the baby. Since this tissue is a part of the baby's body, it has the same genetic makeup as the rest of the baby. This allows the parents to "find out" much earlier in pregnancy (9 to 11 weeks).

Is this chorionic villi sampling safe?

The percent of babies killed by the test is in the 2-4% range.

Also, a British study reported 3% false positives, i.e., 3% tested abnormal, were killed by abortion and then found to be normal.

Br. Med., L. C. van Prooijen-Knegt, 1987
N.Y. Times, G. Kolata, Oct. 9, 1987

It can cause fetal loss through severe oligohydramnios. This is a slow and continuing leakage of amniotic fluid resulting in "spontaneous" abortion at 4 to 12 weeks.

R. Wapner, "Amniotic Leaks & Fetal Loss Linked to CVS," *Medical Tribune*, July 28, 1988

Studies from Oxford, Milan, Chicago and Taiwan

reported clusters of birth defects in infants on whom the test was done. These included missing or shortened fingers and arms, malformed mouths, and brain abnormalities.

"3.3% had major congenital abnormalities."

B. Burton et al., "Limb Abnormalities With CVS,"
OB-GYN News, May 1992, vol. 79, no. 5, p. 726

As did National Institutes of Health Consortium.

Am. J. OB-GYN, vol. 169, no. 1, July 1993

Are there any other invasive tests?

Fetoscopy, or percutaneous umbilical cord sampling, uses ultrasound guidance to take blood from the fetal umbilical vein. Fetal mortality rate from this is $2-6\%$.

Then why do so many doctors push to have these tests done?

To protect their wallets. Doctors have been sued because they did not do the tests and did not discover a handicapped fetus so she could abort. This has produced a compulsion among doctors to have the tests done so as to protect themselves.

But what if she won't abort, even if the baby is handicapped?

Tell your doctor you don't want to risk the life of your baby to satisfy your curiosity. Tell him to write in his records that he has offered the test to you, explained it, and that you refused it. Then you sign his records with witnesses. With this, he'll quit asking.

"If abortion is outlawed, amniocentesis programs in midtrimester would close, since the main therapeutic prerogative would have been eliminated."

Golbus, "The Current Scope of Antenatal Diagnosis,"
Hospital Practice, April 1982

*Note: See RU-486 for fetal deformity from this
drug and its companion, Cytotec.*

CHAPTER 26

EUTHANASIA

*Qualifying euthanasia by calling it
active or passive, direct or indirect,
voluntary, nonvoluntary, involuntary,
or assisted suicide only confuses the picture.*

Euthanasia Is
When the Doctor Kills the Patient

Where and when was euthanasia first legalized?

The *original* euthanasia program was to "purify" the German race. It was a creation of physicians, *not* Hitler. He simply allowed the use of the tools others had prepared.

The first gas chamber was designed by professors of psychiatry from 12 major German universities. They selected the patients and watched them die. Then they slowly reduced the "price tag" until the mental hospitals were almost empty.

They were joined by some pediatricians, who began by emptying the institutions for handicapped children in 1939. By 1945, almost 300,000 "pure blood Aryan" Germans had been killed. By then these doctors had so lowered the price tag that they were killing bed wetters, children with misshapen ears, and those with learning disabilities.

Willke, *Assisted Suicide & Euthanasia,*
Hayes Publishing Co., Cinn, 2001, p. 24

What do you mean "price tag"?

When you take the giant step of placing a price tag on human life, judging that it has only relative value, then you have made a fatal move, for price tags can be marked down. The Nazis marked them down. Holland marked them down. Abortion demonstrated the same thing. Make no mistake, the slippery slope is a startling reality. Recall William L. Shirer who interviewed a Nazi judge condemned to death at Nuremberg. The judge wept saying, "How could it have come to this?" Mr. Shirer responded, "Herr Judge, it came to this the first time you authorized the killing of an innocent life."

Hitler didn't start with Jews, then?

No, Hitler, taking his cue from these physicians, after this eugenic killing of "defective" Aryan Germans, then used their gas chambers and proceeded to eliminate "defective" races. He destroyed an entire race of Gypsies, six million Jews, and perhaps almost as many captured Poles, Russians, and central Europeans.

ibid., Chpt. 3

But the program started with sterilization.

That's true. The first and fundamental law change was the Law for the Prevention of Progeny with Hereditary Diseases, promulgated by Hitler on July 25, 1933. It was aimed at Aryan Germans, and its purpose was to purify the race by eliminating those with supposed heredity diseases. In six years, the law was responsible for the involuntary sterilization of an estimated 375,000 Germans.

W. Deuel, *People Under Hitler,*
New York, 1942, p. 221

This law also legalized abortion for women who were to be sterilized. Later, the "right" to legal abortion was extended to Jews, Poles, Gypsies, and other racial minorities.

ibid., par. 14

But didn't Hitler oppose abortion?

Wrong! Hitler only opposed abortion for "pure blood" Aryan women. He allowed and even encouraged it for others.

In an order to the SS, SD, and police on June 9, 1943, Reichskommisar Kaltenbrunner directed: "In the case of Eastern female workers, pregnancy may be interrupted, if desired." First, a racial exam was to be done and then, "If a racially valuable result is to be expected, the abortion is to be denied . . . if not valuable, the abortion is to be granted."

After the war, the War Crimes Tribunal indicted ten Nazi leaders for "encouraging and compelling abortion," which it considered a "crime against humanity."

"Trials of War Criminals," Nuremberg Military Tribunal,
Washington, DC; USGPO, vol. IV, p. 610

You say Holland is now on this slippery slope?

Yes, Holland was the first modern nation to legalize euthanasia. What began as a few extraordinary cases, has now become routine. One hundred and thirty thousand people die each year in Holland, and over 20,000 are killed, directly or indirectly, by doctors. As many as half did not ask to be killed.

These now include newborn infants judged to have too poor a quality of life. A judge has okayed direct euthanasia for a depressed person who was physically well. Assisted suicide has also been allowed for depressed teenagers.

Hospitalized seniors are routinely visited by an organization that offers to oversee their case to prevent their doctor from killing them.

In April, 2001, the Dutch Parliament passed a law that set up qualifications that must be honored before a doctor can kill a patient. These include being of sound mind, a voluntary request, repeated requests to die, uncontrollable pain, "force majeure" (doctor has no other choice), witnesses, and two doctors who agree.

In practice, few of these criteria are even considered. The big one . . . a voluntary request by a rational person repeatedly made . . . has been routinely ignored.

Acquittal After Assisted Suicide, *Brit. Med. Jour.*, 2/7/94
Willke, *Assisted Suicide & Euthanasia*,
Hayes Publishing Co., Cin, 2001, p. 24

Really — involuntary?

"Documented cases of involuntary active euthanasia have been reported by C. I. Dessaur and C.J.C. Rutenfrans, by myself, and others. K. F. Gunning published his experience with the specialists who, when asked to admit an elderly patient to the hospital, advised the general practitioners to administer lethal injections instead. H. W. Hilhorst, in his extensive study (sponsored by Utrecht University and the Royal Dutch Academy of Science), found that involuntary active euthanasia was being practiced in eight hospitals.

"Anxiety is growing among threatened groups. Warnings have been published that elderly patients, out of fear of euthanasia, refuse hospitalization and even refuse to consult doctors. An inquiry among hospital patients showed that many fear their own families may ask for euthanasia without consulting them. The Dutch Patients' Association placed a warning in the press that, in many hospitals, patients are being killed without their will or knowledge, or the knowledge of their families, and advised the patients and their families to carefully inquire on every step in the treatment, and when in doubt, to consult a reliable expert outside the hospital."

Over 10,000 Dutch people carry a card in their wal-

let which says,
"I request that no medical treatment be withheld on the grounds that the future quality of my life will be diminished . . . I request that, under no circumstances, a life-ending treatment be administered."

R. Fenigsen, "Involuntary Euthanasia in Holland,"
Wall Street Journal, Sept. 30, 1987
ibid., J. Willke,
Nat'l Right to Life News, May 23, 1989
J. Bopp et al., "Euthanasia in Holland," *Issues in Law and Medicine*,
vol. 4, no. 4, Spring '89 pp. 455-487

What of other countries?

The Northern Territory in Australia in 1995 became the second nation in the late 20th century to pass legislation to legalize euthanasia.

This law was reversed by the federal parliament.

The U.S. State of Oregon passed a law legalizing "assisted suicide." This became effective in November, 1997. Substantial details of this are available in your author's book, *Assisted Suicide and Euthanasia, Past and Present*, Hayes Publishing Co., Cincinnati, revised year 2001.

Belgium legalized in 2002.

The courts could legalize?

This is what happened in the Netherlands where euthanasia was routinely practiced for almost two decades until its Parliament finally made it official in 2001.

In the U.S., two cases went to the Supreme Court, *Washington vs. Glucksberg* and *Vacco vs. Quill*. By a 9-0 vote in June 1997, the Court ruled that the federal constitution did not permit assisted suicide or euthanasia. It further ruled that an individual state could legalize, however.

Since then, by referendums, the states of Michigan and Maine have rejected it. In the states of Florida and Alaska, Supreme Courts have rejected it.

But only for the narrow reason of physician-assisted suicide?

Remember how abortion started — only for the most rare and tragic cases? And now 99% of abortions are for social and economic reasons. Plan on euthanasia following the same pattern. It did in Germany. It did in Holland. It'll do the same in other countries.

But I don't want the doctor keeping me alive artificially. Why not a law to permit death with dignity?

Proponents of euthanasia are quick to accuse doctors of not letting a patient die in peace. The typical picture drawn is of an old man strapped in bed, in constant pain, clearly dying. He has tubes in every natural body orifice and in several artificial ones. The doctor is keeping him alive, perhaps to obtain a larger fee, perhaps because the doctor does not want to admit that he has lost the battle for this man's life.

A common observation in a retirement community is, "I don't want to be kept alive with all those tubes and painful and expensive treatments."

Years ago, truly life-saving treatments were limited. Only too often, the physician's role was to comfort and eliminate pain as the patient progressed to an inevitable death. Then, with the advent of antibiotics, better surgery, intensive and coronary care units and new drugs, it became possible to prevent death from occurring. For physicians, there was a learning process, from excesses in keeping dying people alive "too long" to learning how to "let go" and allowing natural death to occur. Today, almost all doctors handle dying patients well. Except in rare cases, the caricature of the old man above is no longer valid.

But what if the pain is uncontrolled?

Pro-euthanasia literature constantly emphasizes pain, uncontrollable pain, constant, intractable pain, unrelieved, agonizing pain. Physical pain, with rare exceptions, can be controlled. Sound advice, when confronted by a story of a person's loved one being in constant pain, is "Get another doctor." If your doctor doesn't know how to control pain, get one who does.

"The claim that serious physical pain is a valid reason to kill a patient does not hold up."

The second type of pain which is the main reason why people ask to be killed, is emotional pain, loneliness, despair, hopelessness, being unloved, anguish, isolation, loss of dignity, meaninglessness and weariness with life. Remedies for this are less apparent.

Editorial, Karl Singer, *Patient Care,* May 30, '94

Recent drug advances have given doctors long-lasting oral, I.V. pumps and dermal patch forms of morphine which now is the drug of choice for severe cancer pain.

"Contrary to popular belief, patients in severe pain are less likely than other cancer patients to approve of assisted suicide. . . . what they are really interested in is getting rid of their pain, not in dying." This study found that most people who do seek death are depressed, concluding, "There is a conflict between the avowed purpose and the probable practice of euthanasia."

E. Emanuel et al., Cancer Patients With Pain, *Lancet,* 6/29/96

Opposition to assisted suicide is strongest among the frail, elderly, and terminally ill, precisely those most directly affected by the issue.

H. Koenig, "Attitudes of Elderly Patients and Their Families Toward Physician Assisted Suicide," 156 *Arch. Intern Med.* 2240

Opposition is also strong among handicapped groups. One of these, openly opposing assisted suicide, in 1997 organized itself under the title, "Not Dead Yet."

Yes, but I don't want all those tubes in me!

Is the intensive care unit such a frightening, painful place, that people do not want to return to it? A major study sheds light on this.

Senior patients, previously treated in an intensive care unit, were asked if they would be willing to again undergo treatment in an I.C.U. "if it prolonged your life as perfectly as it could be?" For 10 years? 96% said yes. The percent remained at a very high level when re-asked for 5, 2 and 1 year each, for 6 months and 3 months. 74% still said yes for just one month.

M.Sanis et al., "Patients & Family's Preferences for Medical Intensive Care," JAMA, vol. 260, no. 6, Aug. 12, '88, p. 797

Is life always preferable to death?

One look at this was a study (in the *American Journal of Medicine*, January '96) that asked critically ill patients how many would want CPR (cardio-pulmonary resuscitation) if their hearts stopped. In this survey of 1,664 such patients in five states, 72% wanted to be brought back, 27% said even a coma was preferable to death, and 42% were willing to stay on respirators indefinitely. These patients were in the advanced stages of acute respiratory failure, congestive heart failure, cirrhosis, lung cancer, etc.

R. Russell, Seriously Ill Want CPR, Beth Israel Hosp., *AMA News*, Feb. 26, '96

What about food and water?

To understand, we look at:

Comfort Care

Comfort care consists of TLC, Tender Loving Care. This includes bathing, clean sheets, a warm room, a smile, a bath, proper positioning, pillows, food, water, and other personal care.

Therapeutic Care

This entails the use of drugs, surgery, etc., directed toward curing a disease, repairing an injury, removing a tumor, etc. Such therapy can be divided into usual and customary, such as administering an antibiotic, splinting a broken bone and removing an appendix, and extraordinary care, such as heart surgery, organ transplants, etc. The caregiver has always been seen as grossly negligent if comfort care is not provided. It is a duty. Extraordinary treatment has never been mandatory and has been judged in the light of many factors.

Mixed Up Priorities

Some have now moved food and water from "comfort care" into "treatment." If then a decision is made to withhold further "treatment," food and water can be removed. If the doctor removes therapy, the patient may sometimes die. If the doctor removes food and water, the patient will always die, and painfully. Removing food and water isn't "letting him die," it's "making him die."

Food and Water?

When a patient is unable to swallow, there are alternate means of giving food and water. Post-operative intravenous fluids and nutrition are, at best, a temporary measure. For a period of weeks, food and water can be given through a naso-gastric tube.

If swallowing is permanently impossible, a gastrotomy tube can be inserted through the abdominal wall into the stomach. This provides a permanent, convenient, painless way of feeding the patient. Euthanasia advocates label the above three methods "artificial feedings." Rather, these are "artificially administered" feedings. Such tube feedings are clean, inexpensive, efficient and use simple nutritive milk-shakes. There are no soiled sheets or clothing to clean up, and the caregiver knows exactly how much was given.

But what of a terminal condition?

Patients who are dying do go on to die. While the proponents of euthanasia constantly speak about such cases, these are not their target at all. They are rather concerned about those who somebody thinks ought to die, but who won't . . . the biologically tenacious. Commonly, such people are not in pain, are not on life support systems, but are, by some judgments, a burden to society. These are people with strokes, multiple sclerosis, Lou Gehrig's disease, head injuries, quadriplegia, etc.

Suicide among those with serious handicaps is almost non-existent. It is the "normals" around them who judge their quality of life to be unacceptable, and who want them dead.

With rare exceptions, those who commit suicide are clinically depressed. Clinical depression is usually a biochemical function that can be helped with drug therapy.

W. Peacock in Shewman, *Active Voluntary Euthanasia,*
Issues in Law & Medicine, Winter 1987, pg. 234

But couldn't billions of dollars be saved if we just let terminally ill people die?

In fact, that is what is happening. In a study of 1,150 critically ill patients who died during the study, in only 14% was there an attempt to resuscitate. Twenty years ago most would have been. If all life-prolonging care would be forbidden, it would only save one out of eight dollars spent on health care. Moreover, most of this saving would come from withholding care for relatively young, critically ill patients.

J. Lynn, Terminally Ill, Forgoing . . . Care, Dartmouth,
Boston Globe, May 21, 1994

After age 85, Medicare expenses decrease per patient in hospice and in conventional care due to less aggressive care.

"Influence of Age on Medicare Expenses, Care in the Last Year of Life,"
J.A.M.A. 9-19-01, pp. 1349-1355

Are there other reasons to oppose euthanasia?

Yes.

- Doctors are frequently wrong in judging that a patient will die.

- When the only remaining living witnesses are the persons who wanted her dead and the doctor who killed her, who is to confirm that she really did ask to die?
- If society approves euthanasia, how many elders will ask for it so as to no longer burden their loved ones?
- How voluntary is "voluntary"? Doctors and family can pressure a vulnerable patient into requesting death.
- Medical societies oppose it in the U.S. (Vote AMA House of Delegates, June 26, '96) and the Am. college of Physicians, Australia, the World Medical Assn., May '01. In Canada, the CMA, in August, 1995 stated, "Doctors should specifically exclude participation in euthanasia and physician-assisted suicide."[6]

Toronto Globe and Mail, 8/17/94, pg. A1-3

What about "Living Wills"?

These are misnamed, for they have nothing to do with living and everything to do with dying. Nor are they wills; they are, rather, "directives." Right to Life agrees that anyone who wants to can sign one, but totally opposes making them binding by law.

Why oppose legally binding "advance directives"?

- The Euthanasia Society started the idea, and that should give us pause.
- Informed consent just cannot be intelligently given in a generic fashion, for an unknown problem, at a future time.
- Legislation is not necessary; we have enough government intervention.
- The patient and family can always get another doctor if the present one seems unsatisfactory.
- A conscious patient can always refuse treatment.
- Many patients change their minds. With a signed

document that is legally binding, it may be too late.
* What does "terminally ill," or "artificial means," or "heroic measures," or "meaningful," or "reasonable expectation" mean? These definitions change with time and are different in each case.

The Euthanasia Society started these wills?

Yes. The Euthanasia Society and its Foundation have since changed their names to The Society for the Right to Die, which then changed its name to The Society for Concern for Dying. They all have been headquartered at 250 W. 57th St., New York, NY 10019. On the Euthanasia Society's advisory council as a founding member is Abigail Van Buren, the "Dear Abby" newspaper columnist, who constantly pushes these misnamed "living wills."

Before his death, Dr. Alan Guttmacher, head of Planned Parenthood World Population, was also a prominent member of the Board of the Euthanasia Society of America.

But what if I've made up my mind?

What a person says at the church social, or even in a doctor's office, is not necessarily what that same patient will say when actually confronted with the possibility of dying. Life, however limited it may become, is a good that most people cling to as long as they can. If you do honor their request, be sure to honor the most recent one, not one casually uttered years earlier.

There is an analogy to abortion?

Yes, they both kill living humans. They both are done for the same reasons.

REASON	ABORTION	EUTHANASIA
Usefulness	a burden	a burden
Wanted	unwanted	unwanted
Degree of perfection	handicapped	handicapped
Age	too young	too old
Intelligence	not yet conscious	not really conscious anymore
Place of residence	in the womb	in a nursing home
"Meaningful life"	"does not yet have" *Roe vs. Wade*	"no longer has" Euthanasia Bills
Cost	too poor	too poor
Numbers	too many children	too many old folks
Marital Status	unmarried	widowed

Is there an alternative to euthanasia?

The real alternative to euthanasia is to provide loving, competent care for the dying. A new concept for the dying arose in England, where institutions called Hospices specialize in compassionate, skilled care of the dying. This concept has spread throughout the Western world.

"Once a patient feels welcome and not a burden to others, once his pain is controlled and other symptoms have been at least reduced to manageable proportions, then the cry for euthanasia disappears. It is not that the question of euthanasia is right or wrong, desirable or repugnant, practical or unworkable. It is just that it is irrelevant. Proper care is the alternative to it and can be made universally available as soon as there is adequate instruction of medical students in a teaching hospital. If we fail in this duty to care, let us not turn to the politicians asking them to extricate us from this mess."

R. Lamerton, *Care of the Dying*
Priorty Press Ltd., 1973, p. 99

I've heard that many doctors are ignoring present laws and assisting at suicide now. Wouldn't it be better to legalize it, along with specific safeguards?

What makes a person think that if a doctor will today disobey the law and commit a felony, that he or she will obey future restrictions when a violation is only a misdemeanor?

So you don't think assisted suicide can be controlled?

No. In Britain, the House of Lords Select Committee on Medical Ethics examined this in detail. That committee, going in, was solidly prepared to accept euthanasia. They went to Holland and investigated it actually happening. They reversed their thinking completely saying that they "do not think it is possible to set secure limits." They found "evidence indicating that non-voluntary euthanasia was commonly performed. Vulnerable people — the elderly, the lonely, sick and distressed — feel pressured to request early death. . . . under this, the interest of the individual cannot be separated from the interest of society . . ."

R. Twycross, Journal Royal Society of Medicine,
Vol, 89, 1996, pg. 61-63

Shouldn't those in persistent vegetative states (PVS) be given a release and allowed to die?

Not unless you want to kill some people who are going to get better, if given enough time. Dr. Kay Andrews, Director of the Royal Hospital for Neuro-Disability, stated, "Over a two-year period, 15 out of 18 patients, thought to be in PVS, came around."

Sunday Telegraph, Feb. 11, 1996

And sometimes patients who have been in "vegetative" states for a long time wake up, e.g., following an anesthetic accident seven years earlier, the health authority in the north of England had discussed applying to the courts to remove a patient's feeding — but — after those seven years he woke up and was "competent enough to indicate his refusal to be interviewed."

Guardian (newspaper London), March 16, 1996

And many are aware. In a British study of 40 patients diagnosed as PVS, 17, or 43%, were later found to be alert, aware and often able to express simple wishes. This vital consciousness in their closed-in state, for some, lasted several years.

K. Andrews et al., *Brit. Med. Jour.*, 7/6/96

A PLEA TO LAWMAKERS

In the event that you do take the tragic step of legalizing euthanasia, please do not have a doctor do it. Rather, hire a professional executioner. For over 2000 years people have trusted their doctor to "do no harm." This trust has been seriously undermined by legal abortion. Please do not complete the destruction of this trust and confidence.

PART VI
SOCIAL QUESTIONS

Chapter

CHAPTER 27

CHOICE?

Does she have a right to choose abortion?
Does this supersede the fetal Right to Live?

THE POSITION IS:

The main question is: "Who decides, the woman or the government?" Clearly, this is a woman's rights issue. This is the basic and only question. Should she or should she not have the right to choose?

- Are you a sincere person who thinks abortion is wrong but still believes the woman should have the right to choose?
- Are you disturbed by the high number of abortions (one for every four live births) and that it is used for birth control?
- Are you comfortable with this position? Or are you troubled by the conflict it presents?

Let's look closer.

A nation in conflict . . .

There are many people today who believe that abortion is wrong. They recognize that medical science has long since proven conclusively that human life begins at fertilization. Accordingly, they cannot and do not deny that abortion is killing. Further, most also believe abortion is against God's will.

But many of these sincere people feel that women's rights are so important that she should be allowed to choose to end the life of her developing baby.

This is an untenable position. A person can't have it both ways. If abortion is wrong, then both mother and baby should be protected, unless it can be shown that one's life (the mother's) might be lost if the pregnancy were allowed to continue. Only the preservation of one life is weighty enough to justify endangering or possibly losing another.

Choice – A live baby or a dead baby!

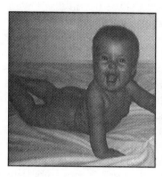 

Once a woman is pregnant, barring a miscarriage or an induced abortion, she'll have a baby. Therefore, her only choice is, "How is the baby going to come out?" Will he or she come out alive and crying, or dead in pieces? For many women this is an agonizing decision.

Truly, her choice is between life and death — a live baby or a dead one. But, for many women, it doesn't end with the abortion. It can impact the rest of her life. There can be physical complications. Perhaps more important, for many, is the emotional aftermath that can result.

On the other hand, if she toughs it out and carries her baby to term, there can instead be good memories — her own child to love and cherish. Or, if she is in no position to parent her child, she can place her baby for adoption in a pair of loving arms of a couple unable to have a child of their own.

The slavery analogy . . .

In 1857 the U.S. Supreme Court decided the Dred Scott Decision. By a 7-2 vote it ruled that black people were not "legal persons," that they were the property of the slave owner, who was granted the basic constitutional right to own a slave. Abolitionists protested, to be met with this answer: "We understand you oppose slavery and find it morally offensive. That is your privilege. You don't have to own a slave if you don't want to. But don't impose your morality on the slave owner. He has the constitutionally protected right to choose to own a slave."

Today the conflict is abortion, and the very same argument is used. In 1973 the U.S. Supreme Court, by a 7-2 decision, ruled that unborn humans were not "legal persons," that they were the property of the owner (the mother) who was given the basic constitutional right to choose to kill her unborn offspring.

Pro-lifers have protested, to be met with the same answer . . ." We understand that you oppose abortion and find it morally offensive. That is your privilege. You don't have to have an abortion if you don't want to. But don't impose your morality on the owner, the mother, for she has the constitutional right to choose to kill, if she wishes.

In the famous Lincoln-Douglas debates, Mr. Douglas defended the right to choose. Abraham Lincoln's answer comes down to us ringingly clear. His reply was, "No one has the right to choose to do what is wrong."

In today's debate the same basic ethic should be our guide.

"No one has the right to choose to do what is wrong."
                                          Abraham Lincoln

Also see chart in Chapter 6.

ANOTHER ANSWER:

Is her "choice" the overriding concern?

This is effectively answered by considering a different issue, one that also raises a significant moral question. Let's consider a hypothetical situation:

A group of young men have just started a "Right to Rape" organization. They explain that they believe they have the right to choose to rape women. The real question, they tell us, is "Who decides, us or the government? We believe the government should stay out of this very private matter." Furthermore, they want the state to set up tax-funded centers where they can rape women in a safe, legal fashion.

What should our response be?

We would promptly reply:

"You can't do that. Rape is wrong!"

Note carefully the answer. The "real question," the first, most important and overriding question, is not "who decides," but a question about the action itself. We must first ask ourselves, "Is rape right or wrong?" Only then can we answer the question of who has the right to choose to do it.

We could use other human actions that also have obvious moral overtones to illustrate this. Does a burglar have the right to choose to rob your house? A husband to abuse his wife and children? Of course not. The most critical question always is to first judge the action itself.

And so it is with abortion. First, one must ask, "Is abortion right or wrong?" Only then can we consider a second question and ask "Who can choose to do this?"

Rights have limits . . .

I have a right to swing my fist, but that right stops at your nose. We have the right to freedom of speech, but not to shout "fire" in a theater. We have a right to freedom of religion, but not if that religion involves human sacrifice.

A woman has a right to her body, but this new being growing within her is not part of her body. Rather, this is a totally different human being, half of whom are even of a different sex.

Compassion for her . . .

In the U.S., pro-lifers, in their concern for pregnant women and their needs, have established numerous women helping centers (4,000). There are also almost 3,000 Right to Life chapters. The volunteers who staff both are overwhelmingly female. In addition, pro-lifers take pregnant women into their homes, collect maternity and baby clothes and adopt children far more frequently than other citizens, very often babies with handicaps. They offer legal, medical and social help for women during and after their pregnancies and after their abortions.

The abortion industry, in contrast, offers a violent "solution" to her problem — abortion. They have no other choices available for the pregnant woman in need of help.

The pro-life movement stands with her. The rights of women and the rights of the unborn should be joined. Loving alternatives, like adoption, must be the focus of our debate. We reach out to every woman faced with the agony of abortion and say to her, "Your life and the life of your baby are both important, and we will not desert either one of you."

"We want to love you both."

CHAPTER 28

ILLEGAL ABORTIONS

*Will dangerous back-alley abortions
return if abortions are forbidden?*

To answer this, first we must look back to what the actual situation was prior to legalization. Two questions are relevant:

1) How many illegal abortions were there?
2) How many women died from illegal abortions?

The head of one of the major pro-abortion organizations in the U.S. said: *"In 1972 there were 1,000,000 illegal abortions and 5,000 to 10,000 women died from them."*

True? Or False?

How many illegal abortions were there?
No one knows. Why? For the obvious reason that illegal abortions are not reported. No one reports the illegal actions that they have done. In this case, neither the abortionist nor the woman report the deed. Because of this, there are no records. There are no statistics, no

numbers anywhere to report.

No one knows! Therefore, if anyone tells you that there were X numbers of illegal abortions somewhere in a certain time, they are guessing.

The pro-abortion leader may guess 1,000,000. Your pro-life spokesman may guess 100,000, but both are guessing.

No clues?

There is only one reported figure that can lead us to some degree of accurate estimate of the numbers of illegal abortions and that is the number of women who died from illegal abortions.

Many nations report only one figure for women who die. They clump together women's deaths from spontaneous abortion (miscarriage), legally induced abortion and illegally induced abortion. Such statistics are no help.

The United States, since the 1940s, has reported such deaths separately, so we know the number of deaths from illegal abortions. Good! Now if we knew how many illegal abortions it took to cause one death, we could easily calculate the total number of illegal abortions. The problem is, no one has the slightest idea how many it took, and so we're back to where we started from.

How many women died?

Let's look. The following chart was used on the floor of the U.S. Senate during the tumultuous debate on abortion in 1981. It was compiled from official U.S. statistics and was not challenged by the pro-abortion forces.

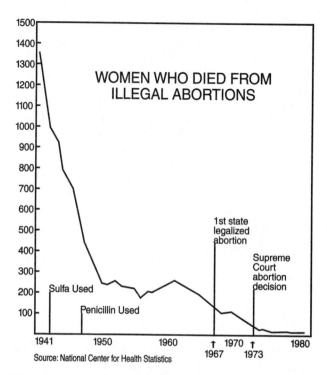

1500
1400
1300
1200 — WOMEN WHO DIED FROM
1100   ILLEGAL ABORTIONS
1000
900
800
700
600
500   1st state
400   legalized
       abortion
300   Supreme
                           Court
200   Sulfa Used   abortion
                           decision
100   Penicillin Used

1941   1950   1960   ↑ 1970 ↑   1980
                       1967   1973

Source: National Center for Health Statistics

Why the early sharp drop?

Largely because Penicillin became available. Note that after Penicillin became available to control infections, the number of deaths stabilized during the 1950s at about 250/year.

e.g., $1956 = 250$

Note that by 1966, with abortion still illegal in all states, the number of deaths had dropped steadily to half that number.

$1966 = 120$

Why the drop after 1960?

The reasons were new and better antibiotics, better

surgery and the establishment of intensive care units in hospitals. This was in the face of a rising population.

Between 1967 and 1970, sixteen states legalized abortion. In most it was limited only for rape, incest and severe fetal handicap (life of mother was legal in all states). There were two big exceptions — California in 1967, and New York in 1970 allowed abortion-on-demand. Now look at the chart carefully.

This legalization reduced the deaths?

In these two large states, legalization should have substituted "safe" for unsafe abortions. It should have saved many women's lives.

Actually, there was no sharp drop in the number of women dying. Let's look further.

By the year before the U.S. Supreme Court decision which allowed legal abortion-on-demand in all fifty states, the death rate for illegal abortions had fallen to:

$$1972 = 39$$

(With 25 additional deaths that year due to legal abortions.)

Now abortion was legal in 50 states. Now back alley abortions should have been eliminated with their alleged toll of maternal deaths.

In 1973 there should have been a really sharp drop in women dying. The chart, however, shows that there was no such drop. The line didn't even blip. The previous rate of decline actually slowed, to flatten out in the late 70s and 80s. According to the U.S. Vital Statistics, as anyone can see, legalization of abortion did not save almost any women's lives.

Canada had a similar record. Its deaths from illegal abortions were:

$$1957 = 32$$
$$1963 = 25$$
$$1966 = 13$$
$$1969 = 11 \text{ (Year abortion legalized.)}$$

But we've been told the opposite.

Correct, but let's recap:

Pro-abortionists claim that in 1972, the year before the Supreme Court legalized abortion, there were 1,000,000 illegal abortions and 5,000 to 10,000 women died.

Actually only 39 women died — less than one per state per year.

But they can't have it both ways.

• Either there were not many illegal abortions

or

• Illegal abortions were all extremely safe.

Since we assume that all illegal abortions were not extremely safe, it seems obvious that

THERE WERE NOT MANY
ILLEGAL ABORTIONS

One other comparison is relevant here. The pro-abortion claim was 1,000,000 illegal abortions in 1972. But with abortions legal without restriction in all states, the total reported for all of 1973 was about 750,000. This climbed to 1,500,000 by 1979 and plateaued there.

But why, then, have I heard time and again that between 5,000 and 10,000 women died annually from illegal abortions?

Those were the figures publicized. Another comment about them is the statement from Dr. Bernard Nathanson, a co-founder of the National Association for the Repeal of Abortion Laws (NARAL) — a man who once ran the largest abortion facility in the Western world and is now pro-life. He stated:

"How many deaths were we talking about when abortion was illegal? In NARAL, we generally emphasized the frame of the individual case, not the mass statistics, but when we spoke of the latter it was always '5,000 to 10,000 deaths a year.'

I confess that I knew the figures were *totally false*, [italics added] and I suppose the others did too, if they stopped to think of it. But in the 'morality' of our revolution, it was a *useful* [Nathanson's italics] figure, widely accepted, so why go out of our way to correct it with honest statistics? The overriding concern was to get the laws eliminated, and anything within reason that had to be done was permissible."

B. Nathanson, Aborting America,
Doubleday, 1979, p. 193

Then, actually, how many illegal abortions were there?

One study quoted in the U.S. Senate debate was authored by Dr. T. Hilgers from Creighton University, who estimated the figure probably was at or somewhere near 100,000 abortions annually in the U.S. prior to legalization.

But were illegal abortion deaths reported accurately? Before legalization?

Almost certainly they were! Back then it was a felony to do an abortion. When a woman was seriously injured by an abortion, she went to another doctor for care. The abortionist was nowhere to be seen. The new doctor tried to save her life, but she died anyway. Was this new, ethical physician going to deliberately falsify the death certificate (which was a felony itself), to protect the abortionist? Not likely! Therefore, prior to legalization, deaths from illegal abortion were seldom covered up.

Are deaths from legal abortions reported accurately? Since legalization?

No, they frequently are not. As an example, let us use the State of Maryland in the year of 1991. There were four women who died in Maryland from induced abortions that year. None of the four were reported to the Federal Center for Disease Control. It receives its information from examination of death certificates. But, just for instance, one of the Maryland deaths above was listed as — "Cause of death = therapeutic misadventure." There is substantial evidence to suggest that the CDC does not report all the abortion-related deaths reported to it (see Chapter 21). But, even if it did operate honestly, the CDC only has the information to work with that is given to it. There are many deaths that are never reported to it.

Why is this?

One reason is that, prior to legalization, a second doctor almost always was the one who tried to save her life. In today's age, however, it can be the same doctor. Since this abortionist does not want to have a reputation for having mothers die from his work, he or she has strong motivation to list some other cause of death. Since abortion is no longer a crime, this can be done with relative impunity.

Another reason has to do with a substantial bias in reporting by the staff at the Center for Disease Control. As exhaustively documented by Mark Crutcher's book, *Lime 5,* the CDC seems to have had an ongoing unspoken policy of under-reporting and minimizing induced abortion mortality and morbidity and maximizing that of full term pregnancy.

M. Crutcher, *Lime 5,* 1996
Pub. by Life Dynamics, Inc., Denton, TX

It is the opinion of all pro-life leaders in the United States that an accurate estimate of women dying from induced abortions is many times the number that is actually reported.

Then there is a difference between illegal abortions and back alley abortions?

Yes! Doctors who did illegal abortions would let a woman in the back door, take her money, and do the abortion. Today, the same abortionist lets her in the front door, takes her money, and does the abortion in the same way. Abortions from untrained "butchers" are increasingly rare and would be in the future.

But isn't abortion safer than childbirth?

Pro-abortion people commonly say that it is. "Maternal mortality" is listed as deaths of women per 100,000 pregnancies. This figure has been commonly listed as eleven, compared to deaths from induced abortion, which are listed as one or two. Therefore, they say abortion is seven times safer. Not so! Maternal mortality, in recent years, has dropped to six and one-half, not eleven.

But more important is the fact that, included in maternal mortality, are all deaths from induced abortions and ectopic pregnancies. Included also in maternal mortality are all women who die while pregnant from almost any cause that is in any way related to pregnancy. Different states require longer or shorter lengths of postpartum time, but, typically, maternal mortality also includes any related death within one year after delivery.

Maternal mortality also includes deaths from caesarean section. To compare comparable risks, one would have to compare the risk of being pregnant in the first three months with the risk of having an abortion within the first three months. When compared in this fashion, abortion is many times more dangerous. Actually, it is probable that induced abortion is more dangerous than carrying a baby to term.

Maternal Mortality Surveillance '82-'96, Center for
Disease Control, M&M, 1998,
Vol. 47, pp. 705-707

How about further proof?

Let's look at the late 1950s. Those were the supposed bad old days. All abortions were illegal, and illegal abortionists were alleged to be busy.

In the July 1960 edition of *The American Journal of Public Health,* there was an article by Dr. Mary Calderone, founder of SIECUS and medical director of the Planned Parenthood Federation of America. She stated:

"90% of illegal abortions are being done by physicians. Call them what you will, abortionists or anything else, they are still physicians, trained as such; . . . They must do a pretty good job, if the death rate is as low as it is . . . Abortion, whether therapeutic or illegal, is in the main no longer dangerous, because it is being done well by physicians."

But what about coat hanger abortions?

Your authors have lectured nationwide on abortion on an average of one city a week for over three decades. We frequently ask the audience to provide documented proof of a self-induced coat hanger abortion. In all this time no one has given us a single case. It may well be — *there never were any coat hanger abortions.*

I've heard of large numbers of women dying from illegal abortions in other countries.

On June 18, 1989, CNN World Report, in an hour-long documentary, stated that in Brazil there are 6 million illegal abortions each year and 400,000 women die. But the U.N. Demographic Yearbook of 1988 lists only 40,000 women, age 15-44, dying each year of *all* causes.

Pop. Research Inst. Review, Jan. 1991, p. 12

In Portugal, the claimed figure was 2,000 deaths. The actual number of deaths of females between the ages of

15-46 was 2,106 in the same year from all natural causes, accidents and illness. There were only 97 listed in
the "complications of pregnancy" of which 12 were
due to abortion, including spontaneous and induced,
legal and illegal.

Portuguese Anuario Estatistico, Tables 11, 16, 111

In Italy, the claimed figure before their abortion
referendum was 20,000. In the age group 15-45, there
were actually only 11,500 female deaths from all
causes.

Primum Non Nocere, vol. IV, no. 1, 1983

In Germany, the claim was that 15,000 women died
annually. In fact, only 13,000 women of reproductive
age died annually in West Germany, and less than 100
died of complications of abortion, legal and illegal.

Kurchoff, *Deutches Arzteblatt,* vol. 69, no. 27, Oct. 26, 1972

At the United Nations Habitat meeting in Istanbul,
Turkey, in June 1996, the following "fact" was given
wide publicity: The UNICEF suddenly claimed that
585,000 women die each year from causes related to
pregnancy and birth.

The pro-life NGO's for the family immediately
answered, "This is wild. According to the U.N. Demographic Year Book for 1990, the total known maternal
deaths worldwide for 1986 and 1987 numbered 11,924
(around 6,000 per year). This figure encompasses
countries covering 35% of the world's population."

U.N. Conference, Istanbul, June 1996

POLAND

A Definitive Answer to a Basic Pro-Abortion Argument

For 44 years under Nazi and then Communist rule, abortion was legal for three months, state paid. In 1960, there were 150,400 abortions. In 1970, 148,000. In 1980, 138,000. By 1990, under the influence of Solidarity, the numbers declined.

In 1993, the new freely elected Parliament passed a law forbidding abortion. The media and liberals screamed: "You now have the legal power to do this, but you won't stop abortions. They will just go underground, and women will be injured and die. They will be instrumented in the back alley and then, bleeding and infected, they will flood into your hospitals as 'miscarriages.' "

The law was passed and the number of abortions dropped precipitously.

$$1980 = 138,000$$
$$2000 = 138$$

Were the ominous predictions realized?

• Miscarriages 1990 = 59,076
               1999 = 41,568

• Deaths due to "Pregnancy, Birth & Confinement"

$$1991 = 70$$
$$1997 = 24$$

• Neonatal deaths/1,000 live births

$$1990 = 19$$
$$1998 = 9$$

• Illegal Abortions

$$1999 = 99$$

251

And total gynecological admissions also dropped. Not only did none of the dire predictions materialize but, instead, Polish women are healthier and have fewer gynecological problems than when abortion was legal and common. Three separate government agencies report annually and agree on these statistics. In the face of this, IPPF claimed that there are 190,000 illegal abortions yearly. When publicly challenged, it was silent.

CONCLUSION

Since the abortion controversy began, we have heard the argument used above that if abortion is ever forbidden by law, it will first "drive women back to the back alley."

Here we have a modern western nation of 40 million people that did forbid it by law. The result there shatters and completely destroys this long-standing pro-abortion argument. In a manner of speaking, this has been a "test market."

"How the Law Protects Life — the situation in Poland;
P. Wosicka, June 2001, Fundacja Glos dia Zyoia
Report of the Council of Ministers on the Implementation in 1999,
of the law of Jan. 7, 1993, Warsaw, 2000 Croatia

CROATIA

This country is walking in Poland's footsteps. The number of abortions:

$$1987 = 48,608$$
$$1988 = 8,907$$

Why? They credit this to continuing massive distribution of pro-life literature, to the clarity and consistency of the Catholic Bishops addressing the issue and to the visits of Pope John Paul II in 1994 and 1998.

CHAPTER 29

PARENTAL NOTIFICATION

*The U.S. Supreme Court's Casey Decision
allowed states to pass laws requiring
parental notification.*

Explain such a law.

Typically, such a law requires the abortionist to notify one or both parents of an unemancipated minor daughter prior to an abortion, a "minor daughter" being under 18 and living at home. Under most state laws this only requires notification. In some states it also requires consent.

The court has also required a "judicial bypass." This means that if the girl feels that she may be abused by her parents when they find out, she may go to a judge and ask for the court's approval to abort without parental notification.

This requires some time?

Yes, and because of this, these laws are often paired with a waiting period. This would be a required 24 or 48-hour waiting period after she has been examined and the abortion agreed upon. Sometimes such a law is paired with parental notification. In some states these laws requiring a waiting period have been passed standing alone.

What has been the usual ruling of a judge?

With few exceptions, cases have gone to judges who have given blanket approval for abortion.

What percent of teenagers tell their parents freely?

The abortion industry tells us at least three-fourths. Experience by pro-lifers has been about one-third. This is supported by a study where 37% told the mother and 26% told the father.

Minor Women Obtaining Abortions:
A Study of Par. Notif. in a Metro. Area, F. Clary,
Am J. Pub H. Mar. 1982, Vol. 72, No. 3, P. 283

Why don't they tell their parents?

The main reason is embarrassment, shame and reluctance to hurt their parents. There's also a certain element of "My mom would just die!," and "My dad would kill me." In fact, such retaliation rarely happens. "The girls go through this alone because they don't want to shatter the good-girl image their parents have of them."

T. Welsh, Fam. Plan. Persp. Dec. '83

But, there is a simple preventive measure.

What is that?

A pregnancy diagnosis is almost always made by a physician. If the girl fears her parents, ideally, that physician should call one or both parents into his office and break the news to them in front of the girl. If not face-to-face, this can be done by the physician over the telephone. The result of this is that the parents, particularly the father, have been notified that this authority figure knows and can and will report any child abuse. As a result, it never happens.

But think of the emotional impact of notifying the parents!

I believe the following article answers that:

Your Daughter — Pregnant?

And under 18 years? What does she think of you, her parents? Should she tell you? Sadly, few girls want to. They think you'll explode, condemn, reject, feel ashamed. She doesn't want to hurt you. She is alone, frightened, defiant, worried, yes, but still a young girl who desperately needs your love and help.

The Supreme Court ruling assures her that she can have her baby killed, can internalize all of the psychic trauma, the loneliness, the bitterness, and never know that . . .

If she had told you — yes, you might have "exploded" initially — but then, with rare exceptions, you would have shared your tears and given her the help, support, and love she so desperately needed. To her surprise, you would not condemn, but offer all the love, help, and understanding you could in this time of trial.

In my 25 years of counseling, I have found that when a girl does come to her parents and receives the help they can offer, it becomes the occasion of a real growth in maturity, self-confidence, and ability to love by the girl. She faces her responsibility and stands tall. The family bond is strengthened by the sharing of the burden.

But no, now the tragic Supreme Court Decision can guarantee that she'll never know that you really love her and would have helped her. Thanks to them, she can have her baby killed in secret and become disillusioned, embittered, hardened.

May God have mercy on those judges for what they have done.

J. Willke, *Cincinnati RTL Newsletter,* July 1976, p. 3

What effect have parental notification laws had on the abortion rate?

In some small states, like Massachusetts, the answer is confused because some teenagers cross into neighboring states for abortions. In a much larger state like Minnesota, where such travel is almost prohibitive, the record is very clear.

What is the result?

The State of Minnesota had such a law in place since 1981. Then the law was challenged in court and enjoined (suspended) in March 1986. The Supreme Court later ruled that the law was constitutional, and it was reimposed.

Hodgson v. State of Minn., 853 F. 2d 1452,
1458 n. 9 [8th Cir 1988]

In that state there were excellent records kept for several years with the law in place, several more without the law, and then again with the law. Results were very clear.

Perhaps not unexpectedly, the number of abortions to unemancipated minors dropped, and by a figure of 34%. Correspondingly, the number of live births to this group increased. The unexpected result was that the number of *pregnancies* in this age group to unmarried girls decreased by 27%.

Impact of MN Par. Notif. Law on Ab. and Birth,
J. Rogers et al.,
Am. J. Pub. Health, Mar. '91, vol. 81, no. 3, p. 294

A 27% decrease in teen pregnancies? That's never happened before, has it?

Correct. It was an amazing and heartwarming result. As everyone knows, government at all levels, private groups, schools, churches, etc., have all been trying to reduce teen pregnancies over the last several decades. The results of all of these have been essentially negative, hardly moving the percentage one way or the other. Then here we saw a full one-fourth decrease in teen pregnancies, an absolutely astonishing and heart-warming effect.

That's exactly what Planned Parenthood has been trying to do. Were they pleased?

Not at all. In fact, they brought the lawsuit which enjoined the law. Planned Parenthood has constantly been telling the world that it wants to reduce teen pregnancies. Here was an outstanding example of an effective method, and Planned Parenthood showed its true stripes. It went to court to stop the only major successful program that limited teen pregnancies. So much for Planned Parenthood's claims that it wants to reduce teen pregnancies.

But didn't the Becky Bell case show otherwise?

The Becky Bell case ranks among the most totally misrepresented happenings in the history of the abortion conflict. Let's recall her story.

Becky Bell is the now-famous 17-year-old Indianapolis girl who died September 16, 1988. Her death has been portrayed by pro-abortion groups all over the country as an example of why parental notification and consent laws are undesirable. The story as told by her parents and others is that she had an illegal induced abortion, became infected, developed pneumonia, and died from the infection. Indiana has a parental consent law that is being enforced. Her parents state that if she could have gotten a legal abortion in Indiana without her parents' knowledge, she would be alive today.

The fact is that Becky never had an induced abortion. She died from massive pneumonia and septic shock.

Becky Bell

She had become pregnant. This was confirmed at a Planned Parenthood clinic. She attended a drug party, became ill and died six days later. Your authors have a copy of the autopsy report which showed no evidence of an induced abortion, but massive pneumonia, lung cavitation, and septic shock as the cause of death.

In the first edition of this book is a six-page detailed description of this case.

Conclusion
Becky Bell did not die from an induced abortion. The entire attempt by the abortion industry to so label her death was a total lie.

CHAPTER 30

RAPE

Pregnant from rape?
Why not abort her?

First, it is important to define terms. This issue concerns assault, or forcible, rape, not consensual, not marital rape. In recent years, semantics have muddied the water, particularly regarding "date rape."

Rape is the forcible imposition of a man on a woman for sexual intercourse. Whether it occurs behind the bushes or on a date, it should be reported to the police and charges filed. (College students, are you listening?)

Are assault rape pregnancies common?

No, they are very rare.

Are there accurate numbers?

The Justice Dept., from 1973 to 1987, surveyed 49,000 households annually, asking questions on violence and criminal acts. Extrapolating to the entire population, the results of those reported were:

1973 — completed rapes — 95,934
1987 — completed rapes — 82,505

The study stated that only 53% were reported to police. Accordingly, the total numbers were:

1973 — 181,016
1987 — 155,667

The Washington *Times*, Jan. 14, 1991, A-5

In 1995, a Justice Dept. report, using a study designed differently with more direct questions, returned a result of 170,000 completed rapes plus 140,000 attempted rapes.

Nat. Crime Victim Report, US Justice Dept.
Aug. 95, R. Bachman

But, in 1997, reporting for the year of 1995, only 97,000 assault rapes were recorded.

"Sexual Offences and Offenders," Bureau of Justice Statistics, U.S. Justice Dept., Feb. 1997

And how many pregnancies result?

About 1 or 2 for each 1,000. Using the 170,000 figure, this translates into an overall total of 170 to 340 assault rape pregnancies a year in the entire United States.

Only one or two out of 1,000? Please explain.

There are about 100 million women in the United States old enough to be at risk for assault rape. Let's use a figure of 200,000 forcible rapes every year. The studies available agree that there are no more than two pregnancies per 1,000 assault rapes.

So much for the numbers. Let's look at it from another angle and see if that figure makes sense.

- Of these 200,000 women who were raped, one-third were either too old or too young to get pregnant. That leaves 133,000 at risk of pregnancy.
- A woman is capable of being fertilized only three days out of her 30-day month. So divide 133,000 by 10, and 13,300 women remain.
- One-fourth of all women in the United States of

child-bearing age have been sterilized. That drops the figure to 10,000.

- Only half of the assailants penetrate her body and/or deposit sperm. Cut it in half again. We are down to 5,000.
- Fifteen percent of men are sterile; that drops the figure to 4,250. Fifteen percent of non-surgically sterilized women are naturally sterile. That reduces the number to 3,600.
- Another 15% are on the pill and/or are already pregnant. Now the figure is 3,070.

Now factor in something that all adults know. It takes from five to ten months for an average couple to achieve a pregnancy. Using the smaller figure, to be conservative, divide the 3,000 figure by 5, and the number drops to about 600.

In a healthy, peaceful marriage, the miscarriage rate ranges up to about 15%. In this case, we have incredible emotional trauma. Her body is upset. Even if she conceives, the miscarriage rate is higher than in a more normal pregnancy. If she loses 20% of 600, there are 450 left.

Finally, we must factor in one of the most important reasons why a rape victim rarely gets pregnant, and that is psychic trauma. Every woman is aware that stress and emotional factors can alter her menstrual cycle. To get pregnant and stay pregnant, a woman's body must produce a very sophisticated mix of hormones. Hormone production is controlled by a part of the brain which is easily influenced by emotions.

There's no greater emotional trauma that can be experienced by a woman than an assault rape. This can radically upset her possibility of ovulation, fertilization, implantation and even nurturing of a pregnancy. So what further percentage reduction in pregnancy will this cause? No one really knows, but this factor certainly cuts the last figure by at least 50%, and probably more, leaving a final figure of 225 women pregnant each year, a number that closely matches the 200 found in clinical studies.

But are there specific studies?

Here are several:

A study of 1,000 rape victims, who were treated medically right after the rape, reported no pregnancies.

L. Kuchera, "Postcoital Contraception with Diethylstilbestrol," *JAMA*, October 25, 1971

In another study, medical treatment on more than 1,000 women was "100% effective," according to Dr. B. Craver at the Wilson Foundation.

B. Craver, "Morning After Pill Prevents Pregnancy in Victims of Rape," *Family Practice News*, Mar. 1972

If the rape victim is not treated, and if it is limited to true assault rape, the pregnancy rate will still be extremely small. If all "reported" rapes, including statutory rape (under 18-years-old, but sometimes with consent given), when drunk (with questionable consent), etc., it is higher.

There are two such large, across-the-board studies of all reported rapes (with no reported attempt to validate them), in Washington, DC for the years 1965-69 and 1969-70. These reported on rape victims seen by private doctors, clinics, and hospitals, with no details as to treatment, if any. Of the 2,190 women in the first study and the 1,223 women in the second, a total of 23 and of 21 pregnancies occurred, or rates of 6 and 17 per 1,000. If these had been limited to true assaults, and the women had been given hormone treatment, the pregnancy rate would have been much lower, perhaps zero.

Hayman & Lanza, "Sexual Assault on Women and Girls," *Amer. Jour. OB/GYN*, vol. 109, No. 3, Feb. 1971, pp. 480-486

Hayman et al., "Rape in the District of Columbia," *Amer. Jour. OB/GYN*, vol. 113, no. 1, May 1972, pp. 91, 97

In another series of 117 assault rape victims, of whom only 17 were given hormone treatment after the attack, none became clinically pregnant.

Everett & Jimerson, "The Rape Victim,"
OB & GYN, vol. 50, no. 1, July 1977, pp. 88-90

In still another series of 126 assault rape victims, only half of those at risk of pregnancy were treated, but none became clinically pregnant.

Evrard & Gold, "Epidemiology and Management of Sexual
Assault Victims," *OB & GYN,* vol. 53, no. 3, Mar. 1979, pp. 381-387

Dr. Alfred Kinsey reported that, of 2,094 single females who had voluntary intercourse 460,000 times, the pregnancy rate was 1 per 1,000 exposures. Many of these women had used contraception, many had not, but it is also true that some assaulted women have I.U.D.s and/or are on the pill.

A. Kinsey, *Sexual Behavior of the Human Female,*
N. Saunders Publishers, 1953, p. 327

In Czechoslovakia, out of 86,000 consecutive induced abortions, only 22 were done for rape.

Why not allow abortion for rape pregnancies?

We must approach this with great compassion. The woman has been subjected to an ugly trauma, and she needs love, support and help. But she has been the victim of one violent act. Should we now ask her to be a party to a second violent act — that of abortion?

Unquestionably, many would return the violence of killing an innocent baby for the violence of rape. But, before making this decision, remember that most of the trauma has already occurred. She has been raped. That trauma will live with her all her life. Furthermore, this girl did not report for help, but kept this to herself. For several weeks or months, she has thought of little else. Now, she has finally asked for help, has shared her upset, and should be in a supportive situation.

The utilitarian question, from the mother's stand-point, is whether or not it would now be better to kill the developing baby within her. But will abortion now be best for her, or will it bring her more harm yet? What has happened, and its damage have already occurred. She's old enough to know and have an opinion as to whether she carries a "baby" or a "blob of protoplasm."

Will she be able to live comfortably with the memory that *"killed her developing baby"*? Or would she ultimately be more mature and more at peace with herself if she could remember that, even though she became pregnant unwillingly, she nevertheless solved her problem by being unselfish, by giving of herself and of her love to an innocent baby, who had not asked to be created, to deliver, perhaps to place for adoption, if she decides that is what is best for her baby.

Compare this memory with the woman who can only look back and say, "I killed my baby."

But carry the rapist's child?

True, it is half his. But remember, half of the baby is also hers, and there are other outstretched arms that will adopt and love that baby.

I don't see how she could!

"Interestingly, the pregnant rape victim's chief complaint is not that she is unwillingly pregnant, as bad as the experience is. The critical moment is fleeting in this area, it frequently pulls families together like never before.

"We found this experience is forgotten, replaced by remembering the abortion, because it is what *they* did."

M. Uchtman, Director, Suiciders Anonymous, Report to Cincinnati City Council, Sept. 1, 1981

"In the majority of these cases, the pregnant victim's problems stem more from the trauma of rape than from the pregnancy itself."

Mahkorn & Dolan, "Sexual Assault & Pregnancy."
In *New Perspectives on Human Abortion,*
University Publishers of Amer., 1981, pp. 182-199

As to what factors make it most difficult to continue
her pregnancy, the opinions, attitudes, and beliefs of
others were most frequently cited; in other words, how
her loved ones treated her.

Mahkorn, "Pregnancy & Sexual Assault." *In Psychological Aspects*
of Abortion, University Publishers of Amer., 1979, pp. 53-72

But many laws would allow for this exception.

That is because many mistakenly think it is best for
the mother. But we should also think of the baby.
Should we kill an innocent unborn baby for the crime
of his father? Do we punish other criminals by killing
their children? Besides, such laws pose major problems in reporting, and also women have been known to
report falsely.

You accuse women of lying?

We don't have to. Radical feminist guru Gloria
Steinem, in a 1985 interview with *USA Today,* said that
"to make abortion legal only in cases of rape and incest
would force women to lie."

The story of Jane Roe, of the *Roe v. Wade* Decision,
is well known. Norma McCorvey (her real name)
fabricated a story — that she had been gang raped at a
circus — in the mistaken impression that this would
permit her to obtain a legal abortion in Texas. Not until
1987 did she reveal that the baby was actually conceived "through what I thought was love." (*Post,* Sept. 9,
1987.)

And:

Up until 1988, Pennsylvania's Medicaid program
funded abortions for women who claimed they had
been raped, without any requirement for reporting of
the purported assault to a law enforcement agency.
Under this law, abortion clinic personnel issued thinly

veiled public invitations for women to simply state that they'd been raped, and the state ended up funding an average of 36 abortions a month based on such unsubstantiated claims. In 1988 the legislature added a requirement for reporting the rape to a law enforcement agency, and the average dropped to less than three abortions per month.

You said reporting was a problem?

The problem is requiring proof. If the woman goes directly to the hospital, her word is accepted. But, sadly, through fright or ignorance, she may not report it and quietly nurse her fears. She misses her period and hopes against hope that it isn't what she thinks it is.

Sometimes months go by before finally, in tears, she reports to her mother, her physician, or some other counselor or confidante. To prove rape then is impossible. The only proof of rape then is to have a reliable witness corroborate the story, and such a witness almost never exists.

What proof would be needed early on?

Reporting the rape to a law enforcement agency is needed. Any hospital emergency room will handle this.

If done within a day or two, she can be examined, given medicine for sexually transmitted diseases and counseled. Her word will rarely be questioned. But if it is many days later, especially after a missed period, her word may not be enough (see above).

What percentage of rape pregnancies are aborted?

Less than half. The balance carry the baby to term. In one study of 37 rape pregnancies, 28 carried to term.
S. Makhorn, in *Psychological Aspects of Abortion*,
Mall & Watts, Univ. Pub. 1979, pg. 58

What is her chief complaint?

Perhaps, surprisingly, it is not the fact that she is

pregnant. Her chief complaint is "how other people treat her." This should be very sobering to everyone. How is she treated? Do others understand the trauma she has experienced, and love and support her? Or, do they avoid her and act as if it was partly her fault, or worse? Just think, if all such victims were given generous love and support, many more than at present would carry their babies to term.

Mahkorn & Dona, "Sexual Assault & Pregnancy."
In *New Perspectives on Human Abortion,*
University Publishers of Amer., 1981, pp. 182-199

Mahkorn, "Pregnancy & Sexual Assault." In *Psychological Aspects of Abortion,* University Publishers of Amer., 1979, pp. 53-72

What if she could not cope with raising the child?

We must let these women know that it is all right to feel that way. We fully understand. That does not mean, however, that the baby is unwanted. There are innumerable arms outstretched, aching for a child to love. Any number of couples will want the child. She should be supported and encouraged if she chooses to place the child in a loving adoptive home.

She had a problem. Abortion permanently removes the problem. Or is there emotional aftermath?

In recent years it has become clear that these women can and do suffer from Post-Abortion Syndrome. When PAS does develop, a woman, so affected, can carry the same burdens of guilt, denial and depression that a woman who aborted a "love" baby often does. Why is this? At least two dynamics seem obvious. Remember that the rape was done **to** her. She was not responsible. She was the innocent victim and should bear no guilt. But, by contrast, the abortion will be done **by** her. She agreed to it. She was a volitional participant in a second act of violence: the killing of her own unborn child.

And it is her own unborn child. This is the other inescapable fact of biology that probably is a factor in the development of PAS. The newly-conceived baby is certainly the "rapist's child," but he or she is also her child, for half of the new baby's genetic material came from her. She may try, but, inside of her, she cannot deny this biologic reality, however unwillingly it happened and however upsetting it may be. And so, to kill this little one by abortion is to participate in a violent, lethal act that destroys a baby who is partly her own flesh and blood.

In loving charity, we should never remind her of this. But we don't have to, for she knows it instinctively and all of her maternal feelings may well rebel when faced with being a part of this killing.

The "treatment" for rape, isn't it abortive?

This is best illustrated by giving two theoretical case histories. Woman "A" is raped at midnight on Saturday and is treated in a hospital emergency room with a female hormone medication beginning at 3 a.m. Sunday morning. In this case, the woman's body was scheduled to ovulate two days later, on Monday. If that were to have occurred, and if the assailant's sperm were still alive in her body, she might have been fertilized two days after the assault and become pregnant at that time. A very small body of medical opinion believes that the dose of medication given might prevent that ovulation, and she would therefore not get pregnant. This mechanism of action would be one of temporary sterilization, or, in more commonly used (however technically inaccurate) terms, the action would be contraceptive.

Woman "B" presents a different case. She had ovulated at 9 p.m. on Saturday, was raped at midnight, and also received treatment at 3 a.m. To her own observation, this lady also does not "get pregnant." In fact, something entirely different happened inside her body. Let us assume that she was one of those very rare cases where fertilization did occur, and had, in fact, occurred prior to the giving of the medication. The life of a tiny new little boy or girl had begun. The cells of this tiny body begin to divide, and divide again, but at one week of life, when implantation within the nutrient lining of the mother's womb should occur, this tiny new human being could not implant and died. The mechanism of action of the drug, in this case, had been to harden the lining of the womb in order to prevent implantation. This effect was one of a micro-abortion, at one week of life and represents the large majority of medical opinion.

Would a Human Life Amendment in America, or a law forbidding abortion in another nation, prevent such treatment?

Most legal opinion agrees that since these drugs have a multiplicity of other beneficial and therapeutic effects, they would never be removed from the market. Since they would in some cases have a legally permissible effect (temporary sterilization or/and contraception), even with a strong Human Life Amendment in place, the use of such drugs after rape could not be forbidden. Therefore, the choice now available to a woman after a assault rape — to use or not use such treatment — would still be available after such a law.

Does anyone win after a rape?

Once, after answering questions on rape on a radio show, one of your authors was called to the phone after the program. A woman's voice said,

"You were talking about me. You see, I am the product of rape. An intruder forced his way into my parents' house, tied up my father and, with him watching, raped my mother. I was conceived that night. Everyone advised an abortion. The local doctors and hospital were willing. My father, however, said, 'Even though not mine, that is a child and I will not allow it to be killed!' I don't know how many times that, as I lay secure in the loving arms of my husband, I have thanked God for my wonderful Christian father."

And so, does anyone win? Yes, the baby does.

What of incest?

Incest is intercourse by a father with his daughter, uncle with niece, etc. It usually involves a sick man, often a sick mother who frequently knows it's happening (even if not consciously admitting it), and an exploited child. Fortunately, pregnancy is not very common. When incest does occur, however, it is seldom reported and, when reported, is hard to prove.

Most pregnancies from incest have a very different dynamic than from rape and must be counseled in a very different manner.

Even strongly pro-abortion people, if they approach an incest case professionally, must be absolutely convinced before advising abortion, for abortion is not only an assault on the young mother, who may well be pregnant with a "love object," but it may completely fail to solve the original problem.

It is also unusual for wisdom to dictate anything but adoptive placement of the baby.

Love object?

When pregnancy does occur, it is often an attempt to end the relationship. In a twisted sort of way, however, the father is a love object. In one study, only 3 of 13 child-mothers had any negative feelings toward him.

H. Maisch, *Incest*,
New York: Stein & Day Publishers, 1972

In incest, is pregnancy common?

No. "Considering the prevalence of teenage pregnancies in general, incest treatment programs marvel at the low incidence of pregnancy from incest." Several reports agree at 1% or less.

G. Maloof, "The Consequences of Incest," *The Psychological Aspects of Abortion*, University Publications of Amer., 1979, p. 74

How does the incest victim feel about being pregnant?

For her, it is a way to stop the incest, a way to unite mother and daughter, a way to get out of the house. Most incestuous pregnancies, if not pressured, will not get abortions.

"As socially inappropriate as incest and incestuous pregnancies are, their harmful effects depend largely upon the reaction of others."

G. Maloof, "The Consequences of Incest," *The Psychological Aspects of Abortion*, University Publications of Amer., 1979, p. 100

A recent book out of the Elliot Institute has added greatly to our knowledge of rape and incest victims. It reports the testimonies of 192 women, pregnant from rape or incest, and 55 children so conceived. Ninety-four percent of the rape victims and 100% of the incest victims said abortion was not a good option.

Of those who carried to term, none regretted doing it. Editor David Reardon summarizes that there is no documented evidence that abortion ever benefits such a victim. There is documented evidence that abortion for rape or incest victims actually makes their problems worse.

Victims & Victors, D. Reardon, J. Makimaa & A. Sobie, Acorn Books, 2000

CHAPTER 31

IMPOSE MORALITY?

"The old law permitted abortion to save one life when two would otherwise die. The new law permits abortion to take one life when two would otherwise live."

Herbert Ratner, M.D.

Abortion was known and practiced in the world of Greece and Rome into which Christianity came. Judaism, having developed a high respect for the family, for women, and for individual life, had condemned abortion but found certain exceptions to it. The Christian message brought a further dignity to the concept of the individual person and the value of life. The idea of an individual, animate, immortal soul given by God to every human person, and hopefully, returning to him for eternity, was a powerful concept which transformed the Roman Empire within two centuries. The value of the unborn person became associated closely with a similar value granted to the born person, and as Christian beliefs crystallized in writing and tradition, condemnation of abortion came to be "an almost absolute value," as Professor John T. Noonan of the University of California at Berkley says in his book.

J. Noonan, *The Morality of Abortion,*
Harvard University Press, 1970, ch.1

By the time the curtain of the barbarian invasions rang down on the glory of Rome, the Christian teaching had codified itself into an extremely firm and certain moral opinion. Abortion was condemned. There was no question about Christian belief.

Does the New Testament oppose abortion? How and where?

The most cogent look at this is through the clinical history of "Mary's Pregnancy" and the Gospel's story.
"Mary's Pregnancy," Hayes Pub. Co., pamphlet, 1989, $23.00/100

What was Thomas Aquinas' opinion 700 years later?

Thomas totally condemned abortion for any and all reasons.

Aquinas did question when the soul was created. He spoke of the then-current scientific conviction that a male child was not fully enough developed to be judged human (and therefore to have a soul) until forty days, and that the female fetus could not be judged fully human until eighty days. This obviously says something about scientific knowledge of that age. Aquinas was reflecting a theological and scientific judgment that mirrored the most accurate scientific information of his time. When, to the most exact instrument available — the unaided human eye — the unborn child looked like a child and the individual's sex could be determined, he or she was deemed dignified and developed enough to be the possessor of an immortal soul, and so Aquinas made his conclusions.

Since that time we have progressed to electron microscopes, ultrasonic stethoscopes, and Realtime ultrasonic movies, and increasingly sophisticated knowledge of chromosomes and genes. We now must make judgments in the light of our new and more accurate biological knowledge. Aquinas' conclusions were the best that could be expected in his day. While not applicable today, they are of historical significance. Had men of his time had today's knowledge of embryonic and fetal development, their conclusions would have been different.

How does religious belief influence the abortion issue then?

Belief in God, in our creation by Him, in His authorship of life, of His Commandments and His justice, and in our brotherhood and sisterhood with the unborn is a powerful motivation leading believers to work for the protection of the unborn. The bottom line is that our religious faith *motivates* us. It can never be the sole legal justification for seeking laws to protect the unborn, the handicapped, and the elderly.

What right has any religious body to impose its morality upon a woman?

If this were a sectarian religious belief, there would be justice to such a complaint. In fact, this is not a religious question except in the broad sense of equal rights, dignity, and justice for all.

If any religious philosophy has been imposed upon a nation, it is Secular Humanism. The U.S. Supreme Court has defined Humanism as a religion. The officer corps of the pro-abortion movement is almost entirely made up of secular humanists who have imposed their beliefs upon our nation.

I have the right to swing my fist, but that right stops at your nose. A woman has certain (not total) rights to her own body, but not over another living human's body just because he or she still happens to live inside her.

The Ten Commandments forbade murder and stealing. So do the laws of every civilized nation. Do those laws impose religious morality? Hardly!

This is a civil rights issue. It is a question of whether an entire class of living humans shall be deprived of their basic right to life on the basis of age and place of residence.

Perhaps the question should be turned around:

**What Right Does a Mother and Her Abortionist Have
to Impose Their Morality
Upon Her Unborn Child . . . Fatally?**

CHAPTER 32

UNWANTED

*Since when does anyone's right to live
depend upon
someone else wanting them?*

Prior to the legalization of abortion in most developed countries, it was widely claimed that unwanted pregnancies resulted in a significant number of unwanted children, some of whom were subjects of child abuse. Legalization of abortion was held up as a panacea for this. It would reduce unwanted pregnancies and lower the incidence of child abuse. Planned Parenthood was a leader here, coining the familiar slogan, "Every Child a Wanted Child."

Shouldn't every child be wanted?

At first glance, yes! "Every Child a Wanted Child" is a great slogan. Who can argue? That isn't the disagreement. It is how to achieve such a goal.

We agree that every child should be wanted. A world with only wanted children would be an idyllic place in which to live. No one could quarrel with that as an idealistic goal. Wouldn't it also be a wonderful world if there were no unwanted wives by husbands, no aging parents unwanted by their children, no unwanted Jews, blacks, Catholics, Chicanos, or ever again a person who, at one time or place, finds himself or herself unwanted or persecuted. Let's all try to achieve this, but also remember that people have clay feet and, sadly, the unwanted will probably always be with us.

A second thought: Women resent that the value of a woman is sometimes determined by whether a man wants her. Yet radical feminists insist that the value of an unborn boy or girl is to be determined by whether a woman wants him or her.

To use *being wanted* by someone as a measure of whether a human life is allowed to live is a frightening concept. Its converse logically awaits us — that the unwanted can be eliminated. Don't forget, Hitler's Germany was ideal for wanted Aryans.

Since when does anyone's right to live depend upon someone else wanting them?

"Every Child a Wanted Child" should be completed with "and if not wanted, kill!" for that is exactly what that Planned Parenthood slogan means. To thus complete the sentence removes the mask from this misleading slogan and reveals it for the monstrous evil that it is.

That certainly makes it sound different!

Yes, and it is of crucial importance that every time we hear that phrase, we should add Planned Parenthood's solution, "and if not wanted, kill!"

Do parents kill teenagers when they are not wanted, or Uncle Joe after his stroke, or Mom, now that she is such a burden? You say no?

Do we give the mother the legal right to kill the two-year-old daughter who is a burden to her? No! Then why and how can we give her the legal right to kill the two-month-old daughter living inside her who is a burden to her?

The U.S. Supreme Court and the governments in many other nations have, for the first time in modern history, granted to one citizen (the mother) the absolute legal right to kill another, if that first person does not want them!

Think of the logic of the inevitable extension of such a freedom to kill. We could solve poverty by killing unwanted poor people, or religious or political groups, or those too old, too burdensome, and on and on . . .

OK, the ethic is horrible, but unwanted pregnancies do result in unwanted children, don't they?

No, not in any greater percentage than wanted pregnancies.

Think of your own pregnancies. Was each planned, or was this or that one a surprise? Were you really happy each time, in the first month or two? Be honest. In the first few weeks or months, were all of your pregnancies really "wanted"?

But now look at your children. Are you glad you have them? Would you give any back — have any of them killed?

You've changed your mind, haven't you? For almost all of you, a pregnancy that was truly unwanted has resulted in a dearly loved and wanted son or daughter.

If we permit abortion for an unwanted pregnancy, we will be destroying vast numbers of children who, by the time of their birth, and through their childhood, would have been very dearly wanted and deeply loved children indeed. If the judgment of being wanted at an early stage of pregnancy were a final judgment, and abortions were permitted freely, a high percentage of everyone reading this book would never have been born.

How many unwanted pregnancies are there?

Some claims are clearly ridiculous. *TIME* Magazine claimed there were at least six million unwanted pregnancies in the U.S. each year.

TIME, Feb. 26, 1990, p. 94

In that year there were 4 million births, about 1.6 million abortions, plus about 400,000 miscarriages. According to *TIME's* claim, *every* pregnancy that year was unwanted.

Are there any scientific studies?

Not many recent ones because now abortion is legal in most developed nations, which are the ones that do such studies.

Back in the '50s and '60s, there were a good dozen well done studies which were reported in detail in your author's editions of *Handbook on Abortion* in the '70s. All of these presumed the negative effects claimed above. They matched groups of pregnant women . . . (1) who wanted abortions, couldn't get them and went on to deliver . . . and (2) women pleased with wanted pregnancies. These investigators studied the resultant children and compared them. Without exception, they found little difference in love, care and wantedness and of neglect and lack of care in the groups that were compared.

Give a few examples.

Dr. Ferriera found no relationship between unplanned pregnancies and newborn deviant behavior. In fact, there were more deviant babies of mothers who had planned their pregnancy than those who had not.

A. J. Ferriera, "The Pregnant Woman's Emotional Attitude and Its Reflection in the Newborn." *Amer. Jour. Orthopsychiatry,* vol. 30, 1960, p. 553

"There is a contention that unwanted conceptions tend to have undesirable effects . . . the direct evidence for such a relationship is almost completely lacking, except for a few fragments of retrospective evidence. It was the hope of this article to find more convincing systematic research evidence and to give some idea of the amount of relationship between unwanted conception and undesired effect on children. This hope has been disappointed."

E. Pohlman, "Unwanted Conception, Research on
Undesirable Consequences," *Eugenics Quarterly*,
vol. 14, 1967, p. 143

"It is clear that mothers who initially believed their pregnancy to be 'the worst thing that ever happened to them' came to feel about the same degree of affection for their children as the mothers who were initially 'ecstatic' about the pregnancy.

"Most women who were most regretful of the pregnancy now claim they would have the child again, if given the opportunity, [whereas] one of every six mothers who were initially pleased with pregnancy would choose not to have the child again.

"[They conclude] . . . initial feelings about pregnancy are predictive of how a mother will eventually feel about her child to only a very limited degree."

P. Cameron et al., "How Much do Mothers Love Their Children,"
Rocky Mt. Psychological Assn., May 12, 1972

Others have conclusively demonstrated a spontaneous change from prepartum rejection to postpartum acceptance of their children by a group of mothers.

M. Zemlich & R. Watson, "Attitudes of Acceptance and
Rejection During and After Pregnancy,"
Amer. Jour. Orthopsychiatry, vol. 23, 1953, p. 570

What of other countries?

• Japan has had abortion-on-demand for five decades. It is used there as a method of birth control, but "cases of infanticide have been increasing so much that social workers have made appeals to Japanese mothers in newspapers and on television not to kill their babies."

The Sunday Times, June 23, 1974

• In England, the Working Party of the Royal College of Obstetricians and Gynecologists stated that the vast majority of unplanned pregnancies become wanted children.

• Aberdeen, Scotland is a unique city because, through an unusual law, it has had open abortion for 20 years in a nation that has had legal abortion only one-third as long. If the availability of abortion did reduce unwanted children, it should have the best record in Britain. In fact, it has the worst record, with 10.2 per 1,000 abandoned, abused, and uncared for children being supported by public agencies — compared with the national average of 6.6.

Annual Report, Chief Medical Health Officer,
Aberdeen, Scotland, 1972

Don't some studies prove the opposite?

No! In the entire world literature on this subject, there are only two studies that attempt to show that there is a negative effect on the children who had been "unwanted pregnancies." Both have been conclusively shown to be invalid.

The first study, from Sweden, concluded that such a child "runs a risk of having to surmount greater mental and social handicaps than its peers . . ."

Forssman & Thuwe, "One Hundred and Twenty Children Born after
Application for Therapeutic Abortion Refused,"
Acta Psychiatrica Scandinavica, vol. 42, 1966, pp. 71-88

Professor Paul Cameron has clearly shown that an evaluation of the mothers in this study showed sufficient differences with the control group so that the authors' conclusions were a "mis-analysis," invalid, and could have been predicted from these differences alone, whether the pregnancy was wanted or not. There were, incidentally, little differences, anyway, between the children in the study and the control.

P. Cameron, "The Swedish 'Children Born to Women Denied
Abortion' Study: A Radical Criticism," Psychological Reports,
vol. 39, 1976, pp. 391-394

The second study concluded that "Compulsory child-bearing has varied and sometimes unfavorable consequences for the subsequent life of the child."

Dytrych et al., "Children Born to Women Denied Abortion,"
Family Planning Perspectives, vol. 7, no. 4, July-Aug. 1975

Professor Samuel Nigro, child psychiatrist at Case Western Reserve University, has published a scathing commentary on this study. He points to the fact that the data found and published in the article "renders the conclusions untenable." He details the "striking differences in the families of the two groups of children," (the study group having more unstable mothers and fathers than the control group), as the obvious cause for the differences in the children.

"The conclusions appear to be contrived by an abuse of scientific method deplorable to the point of discrediting the researchers, of discrediting the Institute which sponsored the research, and of questioning the use of public funds for a publication which takes such license with scientific data."

S. Nigro, University Hospitals of Cleveland, Open Letter to
Family Planning Perspectives, March 10, 1976

In 1989, Henry David reported on the follow up to the above studies and detailed certain less than catastrophic psychosocial problems of children born after unwanted pregnancies.

Report to American Psychological Assn. Meeting,
"Born Unwanted -Developmental Effects of Denied Abortion,"
H. David, et al., Springer Co. 1988

In another critique, Dr. Nigro has written a devastating critique of David's study. He cites "flawed, tendentious, sorry science. It is advocacy." Unwanted pregnancy is held up as a reason to kill before birth. Dr. Nigro then details the "preselection bias," among other problems in the study. Finally he notes that, even if one accepts everything Dr. David claims, by any measurement, the psychosocial maladjustment of these children is minor (e.g., none have raped, robbed, or assaulted anyone). Dr. Nigro asks, "Is the record of these children so socially destructive as to justify their deaths to prevent their existence?"

Review, S. Nigro, M.D., Case Western Reserve,
U. of Cleveland, Sept. 1988

But don't many unwanted pregnancies become battered children?

• Not so. The landmark study on this was done at the University of Southern California. Professor Edward Lenoski studied 674 consecutive battered children who were brought to the in- and out-patient departments of that medical center. He was the first to go to the parents and study to what extent they wanted and planned the pregnancy. To his surprise, he found that 91% were planned and wanted, compared to 63% for the control groups nationally. Further, the mothers had began wearing, on the average, pregnancy clothes at 114 days compared to 171 days in the control, and the fathers named the boys after themselves 24% of the time compared to 4% for the control groups.

E. Lenoski, *Heartbeat*, vol. 3, no. 4, Dec. 1980

• Both parents (or parent figures) lived in 80% of the homes. Two-thirds of the mothers were "housewives" and presumably were at home. Almost all mothers were in the 20-30 age group, and fathers were in the 20-35 age bracket. No special social, racial, or economic class predominated.

Francis, "Child Abuse, A Nationwide Study,"
Amer. Humane Assn. & Child Welfare League, 1963

• The parents commonly ". . . grew up in a hostile environment, and were themselves abused. When the children fail to satisfy their [unrealistic, neurotic expectations of perfection] emotional needs, the parents react with the same violence they experienced as children."

J. Walsh, IL Dept. of Child and Family Services
Newsweek, July 24, 1972

Not much has changed since these earlier investigations. There is much that we still do not know about the sick psychology that leads to child abuse. One thing does stand out, however: *Prenatally, these were not unwanted pregnancies, they were super-wanted pregnancies.*

What if a mother really doesn't want the baby?

There are millions of outstretched arms aching to adopt and love a baby. Her answer is to place the baby in a secure, loving, adoptive home.

I've been told that aborting unwanted babies would leave more wanted ones and, therefore, there would be less child abuse.

Exactly the opposite has happened. In New York City during the '60s, the number of abused children had averaged about 5,000 cases a year. Abortion was legalized in 1970. By 1975, over 25,000 cases were reported.

The figures for the entire U.S. are:

Date	Total Number
1973	167,000
1979	711,142
1993	1,057,255
1996	1,220,000

U.S. Dept. H.H.S., Nat. Center of Child Abuse,
Child Maltreatment

A different department, HHS, listed 879,000 in 2000.

The Adm. For Children and Families, 4-19-2002

Canada's statistics show the same:

Year	Abortions	Child Abuse
1971	16,172	422
1978	38,782	1,762
1994	104,403	30,366*

Child Welfare Branch, Ministry of Human Resource, Ontario, Canada

These are the totals reported from all provinces except PEI and includes physical, sexual, and emotional abuse. Note that provinces vary in definition of "child abuse" and reporting requirements.

Ohio reported 27,248 cases in 1981 and 65,965 in 1985, a 142% increase according to a survey by the U.S. House of Representatives Select Committee on Children, Families and Youth for the largest state increase. The same survey reported over a 55% increase nationwide from 1981 to 1985.

Assoc. Press, March 3, 1987.

Dr. Phillip Ney, Professor of Psychiatry at the University of Christ Church, New Zealand, while still at the University of British Columbia (he is currently at the University of Calgary), published a widely read study of this. His analysis clearly pointed to the fact that abortion (and its acceptance of the violence of killing the unborn) lowered a parent's psychic resistance to violence and abuse of the born.

P. Ney, "Relationship Between Abortion & Child Abuse,"
Canada Jour. Psychiatry, vol. 24, 1979, pp. 610-620

A nation and its people will ultimately be judged not by the fact that there are unwanted ones among them, but by what is done for them.

Are They Cared For?
or
Are They Killed?

CHAPTER 33

THE WEST IS DYING

Overpopulation is largely a hoax

*To determine whether a nation is growing or dying,
we must examine three factors:
birth rate ... death rate ... immigration.*

Birth Rate: This is the ultimate determinant. In a developed nation, the average woman must bear 2.1 children (Mean Fertility Rate) in order to maintain a level population.

In an undeveloped nation the rate must be 2.3 or more because of higher infant and child mortality.

Death Rate: In recent years, fewer people have died than have been born in most countries because the average age of life expectancy has been extended. Everyone will die, of course, but for now this has resulted in increases in population.

Nicholas Eberstadt, the Harvard expert, has summed this up. "World population is increasing, not because people are breeding like rabbits, but because they have stopped dying like flies."

Immigration and emigration: Many want to come into the U.S., Canada and most developed nations. Few want to move to Cuba, Libya, or Russia.

These dynamics explain why the total populations of the U.S., Canada and Australia (to pick three) are still growing, even though their birth rates, except the U.S., are below replacement level. The 2000 census reports the U.S. rate at 2.13

With a much higher percentage of their people aging, but still alive, most Western nations have rapidly aging populations. In the U.S., people born in 1970 had a life expectancy of 70 years. In 1993 it was 76 years. By 2050 it will be 82 years.

U.S. News & World Report, Aug. 14, 1995, P. 9.

With heavy immigration to fill the younger age slots, we see a progressive change in ethnicity, e.g., the U.S. is becoming more Hispanic — Germany, France, Italy, Greece, and Israel more Muslim.

In Italy, the birth rate is 1.2, the lowest in the world in countries keeping accurate records. In '93, there were 5,265 more Italians buried than were born. If this continues unchanged, within 100 years its population will shrink from 57 to 15 million, with half of those over 65 years old.

Italy Birth Rate . . ., *Boston Globe,* July 31, '94, p. 13
W. Montabono, "Italian Baby Boom Goes Bust," *Los Angles Times,*
June 24, '94, A1 & A6

Russia may have the lowest birth rate, routinely killing two in abortion for every one born in its non-Muslim areas. Add poor medical care, sky-high alcoholism, and poverty, life expectancy for men has dropped to 57 years. Each year Russia is burying about one million more people than are being born.

U.S. POPULATION IN MILLIONS

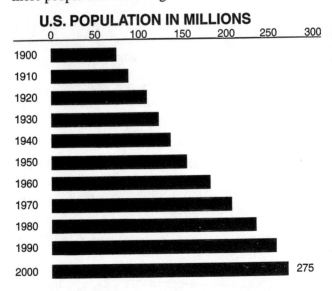

	0	50	100	150	200	250	300
2000							275

But notice the change in age groups

POPULATION BY AGE – 1980

25-44 Years	62.1
44-64 Years	43.8
Over 65 Years	24.5

There were four in the working years for each one retired. Now look ahead.

POPULATION BY AGE – 2020

25-44 Years	16.4*	82.4
44-64 Years		74.2
Over 65 Years		62.1

estimate of number of yet to be born

288

Then there will be only 2.5 in their working years to support each one retired.

The Western world, in the past half-century, has supported its senior and disabled citizens with tax funds on a scale previously unknown. But, unless there are enough taxpaying younger workers, there will be no way that such retirement and medical benefits can continue. Large numbers of young immigrants may modify the figures below.

	RETIRED	WORKERS SUPPORTING
1980	1	3.5
2000	1	3.0
2020	1	2.5
2040	1	1.5-2.0

Only one-and-a-half to two taxpayers to support every retired person? That's an impossible situation! What will happen?

Euthanasia!

Yes, that will be the answer. Today's "Every Child a Wanted Child" will become tomorrow's "Every Grandparent a Wanted Grandparent."

The above figures are from the U.S.A. If we were to examine other developed nations, we would find that, in Europe and elsewhere, with some variations, all reveal a similar pattern.

But hasn't there been a new baby boom in the U.S.?

Call it a mini-boom. Many thirtyish women have finally been having babies before their fertile years are gone. This has upped the U.S. birth rate from 1.8 to 2.13 where it leveled.

The continuing increase in U.S. population has been due to (1) older people not dying yet, (2) a substantial increase in immigration, and (3) a small increase in births to 4,058,814 in 2000.

CDC, Feb., 2002

In the face of this, the teen birth rate per year in the U.S. has dropped 26% since '91 to 45 per 1,000 girls.

HHS, CDC, 6-6-2002

Specifically, what of other developed countries?

With almost no exception, every one will face its major demographic problem of aging in years ahead, e.g., Germany, Austria, and Italy have had mean fertility rates at around 1.3. Japan seems to already be in trouble, burying more than are being born.

And underdeveloped nations?

These all started with very high birth rates. They are dropping rapidly, e.g., in the 1980s the following drop occurred in mean fertility rates.

Tunisia 5.0→4.1, India 5.3→3.9, South Korea 3.2→1.6, Mexico 4.8→3.8, Indonesia 4.1→3.0, Brazil 4.4→3.3.

In the '90s this drop continued and some, like Indonesia and Iran are new at ZPG (zero population growth).

But cities seem so overcrowded.

Over-concentration is a problem in many places, but, overall, the world is not overpopulated.

But what about enough food?

Back when Paul Ehrlich wrote *Population Bomb,* this was a real concern. Since then, world food production has grown much more rapidly than numbers of people, e.g., India now exports food.

For example, the International Rice Research Institute in October '94 announced a breakthrough in unveiling a new "super rice" capable of boosting world rice production by 25%, with a further boost in another decade of 25% more.

New York Times & Gannett, 10/24/94

"Today, India cannot only feed its own growing population but also is emerging as a major food exporter . . . India will have an advantage in any product that is harvested by hand."

Forbes Mag., May 23, 1994, p. 136

"New breeds of corn, developed to withstand droughts and acidic tropical soil, are being tested. The World Bank predicts that, within 10 years, corn production will increase 40%, rivaling the green revolution in Third World wheat and rice production."

J. Nesmith, "New Corn Strains May Feed Millions", *Des Moines Register,* June 24, 1994

The U.N. Predicts:
"A world population of 8 billion by 2030 will be better fed with more people having access to food . . . Growth in agriculture will continue to outstrip world population growth."

UN. Food and Agriculture Org. Report, "Agriculture Toward 2015/2030," July 27, 2000

World population rose from 3 billion in 1960 to 6.0 billion in 1999, but food production grew even faster, outstripping population growth by 20%. The result was a 60% drop in real prices for food commodities. This is the continuation of a trend in prices that started over 100 years ago. Along with this, the incident of outright famine has dropped ten-fold since the early 1960s, and caloric intake per person has risen 25% worldwide in the same period.

Far Eastern Economic Review, Nov. 16, 1995

China's food output per person has increased by more than 40% since 1979-81. The daily food supply now amounts to more than 2,700 calories per capita.

The food problems, and even starvation, which occurred in the past were the result of government policies which taxed farmers in order to subsidize industry, controlled and requisitioned output, drafted farmers to work on poorly planned government projects, restricted agricultural trade and shipping, and prevented farmers from acquiring the land and other resources needed to produce food. The government is gradually reforming these policies and food output is increasing greatly.

J. Kasun, "China: Not Enough Food or Space,"
Human Concern, Spring 1996, p. 3

But can this continue?

Sadly, the world's media seems obsessed with telling only scare stories and suppressing all the good news about food.

The definitive answer has been a report in 1994 entitled "How Much Land Can Ten Billion People Spare for Nature." This is a thoroughly documented, 63-page analysis. It was written by a consortium of 30 major national agricultural societies in the U.S. It was published with the cooperation of the Rockefeller Foundation.

In essence, it details how, even with the growth of the earth's population to 10 billion people, better use of currently farmed land can still feed everyone, while — get this — at the same time returning as much as 10% of current crop land to nature rather than plowing under new virgin areas.

Council for Agriculture Science & Technology,
"How Much Land Can Ten Billion People Spare for Nature,"
$15.00, 4420 Lincoln Way, Ames, Iowa 50014.

But doesn't the U.S. use up a high percentage of the world's natural resources?

It is a fact that there are more such resources available today than there were a decade or two ago. In America one farmer feeds 99 other people. In some countries, one farmer cannot even feed his own family. What is our solution? Should we encourage American farmers and industrial workers to kill their own preborn children or should we stay strong, have children, and help to teach those other farmers and workers to be more productive?

The U.S. now uses less than half the land for farming that it did in the 1920s, even though there are now nearly 200 million more mouths to feed.

Washington Times, editorial, 7-1-2001

The U.S. pollutes also?

Actually, the more developed a free nation becomes, the less it pollutes. A good contrast is the U.S. compared to the USSR's profligate destruction of, and pollution of, its natural resources.

Note that there is less carbon dioxide in the air going into the Atlantic than there is in the air coming in from the Pacific Ocean. "North America is a high carbon sink."

P. Huba, "Saving the Environment from the Environmentalists," Forbes, Mar. 20, 2000, p. 112

How can a Third World country reduce its birth rate?

Coercive abortion and sterilization are short-term measures that cause untold human misery and really don't work well. Further, people resist these measures.

The only humane measures that have worked have been to raise that group's standard of living, to reduce infant and childhood mortality, and to raise expectation of (and provide opportunity for) education. If these changes are accomplished, people will then *voluntarily* limit the number of their children for two reasons: *(a)* they want more for each child, and *(b)* they can reasonably expect their children to survive to adulthood and be alive to care for them in their old age.

So, where is world population going?

"If current trends in declining fertility continue as they are now, the world population could peak at 7.5 billion in 2040. It will then drop by 120 million a year through 2050. After this, it will decline about 30% per generation.

U.N. Division, World Pop Estimates and Projections, 1998

• With this, the world will age progressively. Today, the world's median age is 27 years. In 2025, it will be 35. By 2050 it will be 43.5.

Ibid above

• The U.S. population will peak at about 300 million by 2030 before declining (immigration is the wild card).

• Europe and Japan are dying. Japan has a total fertility rate of 1.4. If this continues in the next century, its population will drop from 125 to 55 million. Europe is in a similar fix.

• Eighty-three countries are now below replacement fertility levels. These encompass 2.7 billion people, 44% of the world's total.

U.S. Census Bureau

• Given this birth dearth, in order to prevent a decline in the working age population, Japan will need 600,000 and Europe 4 million immigrants a year. These will be of other national origins. Will they opt for indefinite decline or ethnic transformation?

N. Eberstadt, "Underpop. The Real Global Problem,"

What about HIV? Will it influence this?

Yes, and its total impact is only beginning to be felt. This is a worldwide pandemic, but so far ⅔ of infections are in sub-Sahara Africa. In Botswana and Zimbabwe, one in four adults is infected. Zambia has over

400,000 AIDS orphans. Life expectancy in Malawi has cut from 51 to 37 years. AIDS is killing 2½ million each year and it's getting worse.

Worldwide, over 40 million are infected and 11 million have died. There are now 23 countries with over 5% of their "low risk" population (i.e., not drug users, etc.) are infected.

Current rapid increase in infection in Eastern Europe, India, Thailand, and elsewhere tell us that this scourge has only begun.

PART VII
ALTERNATIVES

Chapter

CHAPTER 34

WOMEN HELPING CENTERS

*There are more people in the pro-life
movement who give their time, efforts
and support to helping the women than
there are trying to stop the killing.*

I don't believe it.
It's true. In the U.S. there are almost 4,000 pregnancy
help centers compared to about 3,000 right-to-life
groups.

Are these those "fake clinics"?
This is a totally false charge by the abortion industry.
There are really three types:
1. The great majority of these centers are there to
   help the distressed pregnant woman. The help is
   confidential. She needs a place to live? They find
   it. She must drop out of school? They arrange an
   alternative school. She needs medical or legal
   help? They help her get it. A job? It's found.
   Counseling or just a loving shoulder to cry on? It's
   given. Clothes for her or her baby? They furnish it.

   These centers simply meet whatever her needs
   are in order to help her carry to term.

2. Madonna Houses: These are live-in homes while pregnant. Many allow her to return with or without her baby until she can leave and live on her own.
3. Post-Abortion Centers: The best known are PACE, Open Arms, Rachel, WEBA (Women Exploited by Abortion) and American Victims of Abortion. These vary from structured offices to more informal post-abortion counseling in other settings. This service is rapidly coming to be a regular part of the above pregnancy help centers nationwide.

How do I find such help?

Most commonly through a pro-life church or through your local Right to Life office. There are national directories also:

Heartbeat International
Attn: Margaret Hartshorn, Ph.D.
Suite 440
665 E. Dublin-Granville Road
Columbus, OH 43229
(614) 239-9433

and

International Life Services
Attn: Sr. Paula Vandegaer
2606 1/2 W. 8th Street
Los Angeles, CA 90057
(213) 382-2156

Who staffs these centers?

A typical center will employ one or two qualified social workers and have, in addition, 10 to 50 or more volunteers.

Further, about 98% of these workers will be female.

What is the sex ratio in the rest of the pro-life movement?

In Right to Life, women outnumber men by about

2 or 3 to one. Counting both halves, there are about 4 women to every one man, hardly the male-dominated, patriarchal movement that the media often holds it up to be.

And I thought most women were pro-abortion — all the feminists are.

Not so. Most women are pro-life and so were the early feminists: "I deplore the horrible crime of child murder. No matter what the motive, love of ease or a desire to save from suffering the unborn innocent — the woman is awfully guilty who commits the deed."

Susan B. Anthony, 1869

CHAPTER 35

ADOPTION

Adoption Not Abortion

This is a slogan that produces quiet fury in pro-abortion activists, for each adoption is a baby saved and represents a failure to the pro-abortion industry.

Few in the general public realize it but Planned Parenthood "counselors" and the rest of the pro-abortion, anti-child activists have for 3 decades been waging a quiet but successful war against adoption. This is evident in the pregnant girl who would rather have her baby killed than the alternative of "a fate worse than death" (adoption).

How many babies are adopted?
Two percent of non-marital births are placed for adoption. In the U.S. this is about 50,000 non-related adoptions a year compared to 1,400,000 babies aborted.

Why do so few mothers place their babies?
In society, customs change. Right now it is the "in" thing to keep your baby. Part of the reason for this has been the overemphasis on women's "rights" (as in

abortion) over the baby's rights, and the concept of the mother's "ownership," which the *Roe v. Wade* Supreme Court decision taught our nation. Add to this the above insidious influence, the almost condemnation of, and the "poor mouthing" of adoption by many sex educators, Planned Parenthood people, social workers and others.

How many couples are waiting?

There are about two million couples waiting. Furthermore, each of these couples would want two or three, if available. Many will take hard-to-place children with special needs.

Bachrach et al., "On the Path to Adoption"

"When the time comes, as it surely will, when we face that awesome moment, the final judgment, I've often thought, as Fulton Sheen wrote, that it is a terrible moment of loneliness. You have no advocates, you are there alone standing before God — and a terror will rip your soul like nothing you can imagine. But I really think that those in the pro-life movement will not be alone. I think there'll be a chorus of voices that have never been heard in this world but are heard beautifully and clearly in the next world — and they will plead for everyone who has been in this movement. They will say to God, 'Spare him, because he loved us,' — and God will look at you and say not, 'Did you succeed?' but 'Did you try?'"

Congressman Henry Hyde

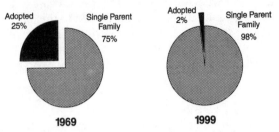

Proportion of Unwed Births Adopted

1969
Adopted 25%
Single Parent Family 75%

1999
Adopted 2%
Single Parent Family 98%

Source: *Abortion Factbook III*, 1999, Nat. Council for Adoption

What does "special needs" mean?

- Those with handicaps. There is a long waiting list for Down's Syndrome babies. There is a national organization of parents of Spina Bifida babies. At this writing, over 100 couples are on the waiting list to adopt such a baby, no matter how severe their problem.
- AIDS babies are a special group. These children need care, and almost all will die. Still, there are homes for them.
- Those of a different race: see discussion below.
- Older children:

All infants can be placed if they are released and if laws and agencies place no barriers. Once a child has been through three foster homes, has been neglected or even abused before being relinquished (or removed by the court), and/or is 6-8-10 years old, there are few homes that want him/her or can even manage the child. Over half of the available, but unadopted, babies in the U.S. are black and over age 5.

What's with minority race babies?

Actually, there are enough couples wanting these babies, but, sadly, they frequently aren't adopted. Reasons include unwillingness of the natural mother to release

302

the child, unrealistically high standards for minority parents to meet in order to qualify, and unwillingness of agencies to allow white parents to adopt them.

E. Lee, "White Couples' Obstacles to Adopt Nonwhites," *Wall Street Journal*, Feb. 27, 1987

Black people make up 12% of the population in the U.S., but 42% of the children in foster care are black. There are 450,000 in foster care, of whom 42% (or 189,000) are black. In an industrialized state, about two-thirds of children awaiting adoption are black, e.g., in Cincinnati 84 of 87 such children were black.

Cincinnati Enquirer, Gregg, May 9, 1996

There is a problem with agencies?

Yes — this was really brought to the nation's attention in the mid-'80s by a series of articles in the *Wall Street Journal* which detailed that if a baby is placed for adoption at birth, the social agency gets X number of dollars. For every child in foster care for a year, the agency gets 3X or 4X dollars. The charge has been made that minority race babies are not being placed at birth because the agency needs the additional money it gets for foster care.

"The system has evolved into an industry, with perverse incentives for social agencies to maintain children in the system because of the increased revenue. Some 70% of the money for foster care is spent for administrative overhead and services. What we have done, according to the National Council of Family and Juvenile Court Judges is 'replace parental neglect with governmental neglect.'"

R. Woodson, "Bureaucratic Barriers to Black Adoption," *Wall Street Journal*, June 26, 1984, p. 34

Then social workers are the problem?

Certainly not most, but we must point out that the National Association of Black Social Workers has condemned transracial adoption. Several decades ago this was a sincere conviction, as many feared a black child in a white family could not adjust. A number of studies, however, have disproved this.

"Transracial adoption has been successful," say Drs. Simon and Alsteen. "On any variable we can discuss about quality of family life, it is no different with these kids ... they'll probably marry non-white, but live in a racially-mixed neighborhood."

"Identity and Commitment, Transracial Adoptees and Their Families," *Praeger Pub., 1986,* from Nat'l Adoption Report, May 1987

"The evidence from the empirical studies indicates uniformly that transracial adoptees do as well on measures of psychological and social adjustment as black children raised inracially in relatively similar socio-economic circumstances. The evidence also indicates that transracial adoptees develop comparably strong senses of black identity. They see themselves as black and they think well of blackness. The difference is that they feel more comfortable with the white community than blacks raised inracially. This evidence provides no basis for concluding that there are inherent costs in transracial placement from the children's viewpoint.

"By contrast, the evidence from the empirical studies, together with professional opinion over the decades and our common sense, indicate that the placement delays of months and years that result from our current policies impose very serious costs on children. Children need permanency in their primary parenting relationships. They may be destroyed by delays when those delays involve, as they so often do, abuse or neglect in inadequate foster care or institutional situations. They will likely be hurt by delays in even the best of foster care situations, whether they develop powerful bonds with parents they must then lose, or they live their early years without experiencing the kind of bonding that is generally thought crucial to healthy development."

"The Politics of Race Matching in Adoption"
E. Bartholet, *Univ. of PA Law Review,*
Vol. 139, No. 5, May 1991

The whole transracial question came to a head in 1996 when the U.S. Congress removed any limits on transracial adoptions. This was tested in the courts and confirmed in a Cincinnati case in 2002.

Sadly, in many areas, social workers have silently or otherwise ignored or deified this new law and continued to "warehouse" black children.

Aside from this race problem, I've heard that adopted children have more problems than biological children.

This has been thoroughly debunked by Marquis and Detweiler. On seven separate measures, adopted persons rated their parents as superior as compared to their non-adopted peers.

"There is not a shred of evidence that indicates any of the previously reported negative characteristics of dependency, fearfulness, tenseness, hostility, loneliness, insecurity, abnormality, inferiority, poor self-image, or lack of confidence."

If different, the adopted are more positive and better adjusted.

Marquis & Detweiler, J. Personality and Social Psychology,
abstract in Nat'l Adoption Report, May 1985

Overall, I've heard that adopted children need more psychiatric care, and generally are in more trouble and are less well adjusted than children in biologic homes.

The studies reporting such problems almost always were comparing apples with oranges and are therefore invalid. Here's why.

Biologic children go home with parents from the

hospital, bond promptly, and, from birth, are reared by two (one) parents.

Adopted children often stay in institutions, in foster care, or in turbulent situations prior to adoption. Their future social and emotional instability is not due to adoption; it's due to their environment prior to adoption.

The only valid comparison is between biological infants and adopted infants, both of whom went from the hospital to the home of their forever parents.

In these cases, adopted children fare better. When compared with those adopted later, born outside of marriage and raised by the single mother, or raised in an intact family, children who are adopted in infancy:
- Repeat grades less often than any other group;
- See mental health professionals less than all other groups, except children of intact families;
- Have better health status than all other groups;
- Have a better standing in their school classes than all other groups, except children raised in intact families; and
- Have fewer behavior problems than all other groups, except children raised in intact families.

And so do their birth mothers. Significantly, teenage mothers who choose adoption also do better than mothers who choose to be single parents.
- They have higher educational aspirations, are more likely to finish school, and less likely to live in poverty and receive public assistance than mothers who keep their children.

Bachrach, Stolley, and London, "Relinquishment of Premarital Births"

- They delay marriage longer and are more likely to marry eventually.
- They are more likely to be employed 12 months after the birth and less likely to repeat out-of-wedlock pregnancy.
- They are no more likely to suffer negative psycho-

logical consequences, such as depression, than are
mothers who rear children as single parents.

S. McLaughlin et al., "Do Adolescents Who Relinquish . . .
Better or Worse . . . Raise Them?," *Fam. Plan. Persp.,* Jan. 1988

All the goals of liberal government programs, like
job training, supplemental education, and family planning, are attained with greater ease, and at lower cost,
through adoption.

P. Fagan, Liberal Welfare Programs, "Data . . . Teen Mothers,"
Heritage Found., #1031, Mar. 31, 1995

Wasn't part of the problem prolonged foster care?

Yes! You're right. Most foster care is certainly better
than either institutional care or some of the inadequate
homes they come from, and we warmly thank those
generous people who offer their foster-love to these
children.

But — and a big but — it is nowhere near as good as
one pair of loving adoptive parents from birth. One
constant and perhaps unsolvable problem is the reluctance of the courts to take children away from mothers
who are clearly unsuitable. Judges quickly place them
in foster care, but they seldom legally terminate the
birth-mother's "rights" and allow adoption.

J. Kwitng, "Nobody's Kids,"
Wall Street Journal, Sept. 6, 1978, p. 1

The problem with not terminating a neglecting or
abusive parent's rights is an overemphasis on "family
preservation." This well-meaning goal too often has
sent children back to an abusive parent and delayed or
prevented adoption.

So the earlier the placement the better?

From the child's standpoint, yes. The ideal is to place
the baby in adoptive arms directly from the hospital.

In recent years we've learned a lot about early bonding between parents and child. The father in the delivery

room, the baby "rooming in" with the mother, immediate breast feeding, etc., are all part of creating that very special and truly unbreakable emotional tie between this tiny one and her parents.

In adoption, the infant, of necessity, must lose those precious early hours and days with her new parents. That generous birth-mother must have a few days to make her final decision. But then what is best for the baby?

Without a shade of doubt, that infant *must be* in his or her adoptive parents' arms as early as possible. Some irreplaceable early bonding is gone, but more slips away every day, every week. Whenever possible, the baby must go directly from the hospital into those new parents' arms.

This is especially true for a handicapped infant. This child has even more need for immediate adoption. What if birth-parents have a handicapped baby? Do they give him back? Of course not. What of a handicapped child to be adopted? Should we keep him in an institution until all medical questions are answered? Or in foster care? Then maybe no couple will want him. How cruel! He needs loving parents from the beginning, and probably even more than a "normal" child.

Please, these infants with handicaps should be adopted directly from the hospital. There are parents who will take them. Once he is "their baby," they will rarely give him back.

Is money a problem?

Yes, many more couples would adopt if they could afford it. The cost of delivering a baby is a tax deductible medical expense — why not the cost of adoption?

The U.S. Congress took a solid step forward in 2001 in giving a $10,000 tax credit to adoptive couples.

What of public or private adoptions?

We need them both. In general, if an agency does most

things right (i.e., early placement, etc.), we believe that there is consistently better parent screening, better records, better follow-up, etc. Private adoptions can be, and often are, all of these good things too, but not always. We believe that both are necessary but that both need improvement and the elimination of abuses.

What of open adoption?

With few exceptions, pro-lifers have little or no objection to this new trend.

What of open records?

This is different. Today there are groups aggressively seeking to pass laws to unilaterally and retroactively open previously sealed records. Increasingly, pro-life people regard such search groups as pro-abortion and anti-adoption and have opposed such efforts. A high percentage of young mothers, in years past, placed their babies in adoptive homes only because the law guaranteed a seal of confidentiality on that adoption. Today, many of these generous women are terrified that this confidentiality will be stripped away. The fair and compassionate answer is a mutual consent registry.

What is a mutual consent registry?

It is the answer to the problems discussed above. Under it, an adopted child over 21 years of age may enter his or her name in a state registry indicating that he or she seeks a reunion. Birth-mothers may also register and request the same. If there is a match, a meeting is arranged. Unless both request it, however, the previous seal of confidentiality is preserved.

One problem in the states where these exist is that there has been no public educational effort to publicize such registries, so very few people know about them.

What if the right to confidentiality is taken away?

This has happened in England and in Australia.

In both countries, adoptions have declined sharply. Your authors have been told that "adoption, as we knew it, no longer exists. What we have now is de facto permanent foster care. . . . If a girl wants permanent confidentiality, the only way to get it is to abort, and that is exactly what they do."

CHAPTER 36

CONTRACEPTION

*Contraception can be divided
into permanent and temporary.*

What is permanent contraception?

The only absolutely guaranteed, permanent contraception is castration. That means removal of the testicles or of the ovaries. Then fertilization is impossible.

Sterilization is usually considered permanent contraception. Sterilization, commonly, is the cutting or ligating of the vas deferens (sperm tubes) in the man and of the fallopian tubes in the woman. This is not absolute and forever, as a small percentage of pregnancies occurs because of recanalization.

About 100,000 women are sterilized each year in the U.S. In a 10-year study of 10,000 women, there was a "failure" (i.e., a pregnancy) in one of fifty. One-third of these pregnancies were in the tube.

J. Trussell, Sterilization Less Effective,
Am. J. Ob/Gyn, May '96

A 1.8% pregnancy rate was observed with one-third in the Fallopian tube in another study.

What types of contraception are temporary?

All of the other known types. These can be divided into mechanical, which includes condoms, diaphragms, Quinacrine, and intra-uterine devices IUD), and chemical contraceptives, which include those taken internally and those applied externally.

Are drugs like RU 486, methotrexate and prostaglandin contraceptives?

No, they are not. They do not prevent fertilization. They do cause very early abortions. See chapter on early abortions for details.

How effective are contraceptives in preventing pregnancy?

There are two measurements — method effectiveness and user effectiveness. Method effectiveness measures the number of times pregnancy occurs when the method is used exactly the way it is supposed to be used. An example of this would be to take a contraceptive pill, without fail, every single day for the 20 days required in a particular month. If, in spite of this, she gets pregnant, that would be a method failure.

Let's take a woman, however, who forgets to take one or perhaps two pills during the month and then gets pregnant. This would be an example of user effectiveness. Dr. Robert Hatcher of Emery University has created tables showing the approximate number of pregnancies during their first year of use. He gives two rates: one for the method when "used correctly and consistently," and the other as the "average U.S. experience among 100 women who wanted no more children." One group used the method exactly correctly every single time in the year. The other group was the more realistic actual "average U.S. experience." There was a significant difference.

C. Kippley, *The Art of Natural Family Planning,*
Couple to Couple League, 1985, p. 18

But how often do contraceptives fail?

Planned Parenthood's Alan Guttmacher Institute reported on 10,000 women getting abortions. Of these, 57.5% said they were using a contraceptive the month they became pregnant. In a similar study in 1987, the figure was 51.3%. The highest percent was in teenagers.

S. Henshaw, Fam. Plan. Perspect.
Vol. 28, No. 4, July/Aug. 1996

Similar findings were reported by the British Pregnancy Advisory Service. Thirty-eight percent of women with unwanted pregnancies had relied on condoms and 17% were on contraceptive pills.

BPAS, July 1999

Why higher in teenage use?

Kippley's results (above) are from experienced married couples in the privacy of their own bedrooms. It is generally recognized that use by unmarried teenagers is use by amateurs in less than private circumstances and carries a surprise pregnancy rate across the board of twice that of married couples. So the Planned Parenthood results are no surprise.

According to this, condoms have a high failure rate for pregnancy. How effective are condoms in preventing AIDS?

Actually, they are not very effective at all. Undoubtedly because a condom retains the bulk of the discharge of semen, the rate is cut down. To become infected with any disease, two things are relevant in terms of the offending, invasive agent. One is the presence of some of those viruses, or germs, themselves. The other is the quantity of that agent entering the body. If there are only a few bugs, the average human will kill them off. If there's a very heavy dose, the chance for an infection succeeding is greater. Therefore, by cutting down on the volume of semen, a condom certainly reduces the chance for AIDS. But AIDS viruses do get through the condom.

Why is this?

Sperm have a diameter of 50 microns. Naturally occurring holes in the wall of a latex condom have a diameter of 1.0 microns. The HIV retrovirus which causes AIDS has a diameter of 0.1 microns. In effect, this would be comparing perhaps an ant crawling on a basketball. AIDS viruses swim freely through the holes in the condom. That is a fact that should be widely publicized.

C.M. Roland, Editor, *Rubber Chemistry & Technology,*
Washington Times, 4/22/92

Sperm – about 50 microns in size

Standard latex holes (voids) – 5 microns in size, or 10 times smaller than sperm

AIDS virus – 0.1 microns in size, smaller by a factor of 50 than the standard holes (voids) in latex rubber

Furthermore, a woman can only become pregnant for 2 to 4 days out of a 30-day month. She can catch AIDS 30 days out of a 30-day month. In addition, pregnancy only goes one way — AIDS can go both ways. He can infect her, but she can infect him.

How does "the pill" work?

The combination pill has three functions. One is to thicken the mucus plug at the opening of the cervix. This can act as a barrier mechanism to prevent sperm entrance.

The main function of the pill is to prevent ovulation.

If there is no egg, there can be no fertilization.

A third function is to harden the lining of the womb. If fertilization does occur, this can and, at times, does prevent implantation at one week of life resulting in a micro-abortion at that time. See chapter on early abortions for more details.

How about chlamydia? Do contraceptives prevent catching it?

No, almost not at all. Non-barrier methods which allow skin contact have no preventive action at all. In fact, women on the pill are more susceptible to chlamydia than would be the case if she were not taking it.

The use of condoms, even if used properly every time, does not prevent chlamydia, as there is still skin contact around the genital organs, and the infection can spread through sweat and skin contact.

Chlamydia is perhaps the main cause for tubal pregnancies and for blockage of the tube resulting in sterility.

And Human Papillomaviruses?

The Federal Center for Disease Control, Division of Sexually Transmitted Disease, in Feb., 2001 stated, "Recent research shows that condoms cannot protect against infection with HPV. Among female college students over a three-year period, 43% became infected. One-fifth of American women and one-tenth of men are infected. It causes 92-98% of all cases of cancer of the cervix.

Would a Constitutional Amendment in the U.S., or a law in Canada or other nation forbidding abortion, also forbid the use of the contraceptive pill, the morning-after pill, or the IUD?

No! Such a law or amendment would only forbid induced abortion. It could not "reach" these drugs and devices. This is because of the legal effect of dual action.

If a drug or device has an illegal action, but also a

legal action, it cannot be forbidden or removed from the market. A good example is a butcher knife. This has a legal function in your kitchen. It can also be used as a murder weapon. Because it has both a legal and illegal function, its use cannot be forbidden.

The "pill," "morning-after pill," and IUD would still have a legal action (contraception, temporary sterilization), even though the other action (abortifacient) would now be illegal. Because of the legal action, the anti-abortion law could not forbid the use of these medications.

The U.S. Food and Drug Administration over two decades ago instructed all physicians who insert IUDs to warn women that its use may cause pelvic inflammatory disease and to make their patients "thoroughly aware of this increased risk and its possible interference with future fertility."

U.S. Food & Drug Administration Drug Bulletin, May-June 1978

What about emergency contraception?

This is more accurately termed emergency abortion. This is also called the morning-after pill. See chapter on very early abortions for more details.

What about Natural Family Planning?

This is not to be confused with the old (and not always effective) calendar rhythm. Utilizing an intimate knowledge of the woman's bodily functions, such as mucous production, body temperature, and other signs and symptoms, this method helps a couple know when her fertile and nonfertile times of the month are. Without using any pills or other artificial means, couples can plan their families by having intercourse when she is (or is not) fertile. The abstinence time can be as brief as one week.

What is Quinacrine?

This is a toxic chemical which is inserted from

below into the womb and into the tubes. This causes acute inflammation and scarring which usually blocks the tubes and sterilizes her. The U.S. FDA has condemned it, but it has been, and is being, used in Third World countries.

What about Norplant and Depo Provera?

Both of these use a form of continuing dose of progesterone. Part of the time they prevent ovulation. Part of the time they allow ovulation and fertilization, but prevent implantation. Therefore, they function both as a contraceptive, at times, and as an abortifacient at times.

Is Norplant safe?

In spite of intense advertising and universal acclaim in the public media, the use of Norplant has dropped precipitously since its introduction. The sales were 800 units a day in April '94. Two years later they were 60 a day.
AMA News, 3/1/96

Its use further declined to almost never. In the meantime, there have been 195,000 lawsuits against it. After years of litigation, its maker agreed to pay cash settlements to 36,000 women.

Are the pills safe?

The early contraceptive pills had a high estrogen content. As many as 500 women a year died from blood clots related to these pills. The estrogen was reduced and so was the number of blood clots. In the past decade there have been newer studies confirming that these low dose second and "third generation" pills still cause clots.

• 3 to 6 times that in non-users
N. Eng. J. Med. Vol. 344, No. 20, 5-17-01

- Death of bride in church — New Zealand

  The Dominion 12-7-00

- Australia, 47 yr. old.

  R. Sheers, Glan Clwyd Hosp. 11-1-94

- 1.9 times increase, for 10 years, studied 46,000 women

  Br. Med. J., Jan 5,99

- Demark, an increase.

  Br. Med. J., 9-25-99, pp. 820-21

- Meta-analysis.
  "definite increased risk"

  Br. Med. J., 7-21-01, p. 121

**Remember,
if "Birth Control" is taught to your children
in your school, these courses often will
promote not just contraception,
but also abortion.**

CHAPTER 37

VIOLENCE —
OR A PROTECTIVE RING?

*The only sure answer to stop violence
against abortion facilities and their
providers would be to eliminate its basic cause,
that is, to stop killing babies inside. Since
that isn't going to happen in the near future, it is
important to closely examine such violence.*

*How does abortion relate to violence in American
society? During a powerful speech at the February
1994 National Prayer Breakfast, Mother Teresa
of Calcutta said: "The greatest destroyer of
peace today is abortion, because it is a war
against the child . . . And if we accept that a mother
can kill even her own child, how can we tell other
people not to kill one another?"*

We believe that sidewalk counselors have been a
"protective ring" around these facilities, and that legislative and judicial actions that have drastically limited and even eliminated such "protective rings" have allowed violence to escalate.

CONDEMN VIOLENCE

Your authors have seldom been a part of sidewalk counseling, but have been anything but disinterested observers. My own (Dr. W's) position has been unequivocal condemnation of violence against the bricks and the persons in the abortion industry. I have held no quarter for those who kill babies, but have consistently stated that violence on the outside will never solve the violence inside. Also, while harboring the deepest respect and admiration for those heroic souls who have sat-in, I have had real reservations about some of their actions because of the negative public image it has created for the pro-life movement.

THE BEGINNING

This being said, let us trace a bit of history. Back in the 1970s, the practice of picketing in front of an abortion chamber began. It spread from location to location, and then from Saturdays only (the heavy "kill days") to multiple days in the week. By the '80s, sidewalk counseling, as it came to be more properly called, was a common practice throughout the U.S.

In the early '80s, fire-bombing reared its head. Using the bully pulpit I had as president of National Right to Life during that time, I would look directly into the lens and say, "If any of you are thinking of fire-bombing an abortion place, please don't. You will hurt the pro-life movement. You think you may save some babies. For a few days, in some cases, you might, although those women may still go elsewhere. What you will do is turn public opinion against our movement and delay the day when we can finally stop the killing completely.

PEOPLE OF PEACE

"Remember, we are people of peace. Our basic ethic is to stop violence, the violence that daily kills 4,000 unborn babies. If we adopt *their* evil ethic, violence, we gut our own. Remaining peaceful is the only way we will win the minds and hearts of people."

Others were saying much the same, and that message slowly got through. Into the late '80s, fire-bombing became much less frequent. We must remember that such fire-bombing was always done at night, directed only against bricks, never against persons.

SIT-INS

Then came the sit-ins. The participants were peaceful, nonviolent and prayerful, adopting the tactics of Ghandi and Dr. Martin Luther King. The physical beatings, jailing and punishment taken by the participants from police, was clear witness to the deep dedication of those involved.

Is it pure coincidence, in the late 1980s when the sit-ins were at their peak, that fire-bombings sank to their lowest levels? Is it a coincidence that by the middle '90s, with rescues beaten back by the courts, that such violent episodes had increased again.

These peaceful sit-ins, however, were publicized by the national media as violent events, exactly the opposite of what they actually were. A local peaceful sit-in, reported in the paper, often had a picture of a burned-out abortion mill (from a thousand miles away) printed along-side of it.

SUPPRESSION

The abortion industry cried loudly in protest. Legislatures and judges listened, and the anti-sit-in juggernaut began to move. Jailing became more frequent. Court-orders set boundaries. The high court ruled the RICO bill could be used. The U.S. Congress passed the Freedom of Access to Clinics Act (FACE), making sit-ins a federal felony. The result, to a significant extent, was to remove the "protective ring" of sidewalk counselors that had been in front of those entrances.

WHY THE ESCALATION?

The question is, why the escalation? A moment's reflection is relevant. There are about 1,200 abortion facilities in the U.S. Abortion has been legal nationwide since 1973. Sidewalk counselors have witnessed in front of these kill centers constantly during these years. There are intense emotional gut issues often involved in the abortion decision, and there are 4,000 abortions daily. How often could not a reaction to "her killing my baby" have caused a rejected, unstable boyfriend or husband to literally go crazy over the frustration, loss and anger generated and result in retaliation?

But, incredibly, 44 million abortions, over all these years, at 1,200 locations have resulted in — (tragically) — *only* five fatal retaliations. These have included three abortionists and two auxilary personnel. This is a minuscule number considering the depth and power of the emotions generated, and considering that we are looking back at hundreds of millions of man and woman protest days. Truly, the news that ought to be publicized is not that five adults have been killed, but that there have been *only* five.

UNBELIEVABLY PEACEFUL

The analogy with the Black Panthers is worth recalling. Dr. Martin Luther King adopted Gandhi's method. He insisted that the civil rights sit-ins and demonstrations be peaceful. His supporters complied, except for the Black Panthers. This small group sought the same goal — civil rights — but employed violent means. They killed people. But there is a crucial difference today. Then the media nearly unanimously supported King's efforts. The Black Panthers were reported as a tiny extremist group not representative of the civil rights movement.

In sharp contrast, the media today is almost unanimously opposed to the civil rights of the unborn. Also in sharp contrast, today's violent extremists have been held up as typical of the pro-life movement rather than the aberrant, atypical, sick exceptions that they so obviously are.

WHO DID IT?

It is an obvious fact that almost all alleged assailants have been mentally unstable and are not members of, nor representative of, the pro-life movement. Responsible leaders of the pro-life movement have unanimously and unequivocally condemned such violence. These assailants may be anti-abortion, but they are not pro-life.

SIDEWALK COUNSELORS PROTECT

It is clear that this vital function of sidewalk counseling has not been generally recognized. Yes, pro-lifers are there as pro-life witnesses. Yes, they are there to save babies. Yes, they are there to help women, before and after the abortion. But they are also there to prevent violence. Their presence has been a "protective ring." These peaceful, prayerful people have undoubtedly prevented hundreds, probably even thousands of episodes of violence.

INFLAMMATORY RHETORIC?

And what of the abortion industry's charges that our "inflammatory rhetoric" is precipitating these new events? This is unmitigated nonsense. It is not because we verbally accuse them of "killing babies" that these tragedies have occurred. No, it is because they **are** brutally killing babies. Our people are just telling the truth. The pro-abortion goal here is obvious. They want to prevent us from informing people of the true nature of their "business." Pro-lifers should see through this immediately.

WHO IS VIOLENT?

The real, ongoing violence is occurring inside the

doors of the abortion chambers. Killing of innocent babies is the ultimate violence, and it occurs 4,000 times every day in the United States.

WHO PICKETS?

Men, but mostly women, boys and girls, young and old of every race and religion. They are heroes and heroines. They volunteer their time. They walk in the rain and snow. They endure insults and sometimes assaults from the guards that the abortion proprietors hire, and they take it — all in hope of saving one tiny life, in the hope of preventing the physical and psychological damage to one woman.

And that is their reward. They sidewalk-counsel and picket peacefully. When a woman goes through their line to enter, they will offer her literature and help. In a quiet voice, they will say, "Please don't kill your baby. We'll help you in any way you need. Won't you let us?"

But I've heard that the picketers threaten and sometimes physically abuse the women.

In fact, it is the abortion chamber people who frequently do such things. Pro-life picketers have been spit on, pushed, cursed, threatened, ridiculed, hit, etc. All they do is turn the other cheek.

There is an entire book available that details the violence perpetrated by pro-abortion people against pro-lifers. It details and documents hundreds and hundreds of such episodes. But not a word of this has been reported by the media.

The Abortion Crime Report, Submitted to the Gov., Atty. Gen., and Legislature of California, CA Rt. to Life, July, 2001 (925-944-5351)

The only unwise thing that we've heard occasionally has been shouting by picketers. This is unwise and probably hasn't saved many babies.

Do you mean the picketers give information the women wouldn't get otherwise?

Yes. A good example is the fact that a heartbeat can be heard seven or eight weeks after conception on an office ultrasonic stethoscope. Is this an important bit of information? Should a pregnant mother know it?

In a series of 327 women at the University of Szeged, Hungary, mothers who wanted abortions were allowed to listen to the "fetal heartbeat." After hearing it, 16% refused abortion.

F. Sontag, Third Internat'l Congress of Psychosomatic Midicine,
OB-GYN, London, 1971

CONCLUSION

Could it be that the judicial, legislative and abortion industry's "solution" to sidewalk counseling and other peaceful protest, such as sit-ins, has been counter-productive? Could it be that the violence that still occasionally occurs is, in considerable measure, a result of the suppression of peaceful, prayerful protest outside of abortion facilities? Could it be that if that "protective ring" was still there, that most of these rare, tragically unbalanced, unstable, atypical individuals would have been "caught," counseled, cooled off, steered away, prevented from doing what they planned?

Jack Kennedy's words back then are worth remembering. "If peaceful protest is made illegal, violent protest will become inevitable."

SOLUTION

The only sure answer to the occasional violence against abortion facilities and their providers is to eliminate its basic cause, that is, to stop the violence inside, the violence of killing babies.

PART VIII
OTHER THOUGHTS

CHAPTER 38

DOCTORS & NURSES

The ancient doctor had a dual role
— to heal and to kill —

Hippocrates introduced a new ethic — to only heal. This passed intact into the Christian area and guided medical practice until the middle 20th century. Then, first with abortion and then with euthanasia, some doctors resumed the old pagan dual role.

The Oath of Hippocrates

"I swear by Apollo, the Physician, and Aesculapins, Hygeia and Panacea and All the Gods and Goddesses that, according to my ability and judgement, I will keep this Oath and Stipulation:

"To reckon him who taught me this art equally dear to me as my parents, to share my substance with him and relieve his necessities if required: to regard his offspring as on the same footing with my own brothers, and to teach them this art, if they should wish to learn it, without fee or stipulation, and that by precept lecture and every other mode of instruction. I will impart knowledge of the art to my own sons and to those of my teachers, and to disciples bound by a stipulation and oath, according to the law of medicine, but to none others.

"I will follow that method of treatment which, according to my ability and judgement, I consider for the benefit of my patients, and abstain from whatever is deleterious and mischievous. I will give no deadly medicine to anyone, if asked, nor suggest any such counsel; furthermore, I will not give to a woman an instrument to produce abortion.

"With purity and with holiness I will pass my life and practice my art. I will not cut a person who is suffering with a stone, but will leave this to be done by practitioners of this work. Into whatever houses I enter I will go into them for the benefit of the sick and will abstain from every voluntary act of mischief and corruption, and, further, from the seduction of females or males, bond or free.

"Whatever in connection with my professional practice, or not in connection with it, I may see or hear in the lives of men which ought not to be spoken abroad, I will not divulge, as reckoning that all such should be kept secret.

"While I continue to keep this oath unviolated, may it be granted to me to enjoy life and the practice of the art, respected by all men at all times, but should I trespass and violate this oath, may the reverse be my lot."

All doctors used to swear this oath when they were licensed to practice medicine. But then two sentences were quietly dropped:

"I will give no deadly medicine to anyone if asked, nor suggest such counsel, and, in like manner, I will not give a woman an instrument to produce abortion."

Some medical colleges substituted:

"I will do nothing illegal," essentially the new American Medical Association position (see below). Subsequently, most medical colleges have dropped the oath entirely.

Are there any other famous pledges?

Yes, here is another, almost as old:

"I will not give my patients any poisonous drug, if they ask first, nor will I advise them thus, nor aid in a miscarriage."

Oath of Arabian Physician

Also, right after World War II and the horror of the Nazi doctors and the Holocaust, this was adopted:

"I solemnly pledge myself to consecrate my life to the service of humanity. I will give to my teachers the respect and gratitude which is their due; I will practice my profession with conscience and dignity; the health of my patient will be my first consideration; I will respect the secrets which are confided in me; I will maintain by all means in my power the honour and noble traditions of the medical profession; my colleagues will be my brothers; I will not permit considerations of religion, nationality, race, party politics, or social standing to intervene between my duty and my patient; I will maintain the utmost respect for human life, from the time of conception; even under threat, I will not use my medical knowledge contrary to the laws of humanity. I make these

promises solemnly, freely, and upon my honour."
Declaration of Geneva,
The World Medical Association, Sept. 1948

Sadly, this one has been largely forgotten, and today few medical graduates take any ethical pledge.

Can anything be done?
Surveying the wreckage of today's medical ethics, a prestigious group of physicians, led by Dr. Joseph Stanton, decided to put forth a new oath, relevant to today's technological age. They clothed it in dignified classical language that expresses the timeless ethic of good medicine. It was released in 1995. Hopefully, it will someday be used widely.

A.D. 1995 Restatement of the Oath of Hippocrates (Circa 400 B.C.)

"I swear in the presence of the Almighty and before my family, my teachers and my peers that according to my ability and judgment I will keep this Oath and Stipulation:

"To reckon all who have taught me this art equally dear to me as my parents and in the same spirit and dedication to impart a knowledge of the art of medicine to others. I will continue with diligence to keep abreast of advances in medicine. I will treat, without exception, all who seek my ministrations, so long as the treatment of others is not compromised thereby, and I will seek the counsel of particularly skilled physicians where indicated for the benefit of my patient.

"I will follow that method of treatment which, according to my ability and judgment, I consider for the benefit of my patient and abstain from whatever is harmful or mischievous. I will neither prescribe nor administer a lethal dose of medicine to any patient, even if asked, nor counsel any such thing nor perform acts of omission with direct intent deliberately to end a human life. I will maintain the utmost respect for every human life from fertilization to natural death and reject abortion that deliberately takes a unique human life.

"With purity, holiness and beneficence I will pass my life and practice my art. Except for the prudent correction of an imminent danger, I will neither treat any patient nor carry out any research on any human being without the valid informed consent of the subject or the appropriate legal protector thereof, understanding that research must have as its purpose the furtherance of the health of that individual. Into whatever patient setting I enter, I will go for the benefit of the sick and will abstain from every voluntary act of mischief or corruption and further from the seduction of any patient.

"Whatever, in connection with my professional practice or not in connection with it, I may see or hear in the lives of my patients which ought not be spoken abroad I will not divulge, reckoning that all such should be kept secret.

"While I continue to keep this Oath unviolated, may it be granted to me to enjoy life and the practice of the art and science of medicine with the blessing of the Almighty and respected by my peers and society, but should I trespass and violate this Oath, may the reverse be my lot."

What is the policy of the American Medical Association?

Stripped to its bare bones, regarding abortion, it

is — what is legal is now ethical. But the AMA has consistently condemned euthanasia.

Does making something legal also make it right?

"In 1944, a physician in Germany could participate in genocide with legal sanction. In America he would have been a murderer. In 1977, in America, a physician could perform an abortion with legal sanction. In Germany, he would have been a murderer. We have come 360 degrees on the moral compass."

M. Baten & W. Enos, "Questions of
Authenticity and
Situational Ethics,"
Cancer Bulletin, vol. 29, no. 4, 1978

How did the AMA deal with physician abortionists back in the 19th century when it was first formed?

In 1871, the AMA recommended dealing with medical abortionists in the following manner:

"These men should be marked as Cain was marked; they should be made the outcasts of society . . . respectable men should cease to consult with them, should cease to speak to them, should cease to notice them except with contempt . . . Resolved, That we repudiate and denounce the conduct of abortionists, and that we will hold no intercourse with them professionally or otherwise, and that we will, whenever an opportunity presents, guard and protect the public against the machinations of these characters by pointing out the physical and moral ruin which follows in their wake."

W. Brennan, "The Abortion Holocaust,"
Landmark Press, p. 189

This is quite a contrast with today.

Yes, and its comparison is chilling.

The American Medical Association on Abortion: An Anatomy of Contrasting Policy Statements

When Does Human Life Begin?

1871 — "No other doctrine appears to be consonant with reason or physiology but that which admits the embryo to possess vitality from the very moment of conception.

"The AMA abortion policy statements of 1967 and 1970 include no references to the scientific fact that human life begins at conception.

What is Abortion?

1859 — "The slaughter of countless children; such unwarrantable destruction of human life."
1871 — "The work of destruction; the wholesale destruction of unborn infants."

1967 — "The interruption of pregnancy; the induced termination of pregnancy."
1970 — "A medical procedure."

What Should the Ethics of Abortion Be?

1871 — "Thou shalt not kill. This commandment is given to all without exception . . .it matters not at what stage of development his victim may have arrived."

1967 — "This is a personal and moral consideration which in all cases must be faced according to the dictates of the conscience of the patient and her physician."

Who Should Perform Abortions?

1871 — "It will be unlawful and unprofessional for any physician to induce abortion."

1970 — "Abortion should be performed only by a duly licensed physician."

Who Are Physician Abortionists?

1871 — "Men who cling to a noble profession only to dishonor it; false brethren; educated assassins; modern Herods; the executioners."

1967 — "Conscientious practitioners; conscientious physicians."

What Should Be Done to Physician Abortionists?

1871 — "These men should be marked as Cain was marked; they should be made the outcasts of society."

1970 — They should be permitted to perform as long as they take place "in an accredited hospital."

W. Brennan, *The Abortion Holocaust*, Landmark Press, 1983, p. 191

You draw a parallel between today's abortionists and the Nazi doctors?

Yes! There is a direct parallel between the two holocausts, neither of which could have happened without doctors.

Excerpted from *The Abortion Holocaust*,
W. Brennan, Landmark Press, 1983.

THEN	*TODAY*
"A doctor may interrupt a pregnancy when it 'threatens the life or health of the mother [and] an unborn child that is likely to present hereditary and transmissible defects may be destroyed.'" (German Penal Code and Hamburg Eugenics Court, 1933)	"A licensed physician is justified in terminating a pregnancy if he believes that pregnancy would gravely impair the physical or mental health of the mother or that the child would be born with grave physical or mental defects." (American Law Institute Model Penal Code, 1962)
"Only persons of 'German or related blood' can be citizens; this does not include Jews." (Reich Citizenship Law, 1935)	"The word 'person,' as used in the fourteenth Amendment, does not include the unborn." (U.S. Supreme Court, *Roe vs. Wade*, 1973)
"The authority of physicians is enlarged to include the responsibility for according a 'mercy death [to] incurables.'" (Hitler's Euthanasia Order, Sept. 1939)	"The abortion decision in all its aspects is inherently and primarily a medical decision, and basic responsibility for it must rest with the physician." (U.S. Supreme Court, *Roe vs. Wade*, 1973)

Obedience to Authority

"The accused did not act wrongly because they were covered by law [and] were carrying out the laws of the land." (Hadamar Euthanasia Hospital Trial, 1945)	"I did nothing which was illegal, immoral or bad medicine. Everything I did was in accordance with law." (Dr. Kenneth C. Edelin, 1975)
"The physician is merely an instrument as in the case of an officer who receives an order." (Dr. Karl Brandt, Doctors' Trial, 1947)	"The physician is only the instrument of her decision." (Dr. Bernard N. Nathanson, 1974)

Subhumanity of the Victims

"The Jewish-Bolshevik Commissars personify a repulsive yet characteristic subhumanity." (Dr. August Hirt, 1942)

"It had nothing to do with humanity — it was a mass. I rarely saw them as individuals. It was always a huge mass." (Franz Stangl, former commandant of Treblinka, 1971)

"Whenever Jews are left to themselves they bring brutal misery and depravity. They are pure parasites." (Adolf Hitler, 1943)

"If it is now pointed out that the Jew is human, I then reject that totally." (Antisemitic speech, Reichstag, 1895)

"For the first four and one-half months the fetus is subhuman and relatively close to a piece of tissue." (Amitai Etzioni, Ph.D., 1976)

"What is aborted is a protoplasmic mass and not a real, live grown-up individual." (Drs. Walter Char & John McDermott, 1972)

"A parasite can commit murder. What attention has Catholic thinking or the law given to the fetus's capacity to murder its mother?" (Dr. Natalie Shainess, 1968)

"It is a wild contention that newborn babies are persons." (Dr. Michael Tooley, 1972)

The Language of Killing

"Fifty-nine thousand persons were evacuated by July 31." (Warsaw, Poland, 1942)

"The Baron de Hirsch ghetto would have to be emptied." (Max Merten, 1943)

"The removal of the Jewish element." (Hans Frank, 1943)

"The treatment was administered to the children of the Haar-Eglfing Institution." (Dr. Pfannmuller, 1945)

"The method of injection is a completely painless method." (Dr. Adolf Wahlmann, 1945)

"The uterus was evacuated." (Dr. David Edelman & Colleagues, 1974)

"The uterine cavity was emptied." (Dr. A.K. Mukerjee, 1973)

"Remove the products of conception." (Dr. Thomas Dillon & Colleagues, 1974)

"Abortion as treatment for the sexually transmitted disease of unwanted pregnancy." (Dr. Willard Cates & Colleagues, 1976)

"Evacuate the conceptus painlessly within 45 seconds." (Dr. Harvey Karman, 1972)

"If you are going to kill all these people, at least take the brains out so that the material could be utilized." (Testimony of Dr. Julius Hallervordan, 1947)

"In the case of abortion, the fetus cannot be 'helped' by being experimented upon since it is doomed to death anyhow, but perhaps its death can be ennobled . . . when the research has as its objective the saving of lives (or the reduction of defects) of other wanted fetuses." (Drs. Willard Gaylin & Mark Lappe, 1975)

"The victims of this Buchenwald typhus test did not suffer in vain and did not die in vain . . . people were saved by these experiments." (Dr. Gebhard Rose, Doctors' Trial, 1947)

"With changes in the abortion laws, fetuses as valuable research material is on the increase." (Dr. Leroy Jackson, 1975)

How did the change come about?

Dr. Leon Alexander, an authority writing after the Nuremberg trials, said it well, and the parallel with the creeping deterioration of today's societal ethics is telling.

"The beginnings were at first merely a subtle shift in emphasis in the basic attitude of the physicians. It started with the acceptance of the attitude, basic in the euthanasia movement, that there is such a thing as a life not worthy to be lived. This attitude, in its early stages, concerned itself merely with the severely and chronically sick. Gradually, the sphere of those to be included in this category was enlarged to encompass the socially unproductive, the ideologically unwanted, the racially unwanted, and finally all non-Germans. But it is important to realize that the infinitely small, wedged-in lever from which this entire trend of mind received its impetus was the attitude toward the nonrehabilitable sick."

L. Alexander, "Medical Science Under Dictatorship," *New England Jour. Med.*, vol. 241, July 14, 1949, pp. 39-47

And in the modern Western world?

The first public admission of this change of basic ethic was an editorial:

> "The reverence of each and every human life has been a keystone of Western medicine and is the ethic which has caused physicians to try to preserve, protect, repair, prolong, and enhance every human life.

> "Since the old ethic has not yet been fully displaced, it has been necessary to separate the idea of abortion from the idea of killing, which continues to be socially abhorrent. The result has been a curious avoidance of the scientific fact, which everyone really knows, that human life begins at conception, and is continuous, whether intra- or extra-uterine, until death. The very considerable semantic gymnastics which are required to rationalize abortion as anything but taking a human life would be ludicrous if they were not often put forth under socially impeccable auspices. It is suggested that this schizophrenic sort of subterfuge is necessary because, while a new ethic is being accepted, the old one has not yet been rejected."

Editorial, *Jour. CA State Med. Assoc.*, Sept. 1970

Don't doctors know abortion kills a human being?

Several decades ago many did not. Doctors are narrowly specialized. Just because M.D. or D.O. appears after their names, don't assume they know everything about fetal development. Remember, most clergymen aren't scripture scholars, and few attorneys know much about copyright law.

In the last decade or so, this ignorance no longer holds true. Today it is common at a baby shower for the expectant mother to show the guests an ultrasound picture of her baby. Today all doctors, even those most distanced from biological facts, such as psychiatrists, know this basic scientific fact.

Why do doctors do abortions?

A few do them for ideologic reasons, but their numbers are dwindling. Most do them because of the money. Many abortionists are unable to earn a living in regular medical practice, so they turn to this, e.g., we have a letter from Shepel Management, Inc. in Brookline, MA soliciting a physician "to perform abortions." It states, "This is a part time position requiring either a morning or an afternoon a week. It is an opportunity to earn upwards of $70,000 a year."

What training is needed to do abortions?

None! There are no laws requiring certain qualifications if done in free-standing facilities. In-hospital abortions involve all of the rules and supervision of regular surgery, but the trend is sharply away from hospital abortions. Today few hospitals do abortions in the U.S. This is not true in many other countries.

What do people think of abortion doctors?

At best, they are regarded as a necessary evil by most citizens. Commonly, they are social outcasts, ostracized by most in their community. People avoid them, and their children often suffer.

A nationwide survey showed that, by their own admission:

- 69% of abortionists say they are not respected in the medical community.
- 65% feel ostracized.
- 87% have been harassed.
- 50% have problems retaining staff.
- 20% have been denied hospital privileges because they do abortions.

64% say that the non-abortion part of their practice has suffered because they do abortions.

M. Crutcher, Project Choice, Feb. 1993

How about psychic stress?

For nurses, this has been a real problem. Except for the unusually high salaries paid, few nurses would work in an abortion chamber.

A detailed accounting of the psychic stress, self-doubts, nightmares, recourse to alcohol and drugs, and the personality deterioration of those doing abortions is described in "Vacant Souls," a chapter in the book, *Lime 5*.

M. Crutcher, *Lime 5,* Genesis Pub., 1996, pp. 171-222

Is this true in other countries?

It varies — some yes, some no. Certainly the trend in the U.S. is clear. Few hospitals do abortions. Fewer doctors want to do them. Fewer medical schools teach how to do them. The abortionist remains an outcast. Malpractice lawsuits against them are more frequent.

CHAPTER 39

WORDS

Words Mean Everything*

Those who support abortion have quite successfully engaged in semantic gymnastics. They have told us that we are for "compulsory pregnancy" and that they are for a "woman's right to choose." "Termination of pregnancy" is "as simple as pulling a tooth." All it does is to gently remove the "products of pregnancy," "the fetus," "the embryo," the "feto-placental unit," "pregnancy tissue," and will "restore her periods." They accuse us of wanting to "impose our morality" and say that she has a "right to her own body," to "reproductive freedom." Most pro-abortionists insist that they "are personally opposed, but . . ." They fear a return to back-alley butchery. They consistently emphasize the problems of "unwanted pregnancy" and "women's rights," while totally ignoring her tiny passenger.

But we call ourselves *Right to Life*. Early on, we who would protect all human life adopted a title that has been startlingly effective. We became "right-to-life." This is the best title. Use it always. We also have said we are "pro-life." This, too, is an excellent title. But many people have used "pro-life" in other ways, changing its original meaning in many minds in an attempt to include those who labor against poverty, against war, against capital punishment, and against nuclear arms. Pro-abortionists have also, at times, claimed to be "pro-life." They have never, and will never, however, adopt the title "Right to Life."

Let's be positive. We are *for* protection for the unborn, the mother, the handicapped, and the aged. If possible, don't accept the negative label "anti-abortion." There is nothing negative about being for life. And their label? "Pro-abortion" is acceptable; "anti-life" is best. *Never* use their "pro-choice." If you do, add "to kill" at the end of the phrase.

What grows within? An "unborn baby or child" or perhaps **"preborn baby"** is better. "Developing baby" is also scientifically and professionally accurate. Sometimes other humanizing terms fit, such as "this little guy." Avoid referring to the unborn child as "it"; use **"he"** or **"she."** The terms "the fetus" and "the embryo" fall on the listening ear as "non-human glob." Never use them. If you can't avoid it, speak of "the living human fetus." Remember that the stage of "fertilized egg" lasts less than 24 hours. What implants one week later is not a fertilized egg, is not a "pre-embryo," but rather is a living embryonic baby. A pre-embryo is several million sperm swimming after one ovum. When one connects, this is no longer a "pre" but an actual embryo.

Who does the procedure? Never call him/her a doctor. They don't deserve the dignity that "Doctor" calls forth. Also, don't use "surgeon." Call them **"abortionists."** Never deviate from that title. The word "abortionist" is one of condemnation, of criminality, of killing. That is the label they deserve.

"Termination of pregnancy" is a pro-abortion propaganda phrase. Avoid it like the plague. It masks what is actually happening. It speaks only to the mother's condition, completely ignoring the baby she carries. Furthermore, it is not specific for abortion. Didn't each of you terminate your mother's pregnancy by your birth?

Use the word **"kill."** Use it repeatedly, directly, and often. It is a non-judgmental, accurate, biological description of what happens. We use it when we step on a roach or when we spray crab grass. Use it here also. What of "murder"? This is a much stronger word. One cannot "murder" a dog or an insect, only a human being. To say "murderer" clearly implies that the abortionist knows that this living being is human and kills anyway. Therefore, use "murderer" with caution. Sometimes it may be too inflammatory and even counterproductive. "Kill," however, is always in order.

Who carries the child in her womb? A "mother." Pro-abortionists hate the word. "Pregnant woman" is accurate, but **"mother"** is much better. Can you imagine a nation accepting a "mother's right" to abortion?

"Womb" is usually a better word than "uterus," carrying a message of love, warmth, and security. "Womb" ties closely with "mother" and leads to "the womb has become a tomb."

Right to control her own body? You might facetiously ask, "Since when has it been out of control?" More to the point, however, is that this is a biologic absurdity, for over half (52%) of the babies born (or aborted) are male. Who ever heard of a woman's body with male organs?

"Right to her own body," if accepted as a feminist credo (*women's* rights), would or should serve to protect the almost 700,000 tiny American *women* whose mothers kill them annually.

"Place of residence" is a catchy and accurate way of remembering that killing in America is legal as long as the baby still lives in his first "place of residence," the womb. We also speak of discrimination on the basis of race, color, age, handicap, and place of residence.

342

The U.S. Supreme Court Decision of 1973 should always be described as "the tragic . . . , the savage . . . ," and like terms.

Clinic? "Abortion clinic" is strong pro-abortion propaganda semantics. Sadly, this term is commonly used by many pro-lifers. The term is a contradiction. A "clinic" is where you go to be healed. There are even automobile transmission clinics. Use **"abortion mill"** or "abortion facility" if you must be neutral. Best of all, use **"abortion chamber."** Why "chamber"? That reminds us of gas chambers — extermination centers — and properly so. Every second human being who enters an abortion chamber is exterminated (the tiny human inside the womb of a mother). Glad you asked.

The American Civil Liberties Union (ACLU) is accurately described as the legal defense and attack arm of the anti-life movement. Since it is so selective in whose right to live it defends, many call it the "anti-Civil Liberties Union." Some call it the "Anti-Christian Liberties Union."

Planned Parenthood needs to be explained and named every time you talk of abortion. Sometimes "Planned Barrenhood" may be in order. Planned Parenthood can always be labeled **"The Largest Baby-Killing Conglomerate in America."** Never fail to mention their abortion chambers kill over 10% of all babies killed by abortion in the U.S.

"Rape pregnancy" is not specific enough. Always speak of "**assault or forcible rape** pregnancy," which is very, very rare and *is* what we're talking about.

"Euthanasia" comes from two Greek words meaning "good death." Euthanasia proponents use this word to make it sound good. A quick retort is that it no longer means good death; it simply means "good-bye."

Similarly, "death with dignity" sounds good, but say it right. We want people to live in dignity until natural death occurs.

"Liberalize abortion"? Horrors! Never use this

phrase. For many of us, to be liberal is to be concerned about those who need help the most. Instead, speak of **"permissive" or "radical" abortion laws.** Similarly, never use "reform" of older protective laws.

Pro-abortionists accuse us of wanting to "impose our morality" on women. Turn that around, and say it correctly: "How much longer will our nation continue to allow mothers and abortionists to impose their morality on their helpless babies — fatally"?

"Every Child a Wanted Child" is their slogan. We must finish their sentence: "and **if not wanted, kill.**"

Always say "salt poisoning abortion." Never refer to "saline abortion" or "salting out." These are pro-abortion terms and do not face what actually takes place.

"Interruption of pregnancy" is an absurd and inaccurate use of words. If I interrupt you, it means that I temporarily stop you, after which you resume. Abortion is permanent. It kills.

The abortionist's "curette" is not a "spoon-shaped instrument." It is "a **loop-shaped steel knife.**" The curette doesn't "scrape" the placenta away; it "cuts and slices" it away.

"Person" is defined in one dictionary in 12 different ways. If you use it, define it first. If they use it, ask, "What do you mean by 'person?'" Pro-lifers do much better to speak of "human life."

"Conception?" Some define it as implantation at one week of life. Better to use **"fertilization."**

"Contraception" is not a Right to Life issue, but I.U.D.s, Norplant, and "Emergency Contraception" are referred to as contraceptives when, in fact, they are **"abortifacients."** Use the correct word.

Perhaps "untimely" or "problem" pregnancy is better than "unwanted" pregnancy.

Are we "compulsory pregnancy" people? Then they are "compulsory death" people.

They want "reproductive freedom." She has it, and

has used it. She is now a mother. She has reproduced. The only question now is whether to kill.

Is abortion a "single issue" in considering a candidate? No. But we do see it clearly as a **"disqualifying issue"** at the ballot box.

"Therapeutic abortion" always used to mean an abortion needed to save a mother's life. But its use in California's first abortion law, by Canada's "therapeutic abortion committees," and by many pro-abortionists in the U.S. has totally destroyed its original meaning. Now "therapeutic" has come to mean "elective."

Some say they want to make abortion "safe, legal and rare" when in fact their actions show clearly that they want it **safe, legal, and everywhere.**

For a few "one-liners" consider:
- Abortion is the ultimate child abuse.
- Abortion equals violence; oppose both.
- Intrauterine-battered child.
- Meaningful life? Meaningful to whom?
- It's a slippery slope from abortion to infanticide to euthanasia.
- Quality of life? Or equality of life?
- Back-alley abortions are now front-alley abortions.

"Since men can't get pregnant, they have nothing to say about abortion." If that were true, doctors couldn't treat a disease unless they had it first. How could we train funeral directors when they have never died? How can we oppose Hitler's genocide if we're not Germans or Jews — or slavery if we were not slaves or slaveholders? In any case, each child has a father. And 52% of all unborn babies are boys.

If one is "incurably ill," that applies to all diabetics, for they are incurable. Let's speak of "terminally ill" instead.

"Potential" life? No. Rather, this is **human life with vast potential.**

Did you "come from" a teenager, a small girl, an

infant, a female fetus, a female fertilized ovum? No, you once were a teenager, a small girl, an infant, a fetus, a female fertilized ovum. You were all there at each of those stages of your life. All you've done is to grow up.

Partial-birth abortion? Yes, or call it brain suction abortion, not a D&X or late term abortion. Best yet, speak of **"killing babies during delivery** — you know, Partial-birth abortion."

"Overpopulation"? Remember, the U.S., Canada, and most of the Western world have had birth rates below replacement level for three decades. Become informed: see chapter on population.

"Health" is not what we think it is. As defined by the U.S. Supreme Court, and as interpreted in law throughout the world, it means **"social, economic, and physical well being"** of the mother.

Euthanasia? Do not confuse things by speaking of direct and indirect, voluntary, involuntary and non-voluntary, passive and active euthanasia and assisted suicide. Call it what it is — **euthanasia is when the doctor kills the patient.**

We want to kill the pain, not the patient.

If a person is "personally opposed, but . . . ," they are in reality, pro-abortion. We'd far rather have a political office-holder admit that even though personally in favor of abortion, he or she will vote for the civil rights of the unborn.

Abortion of "handicapped," preborn babies is "killing the patient to cure the disease." Remember, before birth and after birth, it's the same patient and the same handicap. This is prenatal euthanasia.

"Fetal Deformity"? "Fetal Defect"? Why use such "turn off" adjectives when we use **"handicapped"** for the child already born. The word "deformity" makes us turn away in revulsion. "Defective"? Our culture throws defective things away. "Handicapped," as a word, calls forth a helping hand. To use "fetal deformity" or "fetal defect" is to make the killing easier. To use "fetal handicap" is to call forth a helping hand.

Never forget that abortion for rape is "killing an innocent baby for the crime of his father."

School-based "health" clinics? Never. They are **school-based "sex" clinics.**

Reproductive or research (don't call it therapeutic) cloning are both cloning. It's just that the first is carried to term and the second is killed by two weeks and is best called **"clone and kill."**

Embryonic stem cells come from living 4-5-day-old human embryos. Their term "embryo-like entities" is a transparent attempt to deny human life.

They don't want to admit that a cloned human embryo is really a human being. Some are calling this being a "nuclear transfer-derived blastocyst" or merely an "activated egg."

There is never a "need" for abortion. Rather, talk about a "market."

And, a good one, abortions aren't performed, abortions are committed.

They say that laws forbidding clinics to tell a minor daughter's parents are a "gag rule." Rather, tell them that they want to continue laws that are a "sneak rule" — that cooperate with minor daughters in sneaking behind parents' backs to get an abortion or the pill.

Why not "love them both"?

CHAPTER 40

POLLS

The polls giveth information
The polls taketh away information,
Blessed (cursed) be the polls.

The polls can give information?
They certainly can, but there are many ifs.

They can mislead?
Sure — it happens all the time.

Where do we start?
The most important thing to say about polls is:
• Ignore the headlines and the lead TV comment.
• Go to the question asked.
• Examine the wording of the question.
• Only then decide if it has information useful
  to you.

How does one evaluate a poll then?
Let's look at this. Since there is literally a new poll
out every week, we use the following only as examples
to demonstrate how you should evaluate them. A book

like this obviously cannot keep you up-to-date on polling results.

THINGS TO WATCH FOR

The Words Used

If the wording speaks of "woman's rights," or her "choice", the majority will answer pro-abortion. If the poll asks about rights of the unborn, a strong majority will answer pro-life.

When "doctor," or "and her physician," or "medical reasons," or "medical decision" is used, pro-abortion answers are almost guaranteed. The same for "health." But if "abortionist" is used, or if for "social or economic" reasons is used, then a large majority will answer pro-life. "Terminate her pregnancy" brings a strong pro-abortion answer.

Conclusion: Read the question carefully. Is the deck stacked going in?

Give examples of "stacked" questions.

A classic example of leading the respondent by loading the question was a poll done for the National Abortion Rights Action League.

"The decision on whether or not to perform an abortion rests with the consenting patient and should be performed by a licensed physician in conformance with good medical practice."

Results? Not surprisingly, more than 90% agreed.
Market Opinion Research, 1981,
Bailey and Deardourff

Note the woman's right to decide, that she is a "patient" of a "licensed physician" who uses "good medical practice." Who wouldn't feel impelled to agree?

The same question, with different wording, can bring very different results.
- Here is an example of two questions asked of the same people in the same poll:

    In general, do you think a woman should have the right to choose to have an abortion?

    Yes - 67% No - 29%

    In general, do you think the lives of unborn babies should be protected?

    Yes - 69% No - 19%

    National Werthin poll, Oct. '89

- Now read this one, also asked of the same people in the same poll.

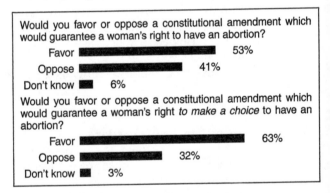

Note that merely adding "to make a choice" to the wording added 10% to the approval.

Boston Globe Poll, Dec. 17, 1989

Who is asked the question?

You will get a different answer from the readership of *Ms.* magazine than from the readership of *St. Anthony Messenger.* That is obvious. What is less obvious is that truly professional polling must ask a valid cross section to be accurate.

What does the person asked know about the issue?

Some questions have asked if the person agrees with the U.S. Supreme Court Decision on abortion, when, in fact, only a tiny fraction have a reasonably accurate grasp of what it decreed. The same is true of a constitutional amendment. What do the respondents know about such an amendment? Which amendment?

Is the question factually accurate?

A frequently used question states: "The Supreme Court has legalized abortion in the first three months of pregnancy. Do you agree?" As our readers know, that statement is flatly false, yet it has been used for years.

In the next questions, the factual error about abortion only in the first three months disqualifies the results, but note also that even subtle differences in wordings bring different results.

1. "The U.S. Supreme Court has ruled that a woman may go to a doctor to end a pregnancy at any time during the first three months of pregnancy. Do you favor or oppose this ruling?"

   Results: Favor - 47%; Oppose - 44%

   Gallup poll conducted March 1974
   The Gallup Opinion Index, Report 106, April 1974

2. "The U.S. Supreme Court has ruled that a woman may go to a doctor for an abortion at any time during the first three months of pregnancy. Do you favor or oppose this ruling?"

   Results: Favor - 43%; Oppose - 54%

   Sindlinger, "Special Hitchhiker on Abortion," for
   National Review, May 1974

The change from "to end a pregnancy" to "for an abortion" changed the results. How much more of a change would there be if "abortionist" were used instead of "doctor"; if the true nine months were stated instead of the incorrect "three months"; or if "to kill her developing baby" were used?

In tracking polls before the 1984 referendum in Colorado on abortion funding, a change from "public funding" to "your tax dollars" added 9% more to those who opposed such funding.

Does the poll contain the Life-of-the-Mother exception?

A *New York Times-CBS* poll asked the same question, with and without the exception, and found a 15% change in results.

"There is a proposal for a Constitutional Amendment that would make all abortions illegal."

Results: Favor - 28%; Oppose - 63%;
        Don't know/no answer - 9%

"There is another proposal for a Constitutional Amendment that would allow an abortion only in order to save the life of the mother. All other abortions would be illegal."

Results: Favor - 43%; Oppose - 48%
        Don't know/no answer - 9%

New York Times, Oct. 14, 1984, p. E3

Is the question multi-issue?

Does the question mix abortion and contraception? The respondent may well favor one and oppose the other. Is the question placed in context with other loaded questions? Or does it stand by itself so that it can be answered on its own merits?

Is the question too general?

"Do you feel that abortion should be: (a) legal under

all circumstances, (b) only under certain circumstances, or (c) illegal under all circumstances?"

Gallup Poll/National, asked annually since 1975

If read carefully and with thought, the only people in "C" would be those who would not even allow abortion to prevent the mother's death, and the only ones in "A" would be those who even approve sex-selection abortions in the third trimester of pregnancy.

A broad, general answer is often rendered invalid (as the next two questions show), when specific details are probed.

1. "As you may have heard, in the last few years a number of states have liberalized their abortion laws. To what extent do you agree or disagree with the following statement regarding abortion: The decision to have an abortion should be made solely by a woman and her physician?"

   Results: Agree - 64%; Disagree - 31%

   Commissioned by Planned Parenthood and asked in a Gallup poll. *The Gallup Opinion Index,* Report 87, Sept.

2. "Do you think it should be lawful for a woman to be able to get an abortion without her husband's consent?"

   Results: Yes - 24%; No - 67%

   Commissioned by Blake and asked in a Gallup poll two months after Question 1 above. (1973)

Note also the slanting of the first question: "made solely by a woman and her physician." This guarantees a pro-abortion answer.

Isn't there some legitimate way to find out public opinion on abortion?

Yes, there is. The question should simply ask for what reasons should abortion be permitted (or legal)? Several major pro-abortion news media did just this at about the same time and the results were almost identical.

Combined Opinion Polls
ABORTION APPROVAL

Life/Health of Mother	90%
Rape/Incest	75%
Fetal Handicap	65%
Can't Afford	40%
Too Many Children	40%
Emotional Strain	35%
To Finish School	28%
Not Married	25%
As Birth Control	16%
Sex Selection	2%

Note that the reasons approved of by a majority constitute only 1-2% of all abortions done, while those disapproved constituted over 98% of all abortions done.

Boston Globe, Mar. 31, '89; N.Y. Times, Jan 22, '89
Los Angeles Times, Mar. 19, '89 and Newsweek Apr. 24, '89.

These are all older polls. Are they still valid, or has public opinion changed?

Until about the mid '90s there had been relatively little change as listed in the combined polls above.

Then came the nationwide publicity on partial-birth abortion, which taught the public that abortion is legal for 9 months. Then came the scandal of selling baby parts.

Then, in 2001 there was a prolonged debate on the first week of life. Is this human life? Does taking embryonic stem cells kill a living human? What about cloning? All of this has further educated people as to when human life begins.

Probably because of the above, there has been a definite swing in public opinion toward pro-life.

This is summed up by the Polling Company in 2001.

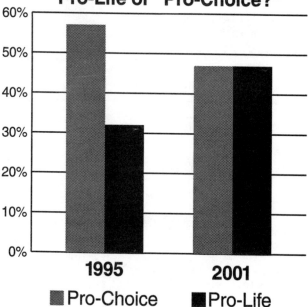

Do You Identify Yourself as Pro-Life or "Pro-Choice?"

Pro-Choice   Pro-Life

Gallup in 1995 found 56% pro-choice and 33% pro-life. In 2001 it was 46% to 46%.

The strongly pro-abortion Center for Gender Equity was shocked when its own poll in January, 1999 revealed:

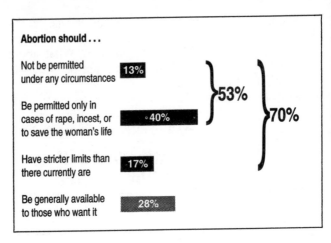

Abortion should . . .

Not be permitted under any circumstances — 13%

Be permitted only in cases of rape, incest, or to save the woman's life — 40%

Have stricter limits than there currently are — 17%

Be generally available to those who want it — 28%

} 53%

} 70%

In May 2000, a Wirthlin Worldwide Poll broke it down to more specifics:

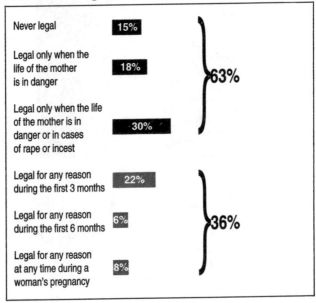

Never legal — 15%

Legal only when the life of the mother is in danger — 18%

Legal only when the life of the mother is in danger or in cases of rape or incest — 30%

Legal for any reason during the first 3 months — 22%

Legal for any reason during the first 6 months — 6%

Legal for any reason at any time during a woman's pregnancy — 8%

} 63%

} 36%

CHAPTER 41

THE MEDIA

*Most are pro-abortion, pro-homosexual,
anti-religion, anti-family, and for more and
more big government and liberal policies
at every level.*

Not all — but most

Give some examples.
- The 1973 decision and its progeny legalized abortion-on-demand even in the late months of pregnancy. For the next 22 years media reports consistently stated it was only legal for 3 months or (sometimes) until viability.
- It took the U.S. Congress' Partial-Birth Abortion Ban debate on C-Span to graphically show the nation this barbaric third trimester infanticide/abortion before the media finally stopped hiding the fact that late abortions were done and were legal.
- We are called "anti-abortion" (a negative label), while they are "pro-choice" (a positive label).
- Large pro-life rallies, marches, picketing, etc., are ignored or grossly underestimated in size. A dozen

"pro-choice" protesters, however, will get equal or often much more time on TV or space in print than even tens of thousands of pro-life people.

- Anti-abortion "fanatics" are contrasted with pro-abortion people with "deep commitments."
- It is okay to identify those who oppose abortion as Catholics, as Evangelicals, Fundamentalists, or right-wing extremists. But who has ever heard of a pro-abortion person being identified as a Jew, an atheist, or a homosexual or lesbian, if such they were.

How about surveys?

Comparison surveys tell us the most. This major one compared media and other leaders with the general public.

"IS ABORTION MORALLY WRONG OR IS THIS NOT A MORAL ISSUE?"

	Morally Wrong	Not A Moral Issue
General Public	65%	35%
Leaders-overall	36%	64%
Religion	74%	26%
Business	42%	58%
Military	40%	60%
News Media	35%	65%
Voluntary Association	33%	67%
Government	29%	71%
Education	26%	74%
Law and Justice	25%	75%
Science	25%	75%

"The Impact of Belief,"
Conn. Mutual Life Report on American Values in the '80s

Another and more detailed report was based on "hour long interviews with 240 journalists and broadcasters at the most influential media outlets, including the *New York Times, Washington Post, Wall Street Journal, Time*

Magazine, Newsweek, U.S. News and World Report, CBS, NBC, ABC, PBS, etc." Among the findings were that 90% said a woman had the right to choose abortion.

Forty-six percent felt adultery was wrong, with only 15% feeling strongly about it, and 76% approved of living with someone of the opposite sex.

On religion, 50% denied any religious affiliation. Twenty-three percent were raised Jewish, but only 14% were practicing Judaism at the time. Only one in five identified themselves as Protestant, one in eight as Catholic. Overall, however, only 8% went to church or synagogue weekly, with 86% attending seldom or never.

They were largely male, white, highly educated, with high incomes. They voted heavily for McGovern and Carter over Nixon, Ford, and Reagan. They were committed to the welfare state, to redistribution of income, and were strong environmentalists and desegregationists. Eight-five percent agreed that homosexuals have the right to teach in public schools, etc.

S. Lichter & S. Rothman, "The Media Elite: White, Male, Secular and
Liberal," *Public Opinion,* 1981

In a study two years later of "Television's Elite," 104 network vice presidents, writers, producers, and executives returned similar results. "Ninety-seven percent of the 'elite' agreed that a woman has the right to decide on abortion."

J. Carmody, "The TV Column,"
Washington Post, Feb. 9, 1983

Does the average journalist share the "media elites' " liberal bias?

Yes. In 1985, the *Los Angeles Times* surveyed 3,000 of the general public and 3,165 more ordinary newspaper reporters and editors nationwide. The same bias was evident in who favored:

	Public	Journalists
Prayer in schools	74	25
Death penalty for murders	75	47
Allowing abortions	51	82
Gay rights in employment	56	89
Stricter handgun control	50	78
Disinvestment in S. Africa	31	62
Reagan's job performance	57	30

R. Irvine, "Charting Media Attitudes,"
Wash. Times, Sept. 9, 1985

What of journalism students?

In a study of 28 candidates for master's degrees at Columbia University School of Journalism, the leftward bias was much more pronounced, showing overwhelming support of women's rights. To sample one other question, in 1980, 4% voted for Reagan, 59% for Carter, and 29% for Anderson.

"Accuracy in Media Review," Dec. 82 reporting on
Dec. 82 *Washington Journalism Review*

What of Opinion Formers in the performing arts?

A study of the 104 top Hollywood creators of TV shows, each of whom had been associated with two or more prime time series, reported that 97% were pro-abortion. Also, two-thirds said that TV should be a major force for social reform. As with the news media elite, they were well paid (two-thirds over $200,000 per year), white, urban, male, most lived in California and the Northeast, and only 7% went to church once a month.

L. and R. Lichter, S. Rothman, "Hollywood and America, the
Odd Couple," *Public Opinion 5,* Dec.-Jan. 1983, pp. 54-58

A study of 149 writers, producers, and directors of the 50 top grossing movies (1965-83) showed 96% pro-abortion, with similar characteristic make-ups as those mentioned above.

S. Rothman & R. Lichter, "What Are Moviemakers Made Of?
Public Opinion 6, Dec.-Jan. 1984, pp. 14-18%

Those surveys are from a few years ago. Perhaps things have changed.

Try May 1996. A survey of 139 Washington-based journalists showed that 89% voted for Clinton in '92, 7% for Bush and 2% for Perot, so no change here. Further, only 2% identified themselves as conservative, while the "moderate to liberal" category claimed 91%.

T. LaHaye, *Capitol Report,* Vol. 10, No. 5, May '96

Let's use just one more example. Anyone reading, watching or listening during Bill Clinton's term from '92-'96 would surely have become convinced of the fact that the Republican Convention in '92 was a disaster and that strongly pro-life speakers like Pat Buchanan and Marilyn Quayle did great harm to Bush's campaign.

During all of those four years, the media hammered away at this. Yet, polls taken before and after that convention tell a very different story.

	Pre-Convention		Post-Convention	
Poll	Bush	Clinton	Bush	Clinton
CBS (7/17;8/20)	35	58	46	48
ABC (7/19;8/23)	29	58	42	47
Louis Harris (7/19;9/1)	33	63	45	59
L. Angeles *Times* (7/17;8/21)	32	52	41	49
Greenberg-Lake (8/16;8/19)	35	50	43	48

No wonder T. LaHaye (above) said, "The nation's press and TV journalists act more like part of Clinton's official re-election campaign than the objective reporters they try to claim they are." (May 1996).

In the presidential election, 2000, 61% voted for Gore, 5% for Ralph Nader and 6% for George Bush (28% refused to answer). As to who they thought was the best president in the past 40 years, they listed Bill Clinton 26%, John Kennedy 17%, Lyndon Johnson 15%, Jimmy Carter 13%, and Ronald Reagan 4%.

Luntz Research Company, Mar. 02

No network labeled Al Gore as a liberal during the '99-00 election cycle. They labeled George W. Bush as a conservative 19 times.

Media Research Center, 6-25-2002

Is this why so many now listen to the likes of Rush Limbaugh, Laura Schlesinger, and to Christian Radio News?

Precisely! It seems that a large part of the listening, watching public is even rejecting network news. In recent years, those who regularly watch plunged from 60% to 42%.

Why? Because these newscasts have all but lost any semblance of impartial reporting and no longer hide their extreme liberal bias.

The book *Bias* by veteran CBS reporter, Bernie Goldberg, a best seller in 2002, is a firsthand, devastating detailing of the secular media bias.

An encouraging development has been the Media Research Center Cyber Alert reporting on the web daily to over 1,000 opinion forming leaders. It details what various reporters and media outlets have said. This has shown a bright light on the unchanged bias of most of the national media.

http://www.mrc.org/

What is the pro-life answer?

After listening to P. Jennings or D. Rather, turn to Marlin Maddox, Family News in Focus, and to the newer talk radio hosts. Remember also to listen to the daily commentaries on Christian Radio by Phyllis Schlaffly, Chuck Colson, Cal Thomas, your author on "Life Issues" and others.

Should we give up on the media? Is it hopeless?

Quite the contrary. Our relationship with the media is getting better.

We must get acquainted with media people. They

will see us as single issue? True, but they must also see us as well-spoken and professional, not irresponsible firebrands. They will then also see us as concerned for the mother as well as her preborn child; broad based, not a single political party or religion or sex; and as a voting block to respect.

We must educate them. Many media people have gross misconceptions of us and what we stand for. When they understand us and our issue better, we will get more balanced reporting.

Local or national?

You won't have much luck with national media, al- though Fox News has been much less biased than the "Clinton" News Network (CNN), but local is different.

Most local media people are sincere, dedicated, and try to do a job. You should praise their professional work, but constructively criticize their unprofessional reporting. Above all, however, respect them and con- tinue to work with them. When we do get to know each other, and do continue to communicate, we will get more balance and, sometimes, even favorable treat- ment.

Reporters and commentators are interested in news, any kind of news. When we make news, we rate time and space and will get it.

CHAPTER 42

CAPITAL PUNISHMENT/WAR

Why are pro-lifers for capital punishment?
Most are not, but many are, including many sincere Christians who see biblical justification for it.

But they both kill, don't they?
Yes. But there are clear differences. Let's list them.

CAPITAL PUNISHMENT	ABORTION
To rational adult	To preborn baby
Punishment for a capital crime	Not punishment, no crime
Judged guilty by due process of law	Not guilty, no due process
Killed by the state	Killed by a private citizen

War kills too. What about that?
If there is a clear-cut justified war, it would be a war of self-defense. Let's list the differences.

WAR	ABORTION
Self-defense	Aggression
Not wanted, unplanned	Wanted and planned
Done by the state	By a private citizen
Against another nation	Against a private individual

What is the position of pro-abortion advocates?

They are the ones who are inconsistent. With few exceptions, pro-abortion leaders oppose capital punishment. They would spare the guilty, but kill the innocent.

CHAPTER 43

Pro-Abortion Organizations And Planned Parenthood

NARAL

Originally, the National Association for the Repeal of Abortion Laws, this group was a prime mover in getting the first abortion-on-demand law in New York passed.

After legalization, it became the National Abortion Rights Action League, and then the National Abortion & Reproductive Rights Action League. It has been a major force opposing the Right to Life movement.

N.O.W.

The National Organization for Women is a national group of radical anti-life feminists heavily influenced by the militant lesbian faction of its membership. While claiming to seek economic and employment equality for women, its two major goals are Reproductive Rights (i.e., abortion rights) and Lesbian Rights.

Its claim to represent the "women" of the U.S. brings a smile when it is compared to the Concerned Women for America which has four times the members. It is often now called the National Organization of (Some) Women.

ACLU

· The American Civil Liberties Union has been consistently selective as to whose civil liberties it protects. Totally blind to the existence of the preborn baby, it has served as the legal defense arm of the pro-abortion, anti-family movement.

National Education Association

The National Education Assn. is the largest and most powerful labor union in the U.S. Tragically, it has embraced a wide range of radical feminist policies, including being aggressively pro-abortion.

YWCA

The Young Women's Christian Association was captured three decades ago by a group of radical anti-life feminists. Its policies today are aggressively pro-abortion. For example, in 1973, its 26th National Convention voted "to support efforts to provide safe abortions to all women who desire them." In 1989, it restated its policy of support for "Repeal of all laws, restricting or prohibiting abortions . . ." There has been no essential change since that time.

YWCA Position on Abortion Rights

Religious Coalition for Abortion Rights

This is a collection of clergy and 'religious' groups who are pro-abortion.

Catholics for a Free Choice

A tiny, militant, anti-Catholic group of former Catholics financed entirely by anti-Catholic sources.

People for the American Way

This heavily funded group has carried on an effective pro-abortion campaign in the national media under the leadership of Norman Lear.

National Abortion Federation
This is the trade association for operators of abortion chambers.

American Association of University Women
In June 1977, AAUW's Biennial Convention voted as a priority issue the "Right to Choose."

National Women's Political Caucus
"From its beginning, it has been pro-abortion. On the issue of reproductive freedom, including abortion, the Caucus remains single-minded and strong."
D. Broder, Wash. Post, A-23, Aug. 26, 1987

Republicans for Choice
This is a wholly owned subsidiary of Planned Parenthood.

League of Women Voters
At its 1982 National Convention, on a 753 to 472 vote, it stated that "the LWV of the U.S. believes that public policy in a pluralistic society must affirm the constitutional right of privacy of the individual to make reproductive choices." (Ninety-two percent of their chapters agreed). It hasn't changed.

Alan Guttmacher Institute
This is the research arm of Planned Parenthood.

Network
A group of Roman Catholic nuns who have defied their church's teachings and adopted a permissive attitude toward abortion.

UNICEF
This U.N. Children's Fund is supporting abortion e.g., the South African "Love Life's" website actively encourages teen promiscuity and abortion and directs

them to abortion providers.

C-Fam Bulletin, 888 U.N. Plaza, NYC, 18 Jan 2002

Pathfinder Fund and United Nations Fund for Population Activity

Both have actively promoted and subsidized abortion in Third World countries.

International Planned Parenthood

This is the largest population control organization in the world. Its 140 national affiliates exert unparalleled influence on national policies. In 25 years, it has spent two billion U.S. dollars in undeveloped countries. It seeks legal abortion in every nation, regardless of how it is achieved.

SEICUS

The Sex Education & Information Council of the U.S. has worked closely with Planned Parenthood since 1970. SEICUS produces national sex education guidelines and materials. Planned Parenthood uses these, through its affiliates, to target every school district in the nation with their immoral and destructive programs.

PLANNED PARENTHOOD

This is the largest, most powerful, most effective pro-abortion, anti-life, anti-family, anti-Christian force in the U.S. and internationally.

The Planned Parenthood Federation of America is one of over 90 national affiliates of the International Planned Parenthood Federation (London). It gets about two-thirds of its U.S. financing through tax money, local, state, and national. It has five regional offices, about 127 statewide affiliates, over 850 local clinics in the U.S. Over 70 of its offices do abortions. Its total

369

cash flow was $627 million in 2000. It concentrates its efforts on abortion, contraception, and sex education.

How many abortions does Planned Parenthood do?

The number increases each year, as it converts more of its clinics to killing centers. In 1985 it had 51 chambers which killed 110,000. This increased to 197,070 in 2000. (See graph next page.) It referred 2,999 for adoption in 1999.

Ryan Report, Vol. 8, No. 3, April 2001

Was Planned Parenthood always pro-abortion?

In its early years of existence, Planned Parenthood limited itself to contraception and specifically opposed abortion. The following is a quote from an official Planned Parenthood pamphlet:

"Is birth control an abortion?"

"Definitely not. An abortion kills the life of a baby after it has begun. It is dangerous to your life and health. It may make you sterile so that, when you want a child, you cannot have it. Birth control merely postpones the beginning of life."

Planned Parenthood, Aug. 1963
Available from Cincinnati Right to Life,
1802 W. Galbraith Rd., Cinti., OH 45239, $3. pp.

Doesn't Planned Parenthood concentrate mostly on contraception?

In its earlier years, to a much larger extent, Planned Parenthood clinics offered contraceptive advice and aid to married women so that they could more responsibly plan their families. Because of this, it generated widespread support from many areas of our society.

Those days are gone. Today its clientele consists largely of unmarried teenagers. It dispenses medically hazardous drugs (the pill) and devices (the I.U.D.) and Norplant without parental knowledge or consent. It is the largest provider of abortions in America, again, to

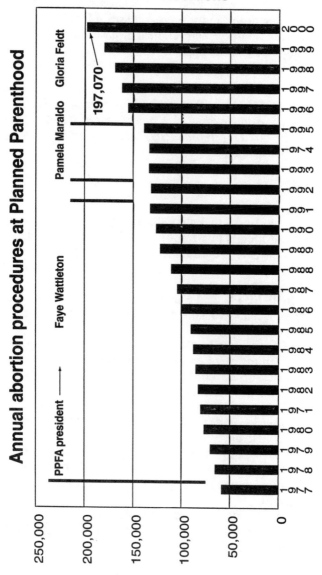

Annual abortion procedures at Planned Parenthood

Number of Abortions

PPFA president ⟶ Faye Wattleton   Pamela Maraldo   Gloria Feldt

197,070

250,000
200,000
150,000
100,000
50,000
0

1977
1978
1979
1980
1971
1982
1983
1984
1985
1986
1987
1988
1989
1990
1991
1992
1993
1994
1995
1996
1997
1998
1999
2000

371

teenagers without parental knowledge or consent. It aggressively promotes sex education that, rather than reducing promiscuity, premarital sex, illegitimate pregnancies, abortion, and venereal disease, has almost certainly had just the opposite effect.

Ryan Report, Vol. 8, No. 3, April 2001

In its Five Year Plan, it openly stated: *Our mission is to serve as the nation's foremost agent of social change in the area of reproductive health and well being* [emphasis theirs].

Planned Parenthood Federation of America,
A Five Year Plan, 1976-1980, p. 5

That is hard to believe. I've heard that Planned Parenthood is pro-family, pro-life, and pro-child.

Their paid TV commercials say that, but their own official documents, their leaders, and their actions say quite the opposite.

In 1976, Planned Parenthood's Five Year Plan (see reference above) laid out in detail what their goals were. We quote:

- Objective #2: "Reaffirming and protecting the legitimacy of induced abortion, as a necessary back-up to contraceptive failure, and extending safe, dignified services to women who seek them."
- Purpose: "To provide leadership in making . . . abortion and sterilization available and fully accessible to all."

"The various activities that we undertake are not 'separate' and certainly not competing. Rather, they are all complementary parts of a single national strategy" (page 5).

"Services to be made available at all clinics include . . . *abortion services (or local referral)*" (emphasis in original, page 6).

• Program Emphasis #2: "Keeping abortions legal and accessible to all persons" (page 9).

"To increase the availability and accessibility of high quality and affordable reproductive health care services [abortion]"

PPFA Five Year Plan 1986-1990, preamble

"Until we reach the millennium . . . Planned Parenthood will continue to provide not only sex education and contraception, but also abortion."

A. Moran, Exec. V.P., Planned Parenthood of New York City, *New York Times*, Dec. 27, 1982

[Planned Parenthood] is not just a social or medical service agency. It is part of a cause, a movement. One of the principles of Planned Parenthood is that reproductive freedom is indivisible. You either have it or not. Everybody has it or none has it."

Don Weintraub, V.P. for Int'l Affairs, PPFA, Madison, Mar. 12, 1985

Family Planning Associations should not use the absence of law or the existence of an unfavorable law as an excuse for inaction. Action outside the law, and even in violation of it, is part of the process of stimulating change . . . of fertility regulation services or specific methods."

Art. 106, p. 28, Int. P.P. Fed., Nov. 1983

Teens are encouraged to engage in "responsible" behavior, e.g., encouraging "outercourse," a "second kind of abstinence that includes lots of sex play as long as they don't have vaginal, oral, or anal intercourse."

Life Decisions International, Report, Vol. 4, No. 1, winter 2001

It is the policy of Planned Parenthood to insure that women have the right to seek and obtain safe legal abortions. Planned Parenthood has the responsibility to provide access to high-quality abortion services. . . .

Federation Policies, PPFA, Jan. 1986

Faye Wattleton, Pres. of P.P., said, "I make it very clear. If you're not clear where you stand on the abortion issue, if you're worried that birth control for teenagers encourages promiscuity . . . this [P.P] is not the kind of outfit you're comfortable with."

"The Faye Wattleton Comeback," P. Span,
Wash. Post, Oct. 14, 1987

Planned Parenthood has aggressively defended abortion rights in the courts in recent years, thus dropping any earlier pretense of neutrality. The most famous case was *Casey vs. Planned Parenthood,* a 1990 decision of the U.S. Supreme Court.

What does Planned Parenthood think of Right to Life?

They have an opinion.

"In every generation there exists a group of people so filled with bigotry and self-righteousness that they will resort to any means — even violence — to impose their views on society. Today, such fanatics dominate a movement ironically called 'the Right-to-Life,' a movement which threatens the most basic of all human rights."

Planned Parenthood Pamphlet, the Justice Fund,
810 7th Ave., New York, NY, 10019

But Margaret Sanger, its founder, opposed abortion.

Not so! Not only did she favor abortion, but she proposed forced sterilization for those whom she considered unfit to reproduce. She worked hard for a "race of thoroughbreds" until Hitler's similar "Master Race" made that goal unpopular. She was a true eugenicist. For example, her April 1933 *Birth Control Review,* devoted an entire edition to eugenic sterilization.

Who did she consider unfit?

Black people, Jews, Southern European immigrants (especially Italians), but also others of "low I.Q." These "feebleminded" people were a "menace to the race."

E. Drogin, *Margaret Sanger: Father of Modern Society,*
CUL Publishers, 1980, Section 1, p. 18-24

This is hard to believe!

Margaret Sanger, the famous founder of Planned Parenthood, wanted "more children from the fit, less from the unfit."

Birth Control Review, vol. 3, no. 5, May 1919, p. 2

This wasn't only related to contraceptive planning. As editor, she printed grossly eugenic material, approving of Hitler's sterilization program (see *Into the Darkness, Nazi Germany Today,* by L. Stoddard , p. 196).

She believed that "Negroes and Southern Europeans were mentally inferior to native born Americans." She found these people, Hebrews, and others "feebleminded," "human weeds," and called them a "menace to the race." In 1933, her *Birth Control Review* devoted an entire edition to eugenic sterilization.

Sanger's famous "Plan for Peace" was almost the same as Hitler's, even going beyond it to suggest, in essence, concentration camps.

"When the world realized the logical consequences of Hitler's hereditarian-eugenic, totalitarian type of government, Margaret Sanger's birth-control movement had to take a quick step away from its overt eugenic language."

E. Drogin, *Margaret Sanger, Father of Modern Society,*
CUL Publications, 1979, p. 28

Tell me more.

Let us quote from her "Plan for Peace." This was little more than peaceful genocide. She wanted the United States:

- "To keep the doors of immigration closed to the entrance of certain aliens whose condition is known to be detrimental to the stamina of the race, such as the feebleminded, as determined by Stanford-Binet I.Q. tests.
- "To apply a stern and rigid policy of sterilization and segregation to that grade of population whose progeny is already tainted, or whose inheritance is such that objectionable traits may be transmitted to offspring.
- "To insure the country against future burdens of maintenance for numerous offspring as may be born of feeble-minded parents by pensioning all persons with transmissible diseases who voluntarily consent to sterilization.
- "To give dysgenic groups in our population their choice of segregation or sterilization.
- "To apportion farm lands and homesteads for these segregated persons where they would be taught to work under competent instructors for a period of their entire lives. [Practically speaking, a concentration camp.]
- "[To] take an inventory of the secondary group, such as illiterates, paupers, unemployables, criminals, prostitutes, dope fiends, classify them in special departments under government medical protection, and segregate them on farms and open spaces as long as necessary for the strengthening and development of moral conduct." (Again, concentration camps.)

M. Sanger, "Plan for Peace,"
Birth Control Review, vol. 16, no. 4, April 1932

But I've read that she was a social crusader for good.
Hardly. She said, "The most merciful thing a large family can do for one of its infant members is to kill it."
Sanger, *Woman and the New Race*

She herself was highly promiscuous and had many lovers. She favored "free love" for women without any sexual limits but without the burden of children. She saw "the marriage bed [as] the most degenerating influence in the social order."

Kennedy, David M. *Birth Control in America: The Career of Margaret Sanger,* London: Yale University Press, 1970.

But Planned Parenthood wants to reduce teen pregnancies, doesn't it?

Let's be specific. Planned Parenthood wants to reduce teen *births*. It is not trying to reduce teen sex activity; in fact, its sex education programs do exactly the opposite.

CHAPTER 44

TAX-FUNDED ABORTIONS

This has been rather definitively answered in the U.S. A large majority of citizens do not want to pay for welfare abortions. With almost no exceptions, every poll with unbiased wording has confirmed this time after time.

Most of the investigations of this issue were done in the '70s and '80s when there were dire predictions of women dying if such abortions were not paid for.

What happened when public funding of abortions was cut off?

There was an excellent example. In 1977, the federal government of the U.S. paid for 295,000 welfare abortions. In 1978, it only paid for 2,000 abortions because the Hyde Amendment had cut off the funding.

The U.S. government's chief pro-abortion biostatistician, Dr. Willard Cates, predicted "a total of 77 excess deaths to women" who would turn to illegal abortions, plus five additional deaths due to delay of abortions into the later weeks of pregnancy.

Petitti & Cates, "Restricting Medicaid Funds: Projection of Excess Mortality," *Amer. Jour. Public Health,* vol. 67, no. 9, Sept. 1977, pp. 860-862

In fact, his projection proved to be completely unfounded. An article by the same department, which later surveyed 13 states and the District of Columbia, revealed, "No increase in abortion-related complications was observed. . . . No abortion deaths related to either legal or illegal abortions were detected, [and there was] no difference between institutions in funded and non-funded states."

Morbidity and Mortality Weekly Report, CDC,
U.S. Dept. HEW, vol. 28, no. 4, Feb. 2, 1979

A later attempt to link three deaths as "abortion funding-related" was shown not to be related to the funding cut-off at all. Total maternal abortion deaths were actually lower than before the cutoff in 1976.

"Medicaid funding restrictions are associated with a reduction in both the number of abortions and of pregnancies."

"The Effect of Medicaid Abortion Funding
Restrictions on Abortions, Births and Pregnancies,"
Levine et al, National Bureau of Economic Research,
Working Paper No. 5066, 1995

But poor women want this help.

Not as much as rich people. In 1984, the strongly pro-abortion University of North Carolina polled its state to find that only 32% favored tax funding. An important finding was that 43% of the college-educated favored such government "assistance," while only 17% of those with less than a high-school eduction concurred. Also, 36% of men favored assistance, but only 28% of women.

So, those who would receive the "benefit" of tax-funded abortions wanted them the least. One might conclude that the elitist social planners see this as a way of reducing poverty — killing the unborn children of the poor.

From a strictly economic standpoint, isn't it cheaper to abort than to have another person on welfare?

Planned Parenthood did one of the definitive studies on this which showed that at the time of the study there were welfare costs of $13,900 for each first birth to a teenager (married and unmarried), and $8,400 for each first birth to her if she was 20 years or older. Compare this with the average of nearly $50,000 each will ultimately pay in taxes as an adult.

M. Burt, "Public Cost of Teen Childbearing,"
Family Planning Perspective, vol. 18, no. 5, Sept. 1986

The average time a family stays on welfare in the U.S. is 27 months, not 18 years. When we peel away the outer layer of the rhetoric, what we expose is a callous, cost-benefit analysis of solving poverty by killing the unborn children of the poor.

This continues to happen. In 1982, Michigan for instance, only 14.7% of pregnancies of non-welfare mothers were aborted. This clearly suggests coercion when we realize that the minority classes who make up a large share of the welfare people are more against abortion than are white affluent people.

ibid.

**It isn't the poor who want abortions.
It's the rich who want abortions
for the poor.**

PART IX
WHAT TO DO

CHAPTER 45

WHAT TO DO

"When the time comes, as it surely will, when we face that awesome moment, the final judgment, I've often thought, as Fulton Sheen wrote, that it is a terrible moment of loneliness. You have no advocates, you are there alone standing before God — and a terror will rip your soul like nothing you can imagine. But I really think that those in the pro-life movement will not be alone. I think there'll be a chorus of voices that have never been heard in this world but are heard beautifully and clearly in the next world — and they will plead for everyone who has been in this movement. They will say to God, 'Spare him, because he loved us," — and God will look at you and say not, 'Did you succeed?' but 'Did you try?'"

Congressman Henry Hyde

therefore

The most important thing that you can do is to become personally involved. Unless you do, nothing will change.

Educate yourself and others

Start by reading pro-life materials. Commit to reading at least one piece of educational material every month. Share your newfound knowledge with family, friends, neighbors, coworkers and members of your church. Don't assume that, because someone is a religious person, they already have this information.

Lobby your elected officials

One of the most effective ways to reach an elected official is to send a brief, hand-written letter. Make it factual, respectful and calm. Clearly state what it is you are requesting from them, i.e., a vote for pro-life legislation or a vote against a pro-abortion bill. This is a **highly** effective tool that is often underestimated by pro-life people. Mail letters to your federal elected officials at the following addresses:

Honorable Senator _____
United States Senate
Washington, DC 20510

Honorable Congressman _____
United States House of Representatives
Washington, DC 20515

Or phone them by calling the Capitol Hill switchboard at (202) 224-3121. You can often avoid the expense of a long distance call by phoning a local office in your town. Look for their last name in the phone book. Don't forget to lobby your local and state elected officials also.

Letters to the editor

This section of your local paper is one of the most widely read. Be brief — usually 200 words or less is required. Be factual, respectful and calm. Many people formulate opinions based on the comments of others.

Use this opportunity to educate, persuade and motivate those in your community. Also write to your radio and TV stations.

Collect items

needed by pregnant women and their babies, such as baby and maternity clothes, cribs, car seats, toys, etc. These can be used by the local Pregnancy Help Center. Look under abortion or abortion alternatives in your local yellow pages to contact them.

Volunteer your time.

Pregnancy Help Centers have a wide assortment of jobs you can do besides counseling. In addition, your local right to life chapter is **always** in need of volunteers. Jobs vary from stuffing envelopes to lobbying elected officials, and everything in between. Call them to see which job suits your talents. Look under "R" in the phone book for Right to Life.

Vote.

Nothing will change unless **you** do. Remember that any candidate for public office who permits, supports, or wants you to pray for the direct killing of almost every third baby conceived in America is simply disqualified from holding public office.

Support our efforts financially.

Most everything we do to protect the lives of unborn babies and their mothers requires financial resources. When you financially support the pro-life movement, you become a partner in the effort to protect innocent human life. There are few investments that provide such a wonderful return! Henry Hyde is clearly also speaking of such tangible support.

Utilize other pro-life organizations.

Volumes of pro-life resources are only a click away on the World Wide Web. Take advantage of what they have to offer. Some of these include:

www.lifeissues.org
www.abortionfacts.com
www.prolifeinfo.org
www.nrlc.org
www.ohiolife.org

Pray

as if everything depends upon it — it does. Pray that God will stay His hand. Even though we, as a nation, may not deserve His help and mercy, pray that He will extend it.

Now that you're aware of things you can do to help save the lives of unborn babies, I hope that you will move into action. If you and I don't help the babies, who will?

"The care of human life and happiness, and not their destruction, is the first and only legitimate object of good government."

Thomas Jefferson
"To Republican Citizens
of Wash, County Maryland."
March 3 1, 1809

INDEX

A

D

I

L

M

Mother Theresa, 319
mutual consent registry, 309

N

NARAL (National Association for the Repeal of
    Abortion Laws), 245, 349, 366
Nathanson, Dr. Bernard, 103, 145, 245
National Abortion Federation, 368
National Association of Black Social Workers, 303
National Education Association, 367
National Institutes of Health, 114
National Organization for Women (N.O.W.), 366
National Women's Political Caucus, 368
natural family planning, 316
Nazi doctors, 329, 332
network news, 362
neurotransmitters, fetal, 90
Ney, Phillip, 58, 285
Nigro, Dr. Samuel, 282
nociceptors, fetal, 102
Noonan, Professor John T., 272
Norplant, 148, 311, 341, 370
Nuremberg trials, 11, 336
Nurses, abortion 339

O

Offenses Against Persons Act, 31, 96
oligohydramnios, 218
Open Arms, 298
open records, 309

P

PACE, 298

T

X

Y

Z

Video Tape

Video version: Here is the entire Pro-Life story for a first-time audience, youth or adult, civic or in a church setting, classroom, crisis pregnancy center, etc.

One Tape

- *Part I* – Human life, Human rights, discrimination, choice- 28 minutes

- *Part II* – Euthanasia, illegal, unwanted, rape, Post-Abortion Syndrome, disqualify, love both- 26 minutes

- *Part III* – Abortion – 10 minutes

VHS   **$25.00**   *PAL*

Why Can't We Love Them Both Slide Set

94 Slides – 2-sided cassette – manual

$50.00

Assisted Suicide and Euthanasia
J.C. Willke. M.D.

This book includes:
- The Nazi experience
- The ongoing Dutch Saga
- The reversal of a permissive law in Australia
- The passage of one in Oregon
- The present worldwide threat in many countries
- The groundbreaking formulation of anti-euthanasia answers to "their" arguments in the 45 friend of the court briefs presented to the Supreme Court
- The answer, compassionate care

1-4 copies = $7.95 ea; 5-9 copies = $6.75 ea;
10-24 copies = $6.00 ea; 25 or more copies = $5.50 ea
Hardbound $12.00 ea

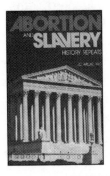

Abortion and Slavery
History Repeats
J.C. Willke, M.D.

Dr. Willke has drawn a well documented analogy that is devastatingly convincing.

1-9 copies	$6.00 ea
10-99 copies	$5.40 ea
100 or more	$4.75 ea

By Dr. & Mrs. Willke

For Pre-School to Pre-Teens

A fully accurate,
scientific, easily
understood showing
and telling of the
beautiful story of
growth of the baby
from conception to
birth.

For fair booths!
Excellent for
continuous
showing in
public place.

Completely
positive
education.
Does not
mention abortion.
Ten-minute presentation. Video has three
consecutive showings on a 30-minute tape,
so structured for fair booth use.

Full color

One copy **$24.95**

VHS   *PAL*

8 Week Flyer
for mass distribution
by Dr. and Mrs. Willke

- at lectures
- sidewalk counseling
- at fairs
- to school children
- in Sunday School
- in churches
- in mailings

English, Spanish, French, Russian, and Ukrainian

100 copies	5 ¢ each
1,000 copies	4¢ each
10,000 copies	3½¢ each

DID YOU KNOW

This is how big you were when you were only 11 weeks old. From then on you breathed (fluid), swallowed, digested, urinated, and had bowel movements, slept, dreamed, and awakened, tasted, felt pain from touch and heat, reacted to light and noise, and were able to learn things.

After 11 weeks no new organs began functioning; you just grew more mature.

4 sides 3½ x 8½

An Envelope Stuffer — Mini Brochure

In English, Spanish, French, German, Italian, Portuguese, Croation, Swedish, Japanese, Cambodian, Russian, and Ukrainian
By Dr. and Mrs. Willke

- Brief hard hitting facts on development in womb
- Envelope size
- Easy to include with every letter, bill, or mailing you send
- Pass out at a sports event, a fair, a convention, or at an abortion clinic

100 copies	9¢ each
1,000 copies	7¢ each
10,000 copies	6¢ each

410

The Deadly After-Effect Of Abortion — **Breast Cancer**

Hard facts concerning the increased risk of breast cancer for women choosing abortion.

By Dr. J.C. Willke

Is **Planned Parenthood** the nation's leading provider & promoter of abortion?

Leaves no doubt that they have a vested interest in keeping abortion legal and flourishing.

By Edward Szymkowaik

EUTHANASIA . . . when the doctor kills the patient!

Clearly defines the problem and addresses the misconceptions and probable abuses

By Dr. J.C. Willke

Every person must answer **2 basic questions**. When does human life begin? Should human life be given equal protection of the law? Questions and answers.

By Dr. J.C. Willke

1-499 = \$.23 ea; 500-999 = \$.20 ea; 1,000 up = \$.17 ea
Quantities of similar priced items can be combined for discount.

411

Women Hurt

Discusses the very real problem of Post-Abortion Syndrome (PAS) and what we can do to help.

By Dr. J.C. Willke

Men Hurt Too

The feelings of guilt that result from an abortion can also have a profound affect on men. How to help.

By Bradley Mattes

CHOICE

What is the real question?
What are the real choices?
Take a closer look.

By Dr. J.C. Willke

Mary's Pregnancy

Mary's pregnancy in the New Testament speaks clearly against abortion. Read how.

By Dr. J.C. Willke

1-499 = $.23 ea; 500-999 = $.20 ea; 1,000 up = $.17 ea
Quantities of similar priced items may be combined for discount.

RU-486 A Human Pesticide
A factual account of what it is
and the inherent danger.

By Dr. J.C. Willke

**Never Again?
Never Was!**
Exposes the greatly exaggerated
numbers commonly used to describe
illegal abortion prior to legalization

By Dr. J.C. Willke

By Dr. J.C. Willke

Life or Death
A factual and graphic presentation of fetal
development and abortion. A must-read
brochure for everyone.

Life or Death available in: **English, Spanish, French,
German, Italian, Portuguese, Dutch, Norwegian,
Hungarian, Polish, Japanese, Chinese, Swedish, Turkish, Greek.**

1-499 = \$.23 ea; 500-999 = \$.20 ea; 1,000 up = \$.17 ea
Quantities of similar priced items may be combined for discount.

El libro más importante del mundo en la lucha contra el aborto existe ahora en español.

Spanish version of the Willke book *Why Can't We Love Them Both?* An indispensable tool with scientifically documented answers to more than a thousand questions to teach the pro-life story!

Paperback $7.00

The Supreme Court has ruled that it is legal to abort a child **any time** before birth. This brochure includes a pictorial timeline from conception to natural death.

After 44 years of Communist sanctioned abortion, Poland made abortion illegal. What happened next has unraveled the pro-abortion rhetoric.

By Dr. J.C. Willke

1-499 = $.23 ea; 500-999 = $.20 ea; 1,000 up = $.17 ea
Quantities of similar priced items can be combined for discount.

Español

1-499	$.23 cada uno US
500-999	$.20 cada uno US
1,000+	$.17 cada uno US

FOLLETITO / CABE EN UN SOBRE

HOJA SUELTA DE 8 SEMANAS

Para distribución en masa

SABIA USTED

Hechos sucintos y trágicos sobre el desarrollo en el útero y el aborto.

1-999	$.05 cada uno
1,000-9,999	$.04 cada uno
10,000+	$.03½ cada uno

1-999	$.09 cada uno
1,000-9,999	$.07 cada uno
10,000+	$.06 cada uno

PRO-LIFE POSTCARDS

HUMAN LIFE AT 8 WEEKS

6-WEEK EMBRYONIC BABY

A 14-WEEK LITTLE ONE

TINY HUMAN FEET

Full-color reproductions of 4 of the most effective Pro-Life documented photos, each with a brief educational message.

An impressive and inexpensive way to promote the Pro-Life message and raise public awareness.

CAN BE USED FOR:
- Pro-Life chapter meetings
- Legislative awareness
- School Educational Programs
- Clergy/Church organizations
- Membership drives
- Notes to public officials
- Personal writings
- Group meetings

units of 16 cards (containing 4 of each)

1-9 units . . . . $4.00 per unit (plus $3.00 S&H)

10-99 units . . . . $3.00 per unit (plus $4.50 S&H)

100-500 units . . . . $2.60 per unit (plus $6.50 S&H)

Wall Posters

16 x 30

23 x 35

23 x 35

Color

One . . . . . . $5.00 each
10 . . . . $4.00 each
100 . . . . . . $3.00 each

24 x 36

Black & White

One . . . . . . $3.00 each
10 . . . . $2.00 each
100 . . . . . . $1.50 each

24 x 36

24 x 36

To order copies of materials shown on preceeding pages, use this order form.

Quantity prices for

Abortion: Questions & Answers
Love Them Both

1-9 books . . . . $6.95   50 books $4.50
10 books $5.00

Please send me:	Copies	Cost
Why Not Love Then Both	_____	_____
OTHER ITEMS from preceeding pages (list)		
_____	_____	_____
_____	_____	_____
_____	_____	_____
_____	_____	_____

Postage (1 book $3.00)
Inquire for quantity orders   _____

Please include payment with order   Total: $ _____

Name _____

Address _____

_____

Phone _____

City _____ State _____ Zip_____

HAYES PUBLISHING CO.,INC.
6304 Hamilton Avenue • Cincinnati, Ohio 45224
Phone (513) 681-7559 • Ph/Fax (513) 681-9298
e-mail: hayespub@aol.com
web: hayespub.tripod.com

To order copies of materials shown on preceeding pages, use this order form.

Quantity prices for
Abortion: Questions & Answers
Love Them Both

1-9 books $6.95	50 books $4.50
10 books $5.00	

Please send me:	Copies	Cost
Why Not Love Then Both	_____	_____
OTHER ITEMS from preceeding pages (list)		
_____	_____	_____
_____	_____	_____
_____	_____	_____
_____	_____	_____

Postage (1 book $3.00)
Inquire for quantity orders   _____

Please include payment with order   Total: $ _____

Name _____

Address _____

_____

Phone _____

City _____ State _____ Zip_____

HAYES PUBLISHING CO.,INC.
6304 Hamilton Avenue • Cincinnati, Ohio 45224
Phone (513) 681-7559 • Ph/Fax (513) 681-9298
e-mail: hayespub@aol.com
web: hayespub.tripod.com

This tiny human was yet alive at this moment, only 6 weeks after first day of last menstrual period, a just removed tubal pregnancy.
(Photo by Robert Wolfe, with permission Bell Museum of Pathology, University of Minnesota.)

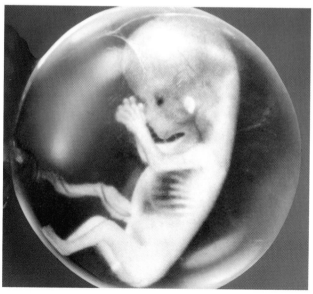

8-weeks-old heart beat can be heard on office instruments

ALIVE & GROWING

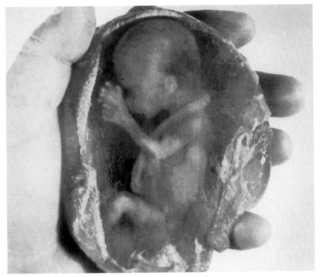

Eleven weeks old, almost 3 months. All organ systems now function.

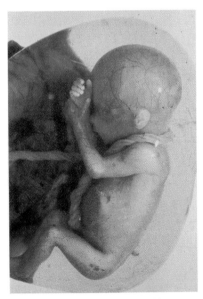

3½ months old just growing bigger

Little Sam at 21 weeks

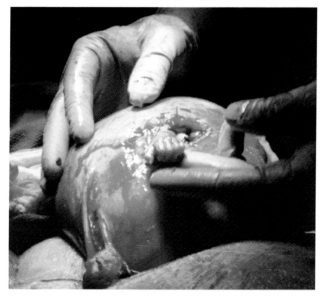

KILLED BY ABORTION

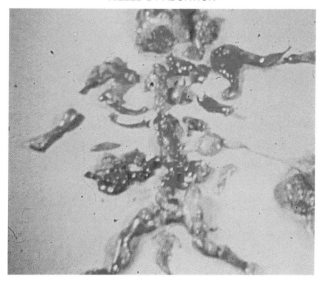

D & E Abortion at 4 Months

KILLED BY ABORTION

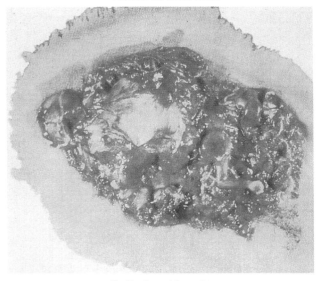

By Suction at 8 weeks

By Suction at 8 weeks